# Munching on Existence

CONTEMPORARY AMERICAN SOCIETY THROUGH LITERATURE

# Munching on Existence

EDITED BY Robert Gliner
AND R. A. Raines

The Free Press, New York

A DIVISION OF THE MACMILLAN COMPANY

Printed in the United States of America



The Free Press
A Division of The Macmillan Company
866 Third Avenue, New York, New York 10022

Collier-Macmillan Canada Ltd., Toronto, Ontario

Library of Congress Catalog Card Number: 72–141937

*printing number*
1 2 3 4 5 6 7 8 9 10

# CONTENTS

# INTRODUCTION

This reader is designed for students of the social sciences, the humanities, literature and American studies who are trying to develop a sense of the quality of American life today. American society as studied in universities has come to be viewed in terms of categories: institutions, conflicts, ideologies, and relationships. Elaborate descriptions are made of these categories and studies are undertaken to determine not only how our society works, but who suffers because of such processes—who is being discriminated against, why a specific war exists. Such a perspective is confining, for both descriptions rendered and solutions posed can be limited by academic rhetoric. Such analyses rarely tell how it *feels* to live in contemporary America.

In this book we provide literary renderings of contemporary American society in some of its more problematic aspects. For these are the aspects in which America is changing, whether this process is considered positive evolution or decay. The way you respond will eventually determine our national future. Yet only when you come to feel the existence of these changes can you sense the urgency of acting; only then can you escape the plane of abstraction at which changes seem far away, distant eruptions which you know exist, but which do not seem relevant to your situation.

One of the assumptions underlying this reader is that literature can provide a needed approach to academic discussion of American society, especially since growing numbers of social scientists are questioning the possibility of an "objective" social science. Literary artists often convey very involving descriptions of society. They are sometimes able to show the direction a given society is taking, and to describe inconsistencies within it—they are often prophets of the future. The literary artist does not avoid value judgments, for in portraying the lives of members of society, he is able to show that life *is* value judgments. The literary artist is not a passive reporter, an "objective" observer; he swims through the mud with the characters he creates. Many literary artists have taken it upon themselves to portray the anguish of American society and to assume responsibility for commenting upon the social issues of which they are a part. These selections demonstrate that you cannot be neutral, nor can you remain indifferent. *The purpose of this reader then, is to enable you to get a feeling for the scope and depth of some of the more problematic aspects of contemporary American society.*

This reader approaches American society in six problematic dimensions. First, our culture is seen from a white middle-class point of view. Within this dimension, the selections illustrate the alienation of both youth and adults. Following this overview are four dimensions of American society: (1) the education that American society provides to insure its continued existence; (2) the relationship of minority-group members to the societal majority; (3) the means that America has traditionally used to resolve international conflict; (4) the occupational tasks the American system provides. The final section brings the reader to a way of viewing American society from outside traditional value frameworks. This "reality busting" section includes avant-garde American literature, as well as cross-cultural works, in an effort to conceptualize different types of feeling and thought patterns as a means of helping to cope with and solve some of the dilemmas currently facing American society. No solutions are offered. Rather, the future is open-ended; everything is a possibility. What is important now may not be in ten or even five years—thus it is necessary to broaden ways of viewing your world and the relationships within that world. For example, by changing your attitude toward time, cause and effect, and individuality, you can fundamentally change how you respond to institutions in American society. As you come to be able to experiment with ways of viewing yourself and your society, so too you come to be open to new ideas and ways of dealing with crucial issues. It is hoped that this section will aid in this enterprise.

Choice of the selections is based upon the relevance of the author's work to contemporary American society. Chronology is particularly important; most of our selections are from the recent past, but we have also included works from other periods which illuminate the themes of the book. Of course, selection of material is based on the editors' own particular tastes. We feel that these authors are representative of the most interesting and creative writing today. There are many authors we could not include because of copyright problems. All literary genres are included: plays, poems, short stories, and excerpts from novels. We hope that the breadth and depth of the works selected will enable the student to grasp many different ways of looking at American society and will also provide a means for him to identify with important issues and seek solutions to them as a participant rather than as an innocent bystander.

R. G.
R. A. R.

# Munching on Existence

# The Sounds of Silence: Middle-Class Culture and Alienation

For perhaps the first time in history there is a society that contains a relatively affluent majority that feel vaguely estranged from the manifestations of their society's abundance—enough to eat, a good roof over their heads, two cars, two martinis, two "wives," two homes, two alimony payments, and two headaches. *Alienation* is a term originally employed by Karl Marx to refer to a worker's estrangement from the tools and products of his labors. However, *alienation* has been used more recently to describe disenchantment with occupations and relationships and the value framework that is supposed to validate them. The members of the middle class, alienated in this latter sense, have become increasingly susceptible to fads and foibles —in fact anything which looks as if it might provide meaning for their lives. This has bred a kind of otherdirectedness, or mass conformity: other people tell you who you are, who you are supposed to be, and who you are to become. To question their opinion is to risk invalidation, for there is seemingly nowhere else the individual can turn to find justification for his life. Such a position is unsatisfactory, for the needs of the group constantly change, and one is kept in a constant state of anxiety attempting to keep up with these changes lest he be left behind with last year's fashions. Persons come to be treated as things—possessions to be bought, sold, and manipulated on the open market in much the same manner as vaginal deodorant sprays, new cars, and detergents are marketed and consumed. As other individuals must be constantly "consumed" in a never-ending search for meaning in an empty society, so too does the individual become susceptible to advertisers who urge him to get that new car and thus find meaning for his life. It is a sometimes vague, sometimes deeply felt disenchantment with the entire "system," life style, or just the way things are working out, rather than specific problems, that is at issue. Nowhere has this disenchantment been more personally felt or seemed more immediate than among the youth of America, who have expressed their dissatisfaction through drugs, new ways of physical appearance and relating to others, and a general unwillingness to cooperate with the system and legitimate its values.

With the above in mind, this section begins with two selections dealing with alienated white middle-class youth. Following are selections which are expressions of general interpersonal alienation and, finally, selections that portray alienation from the entire society or "System."

## MICHAEL MC CLURE

*was born in Kansas in 1932 and became prominent among the beat poets and writers who made San Francisco a new center of literary activity in the 1950s. McClure has published poetry and other writings in various periodicals, including* Evergreen Review, The Nation, *and* City Lights Journal. *He is also the author of a controversial play,* The Beard, *which uses Jean Harlow and Billy the Kid as archetypes of American cultural myths.* The Beard *was closed numerous times by the police during its Los Angeles and San Francisco runs because of its overt sexuality. In this selection from McClure's novel* The Mad Cub *(written in 1963 but unpublished until 1970) American youths are seen in perhaps their most alienated condition, where neither love, sex, drugs, nor ideology can rescue their lost souls from the constant instrusions and deadening impact of the American way of life with its constant shouts of "Cut your hair! Get a job! Grow up to a suburban life! Fight the commies! Live monogamously, and if you can't, lie continually!"*

*McClure's latest volume of poetry is* Star.

*From*

## THE MAD CUB

I SEE MYSELF! . . . THAT I AM BEAUTIFUL! THAT I AM REALLY BEAUTIFUL but I am not able to get on top of the realization. I can't encompass the realization that I'm beautiful. I see how I must look to other people for a moment . . . Yes, I am beautiful and that should give me some assurance but I can't believe that I'm beautiful.

Since I was fifteen years old, people have told me that I am handsome or beautiful but I don't believe it. My mother is beautiful but my beauty is weaker than hers. My grandfather was nobly handsome . . . In my mother it becomes beauty and finally in me it is a kind of shallow mockery of beauty . . . When I was young I romanticized that there was elf-blood in our family—but maybe it's true. It is the way that I move that's beautiful not the way I look. My appearance is weakly handsome but there is a strong spark of life in my eyes when they come to life. What I have is the knowledge that I am an animal—and I'll never give that up. Even when my eyes are glazed and when I stumble against the furniture or sit in aching stupidity dumbed by the pain in my forehead there's another part of me that knows I am an animal and it is right . . . No matter what happens to me I'm going to be o.k. I am nearly twenty-three.

For a moment I can see that I'm beautiful and then it goes away . . . It does not even matter to me. What matters is that the animal warmth does not go out . . . and it does not go out even when I'm glazed and blunted and numb and dumb and stupid. I'm going to be o.k.

I walk through the lovely rooms of the apartment. It is my huge white cave and I am a baron of the human spirit living high in the air in majestic simplicity in a city that is a modern jungle . . . but it's not *that* I care about. What thrills me right now is that sensation is coming in through my senses and I am o.k. I am o.k., and I am in love with the universe whether it is the dark stars far away that I cannot see because it is daylight or just the lovely colors that gleam up through the old coats of paint on the floor. It is the sensation of being alive that I love—the idea that I am beautiful is nonsense . . .

But if I could only surround the idea that I'm beautiful—get the realization inside of myself and make it a part of me it would give me such self-assurance.

I love the plants here in the house and I love to see that they are alive and tremble when I walk past them with my foot shaking the floor ever so lightly—and they respond by quavering . . .

The dream is a painting of velvet and lathes of wood are being laid across it . . . Tentacle-like shapes weave across the velvet—the lathes of wood shift themselves . . . It dissolves and becomes a painting of purely tentacle shapes . . .

The peyote man rises up . . . He is flat and one-dimensional like a shadow . . . I know he will get bigger and I feel myself draw away from him in the dream . . . He gets bigger and bigger. Now he is twenty feet tall. He is like the Phantom in the comic strips except that he is neither good nor evil. He is only threatening and his costume is not a costume but his being—he is glabrous and featureless . . . He does not know love or fear or hate or any human thing. Many people who take peyote dream of the peyote man . . . a huge figure sometimes threatening, sometimes pursuing and sometimes just there . . . In dreams he sometimes pursues me . . . My dreams give me the creeps . . .

Jeanie has just gotten out of a mental institution and I talk to her over the phone . . . "I am having dreams about a peyote man . . . I can't think right . . . Everything glows and gives off light . . . I am having a dark night of the soul . . . nothing matters to me."

"It's the peyote that is doing it . . ." she says. "I dreamed about the peyote man also," she continues.

"What can I do?"

She tells me to take sleeping pills and to avoid peyote . . . It helps and I hope it will be the ending of a kind of hell.

"The peyote man rises up out of the darkness— he is twenty feet tall! He is chasing me . . . He looks like the Phantom in the comic strips, he is almost featureless, he is black and he chases me down long halls that are not halls but are vistas overlooking eternity . . . I run through the emptiness of space as if it were a hall . . . He does not breathe and I do not scream . . . My feet make no noise on the surface I am running on—it is absolute silence . . . I stop running . . . there is only nothingness. The peyote man rises up again in front of me. He is twenty feet tall and like the Phantom in the comic strips except that he is black and has no features . . ." I write down the dream to remember it and as I write the blankness comes over my eyes and I feel that my head has already gone numb and thoughtless . . . I am fighting to regain my sense . . . There is no meaning to anything . . . It is morning but I imagine the noon ahead of me. Noon is a glaring meaningless thing. Perhaps at noon I will be able to feel again.

The night madness is blue and its swirls around me in a dark-blue envelope—I beat on the walls. They boom and plaster shatters and I scream, "Love me! LOVE ME! LOVE ME! LOVE ME! LOVE MEEEEEEEEEE! OH GOD, PLEASE LOVE ME, LOVE ME, BABY LOVE ME!"

I see myself doing it. The pain is so terrible I become somebody else watching. I can be either myself bashing around in the room or I can be a free spirit watching. In the daytime when my eyes glaze over and blunk-out I walk into furniture—I walk into the edge of the table or into chairs . . . I step on anything on the floor . . . I knock down the phone tumbling over the phone wire and it falls on my foot and I curse, scream, and yell . . . for a few moments my head gets clear. There is a constant dull ache in the front of my forehead . . . It feels like wood or lead . . . I get so I can't stand the dull ache . . . The ache is like the glaze in my eyes.

"Oh God, help me baby," I fall by the edge of the bed tugging at the quilt and she turns away from me in rage—she hates me. I mock her viciously. I say everything I can think of that will torment her and make her angry . . . I spit at her, I turn her over, I pull her hair . . . She gets up and slowly and angrily dresses and says she is leaving me. I fall down weeping and repentant and beg her to stay . . . We both end up weeping and the night madness dissipates. We have sex . . . I force her—making love to her . . .

Bond is strange—once Bond was a kind of happy-go-lucky kid and now he is cranky and almost warped. He's full of anger. When we grew up together I picked on Bond less than the others did and was like an older brother. He idolized me . . . Now he thinks he is more of a success than I and he resents how much I picked on him or helped him. He wants to make me pay for it. I don't blame him. I was pretty mean—but I don't want to pay for it . . . Some kind of sickness has come over me . . . My eyes glaze . . . I can't feel anything.

The night madness happens. I can't sleep. It is a kind of horror . . . I begin telling Cathy that she must love me—she will not answer . . . I demand that she love me and still she won't answer. She pretends that she's asleep. I shake her and she won't wake up—she sets her face into vicious lines—it scares me and I feel more unloved. I try to roll her over and she swears at me. I persuade her to wake up and talk to me but she's angry . . . She sits glaring at me. I get sick and fearful—I beg her to love me and give me love . . . She won't answer me and I tell her to go back to bed—she rolls over and pretends she's sleeping. I begin to threaten her and curse her and mock her . . . She cries and gets more angry . . . I go into despair . . . I'm totally alone in the universe. I beg her to love me . . . She is angrier—I forcibly turn her over. She is really angry . . . I fill up with tension and I stand up and walk around in the room swinging my arms and yelling and weeping and begging for love. I run to the bed again but she will still not have anything to do with me . . . It goes on for hours till I am exhausted enough to sleep.

I sit horrified with reality. The kitchen ceiling is finished in swirls of plaster done long ago by a hand that is now far away—ugly cracks have broken in the plaster and years of cobwebs and dust and grime stick to the plaster swirls. Kitchen grease floats up and acts like glue to hold the filth in the air to the plaster. The kitchen is frightening—it is hideous and pristine as only old buildings can become with the touch of a master's hand. I am obsessed with order, neatness, and cleanliness but I like the ceiling the way it is. The walls are painted white but the white coat is thin and the brown paint beneath looms through in the afternoon light. There is not one extra object in the kitchen, on the shelves, or tables. Each dish is washed—I wash each one as it becomes dirty.

Over the sink is a color reproduction of the Madonna of the Rocks by Leonardo Da Vinci. The babe Jesus holds up his little fist—he sits beside a heap of huge pine cones. The picture is dried-out and yellow even through the color.

A glass jar of pussy willows looms up into the air . . . but they are dead as the room is dead . . . Out the window is a view of the sky over the brick wall—there is dead moss on the wall.

My eyes are glazed and I can't feel anything. Bond comes by to see me and I listen to him. He's angry about something and he wants to argue but I do not have the spark to argue . . . He becomes more angry and depressed . . . I clip my nails and we disparage each other with our glances. All of the world is dead.

I want to ask Bond why he doesn't get out, but I am afraid to be alone and Bond is trapped by the inertness of the room.

I tilt back onto the two back legs of the chair and stare at Bond. He leaps up and runs out.

Drifting in my thoughts I remember Neeland . . . Small Neeland comes in sliding around the edge of the door yet somehow appears directly in the doorway and walks in fast and straight. Neeland has been high on marijuana so many years that he looks like a terry toon wolf—a harmless wolf but a wolf . . . He has come to be what he is while he's high because he is high constantly . . . Neeland's shoulders hunch together, he smiles in a boyish and wise way.

"Have you got the buttons?" I ask him anxiously. I want to get turned on to the peyote right away—my first turn on.

"Sure baby, you think I'd forget you?—I didn't zip all the way over here for nothing . . ."

He reaches into the pocket of his undersized boy's trench coat and walks me into the other room. Neeland is about thirty-three.

"You want some coffee, Neeland?" I ask.

"Nah, not yet . . . I'd like some water in a while though."

Neeland lays a packet wrapped in a torn brown paper bag on the table. He does it in a hip way but there is an element of ceremony about it. Neeland has the hands and thin wrists of an artist.

Like Neeland tells me, I do not drink anything alcoholic for several days before this sunny morning and I eat a light breakfast early on arising.

"How do you feel?" asks Neeland as I reach for the packet.

"Like taking this," I say. I take the packet and begin unfolding the brown paper. Inside are five small wrinkled leathery disks of dried cactus called *buttons*.

"It's not enough is it?" I ask Neeland.

Neeland smiles at me brightly with a wise grin. "It'll do, it'll do," he says.

Neeland is a decorator of the soul . . . If Neeland were ordinary he would be an interior decorator or a painter of small perfect works of sensitive art but Neeland is extraordinary. He wants everything he says to have the intention of poetry and all that he does to have a touch of hip perfection. He believes so deeply in art that he wants life to be a work of art.

If Neeland has nothing to say he's quiet and looks hip and wise. Neeland does not have much to say because most of what can be said is not art. He's quiet and his eyes twinkle or grow dim—but he stays on top of the scene and he stays cool. He has a *mystique* of dope . . . he believes in drugs and in turning-on people, 'cool people' as he says, at just the right time in their lives.—He gets vibrations about what is cool and not cool.

Neeland's apartment and wife and child are perfections of art. If he has a broken vase then it is a small perfect tiffany vase valueless to the used-goods stores. His Indian incense burner lies next to a brass Arabian water pipe. There is a bouquet of peacock feathers—a small bouquet. There are a few far-out books on mysticim or rare verse casually and perfectly placed on his low table. One of the best drawings that Bond has ever done is stuck to the wall with a thumbtack next to a photo of Neeland and his wife holding hands and looking into each other's eyes.

Tarna is Neeland's wife—behind her head in the half-light is a reproduction of a Byzantine madonna from an old fresco. Tarna looks like the madonna. Candlelight flickers on the face of the picture—the room is cool—everyone is warmed by their own thoughts and they don't feel the chill. Brooder looks off into space, dazedly into the corner of the room, with his jaw hanging down. Brooder is not at ease with Neeland but he senses he should like Neeland. Bond talks to Neeland about a group of negro singers he went to hear.

"Oh yeah, they are too much, man," Bond says. "We went into the back to stand and they all ignored us so cool . . . After a while we began to sing with them and they turned around and smiled at us and we became a part of the whole thing . . ."

Neeland looks agreeable and wise listening to Bond. Bond goes on working himself up—he is being too affable. He feels something deeply and religiously moving and he does not know how to say so to Neeland. Neeland senses it and wants to keep things cool—not mentioning the religiousness of the singing Bond has heard—but keeping the aura of it in the room.

Lovely Tarna with short black hair and long slender neck is speaking to Cathy in a happy voice. "I had a dream last night . . . I dreamed that Karen, an old friend of mine from San Diego, appeared to me in a dream . . . She said, 'Tarna, I am in Mexico and everything is good here.' It was almost like a vision. Then she turned and clouds came up and folded around her and she turned and smiled just once and that was the end of the dream."

Tarna leans forward with the pleasure of her story and smiles at Cathy who smiles in return—two beautiful women smile at each other . . . Tarna's short black hair is as dark as the lines of make-up on her eyelids—it is the only make-up that she wears. Her skin is pale, soft, and unwrinkled—the face of a sexy madonna almost decadent in beauty . . . "When I went to work this morning," she continues, "I stopped by one of those little machines that stamp out words on a circle of aluminum—the kind that you can use on key chains for a fob if you want . . . and I stamped out a message for myself. Do you know what I wrote on it . . . ?" Cathy smiles at her questioningly enwrapped in the story . . .

"I wrote out—IN MEXICO AND SWINGING."

Tarna and Neeland's daughter comes in through the candlelight to sit on Tarna's lap. She moves quietly—a graceful creature with pale face and gentle manners—never speaking, silent, never enthusiastic except in the most subtle movement of face or gentle smile. Tarna works and Neeland cares for the daughter—sleeping till noon and arising spooky to turn on to a joint of pot . . . I am able always to forget that Cathy is working and that I care for our child after school in the noon . . . My child seldom enters my consciousness except in rage or anger that I direct toward her . . . I see myself repeating the bad gestures of my father. I never speak of my parents—sometimes I receive a letter and weep with anger or rage or I feel nothing. I am blunked-out in the light of day heading for a new night-madness.

Cathy kisses me with a very wet-mouthed kiss—she clings to me and I turn away from her slightly . . . She clings again, clutching at my shoulders . . . I pull my lips away from hers. She frightens me. She pulls me to her again and kisses me on the lips . . . A well of all my guilts opens . . . I think of Ferna and Dolores . . . I pull away from Cathy. I push her away from me a little . . . She looks at me with face of desire and anguish . . . Her face is lighted with desire and twisted to one side with anguish. Cathy's hair is like a beautiful Greek helmet—it falls to her shoulders—hair of many colors—of dark and light brown and blond and pale all intermixed. Her face is smooth and angelic. She frightens me. Her arms and bosom are soft and they challenge me to take them of my own accord but I can only be the passive receiver of pleasure . . . I am no good! I have hurt her. She stares at me in anger and resentment . . . glints shoot out of her blue and hazel eyes. I see the face of a hurt child alight with almost extra-human anger . . . She turns from me fiercely. I have just masturbated and made myself sexless . . . I would go masturbate again thinking of some act . . . Ferna, Sarie, Dolores . . .

I walk away . . . sit in another room at a black desk . . . I am blanked . . . Horrible things happen inside my head . . . I want to die. Out of the window the city is meaningless. Children and grown-ups pass like robots in the glare of light . . . It is better at night and when it rains . . . A long time passes . . . I feel numbness and a spreading sensation inside of myself . . . I don't feel anything . . . I get tense and jump up. I throw my arms about and I sit down again. I stare broodingly into the corners of the room and out the door of the room . . . I know now that I am looking intensely out but I see nothing . . . Cathy walks by the door. She does not look in at me. I think how angry I am at her and how she has treated me . . . Kissing me like that . . . I know I am wrong . . . I watch her pass by the door like a lamb of beauty. I know I am wrong . . . Her face is twisted up with anger and hatred for me . . .

Cathy will not speak to me . . . Her face is utterly impassive except for the lines of detestation that show about her eyes. She turns away from me as I walk in. She turns to the sink and turns on the hot water and washes a dish . . . I come up behind her and stand behind her. I am filled with rage that she will not speak to me . . . I want to hit her to make her speak to me . . . I need help . . . I am in anguish in guilt . . .

"Baby . . ." I say in almost a whine.

She does not turn around. She turns on the cold tap of water.

"What's the matter?" I say. "Why don't you talk to me?"

She does not say a word. There is a fierce angularity to the movements of her arms. I feel rage rising in myself that she should hate me.

"Don't you love me?"

There's silence.

"What's the matter, baby?" I will not admit to myself that she needs sex and loving . . . there is only a faint stirring of the admission within myself at a rooty core—I want to hit her.

"CATHY! Speak to me!" She won't answer.

She walks into the other room leaving only a swirl of her movements behind her . . . I follow her.

"Speak to me. Please! I can't stand it . . ."

Peyote teaches me the separate consciousness of my being and I am aware of the creature that is stomach and the one that is solar plexus and the one that is brain and chest and all the fragmented creatures of my being that form the totality . . . In reading biology I hope to make the discoveries that will liberate man to exist in timelessness and state of superconsciousness. I blank out, my eyes become dulled, and the pain in my forehead has started, but if I can begin a thought process before that happens I become at one with the primitive creatures who scientists claim are the relatives of our ancestors—actual living beings of plasm close to what our genetic structures once evolved from. We are separated from those creatures only by time and I know from the drugs that time does not exist, and to ever have being is to be real in all space forever . . . My eyes begin to grow farther and farther apart and I feel my being spreading through space. I cannot stand the sensation but I realize this is the sensation that the primordial cousins feel as the total of their existence . . . They are only their desires and hungers and sensations and nothing more, except for the vast philosophical awareness of the universe that we have become separated from genetically by our self-consciousness . . . I go off in my state of feelinglessness, becoming *those* creatures, and I feel the individual parts of myself rebelling against the control that I hold over them . . . That is all that I feel sometimes—it is terrifying but I know I can make my achievement and bring back a new glory for mankind . . . Surely I know too that it is hideous but only because . . .

This is the most beautiful night of my life . . . Cathy and I make love. I do not know why everything has been so wrong between us . . . It is the most beautiful love-making that anyone has ever done. Cathy almost always comes when I can bring myself to fuck . . . but how loudly she moaned . . . I lay here feeling the absolute bliss of completed pleasure—the walls are soft things that smile to me . . . The air is still and warmly cool . . . I hear the hum of cars as they pass . . . The darkness is a blessing . . . Bars of reflected neon light stripe the floors in pale blue and pink . . . Angelic beings drift in the air harmlessly and pass love from one to another . . . Invisible blossoms of heather explode in scented flashes . . .

Cathy's smooth body beneath me is a tiny continent of pleasure and sleekness . . . Her thin happy face looking up at me in the darkness was a face of demonic joy transported in the ecstasy of coming . . . Her features changed and she became even more lovely—a different person . . . She became the pleasure-person that she always is beneath the dailiness . . . My whole body became tense and uncontrollable . . . What relief not to be in control but fucking involuntarily seeing only Cathy's beauty as I move over her and feel my body out of control seeking only pleasure . . . Visions coming into my head of bright colors and shapes like pitchers and chalices to the final enormous pleasurable shudderings and twitches and knottings of toes and shoulders in final spasm of release . . . And now side by side stroking and loving and looking off into the small distances in the room as if they were the whole universe, for now there is no war with the universe—no spiritual battle but only a oneness of tension, release, and desire for pleasure satisfied.

I turn the pages reading the Odes of Anacreon, the early Greek poet. The sheer beauty overwhelms me . . .

Nature gave horns to bulls, and hooves to horses,
swift-footedness to hares, to lions wide-parting of teeth,
to the fish the power of swimming, to the birds to fly,
to the men thoughtfulness; for women she had naught besides.
What then does she give? Beauty, instead of all shields,
instead of all spears: and anyone being beautiful
vanquishes both steel and fire.

The sunlight on the page does not gleam back the radiant light of my own fears and horrors that I feel. My hand does not seem cold and blue and pink gleaming colors as it does in a dark night of the soul but it is the color of flesh again and the color of reality that men accept. I am not afraid of the coldness and night madness. I am making a new reality where the old one could no longer make it. The drugs and not religious revelations have showed me that I cannot grip the accepted reality of men. Religion and poetry show that the states of consciousness do not matter but only the acceptance of truth and liberty and beauty matter . . . not how they are seen.

. . . the midst of the furrow shines through the waters,
as a lily wrapped in violets. And over the silver,
ride on dancing dolphins, Love and Desire, laughing
and guileful with youthful forehead . . .

The sunlight on my hand is warming and it is good . . . Drunken Anacreon and sober Jesus were similar men. My head begins to hurt and become thick and stupid.

Fucking Cathy her face changes—the saintly face of intense sweetness surrounded by a helmet of graceful hair becomes an almost demonic face—not demonic in the sense of bad but demonic in the sense of completion and satisfaction. Cathy becomes wholly absorbed upon the one point of the desire to come. She closes her eyes and the whole consciousness of her being moves toward her pussy but the revelation of what she is feeling glows on her face and draws it into a new shape of utter consciousness of that *one* thing that she's working for—the orgasm. The pleasant and almost mystic face becomes a face of divine concentration . . . Her eyes close, the hair falls out of place and the locks of it become living with a life of their own—she is electrified but tuned only toward an internal sensation . . . She becomes even more beautiful if that is possible . . .

My body is like a platform that moves up and down upon the pillowyness of her stomach and breasts and I do not close my eyes but hold them open to watch the changes upon her face and her delicacy of concentration . . . My eyes close blinking hard with pleasure . . . and I know that my face is changed too . . . and that I have become the submerged part of myself. We beat against each other mindlessly and in unison . . . Where a beat of pleasure is lost the enormous body of what we are in the darkness seeks to regain the lost beat and garner pleasure from even the missing of a stroke as a variation in the fugue of flesh that we are playing . . . My eyes press close again . . . I know that my face is elongated like hers and drawn tight in a concentration of pleasure. All men and women are trained and become less autonomous in life and this is our escape from that—for we become momentarily eternal. I think of hummingbirds.

There is not enough money and everything is filled with despair.

Cathy leans to me gently and says, "I'm going to have to leave you baby, if there are any more troubles like last night . . ." We look at the apartment. The table is broken where I kicked it last night . . . The broken dishes appear out of the sack the garbage is in . . . I have given away or destroyed everything that was not of immediate use to us. Now in our fights we have begun to destroy even the pitiful necessities that are left. The apartment is huge and sprawling at the top of a building of apartments—the rooms are almost empty . . . chairs . . . a desk . . . a table . . . a bookcase . . . paintings . . . child's toys . . . nothing else . . . It is a graceful and poetic decor—empty and proud but haunting and free showing we desire freedom from possessions. Now even the last necessities have begun to be destroyed. Soon not even the necessities of pride will be left.

Cathy is gentle and worn out—there is a softness of exhaustion to her body. "I love you but I can't stand any more of this. I'll have to take the baby and leave . . ."

"No, everything is going to be o.k."

"Nothing can be o.k.," she says. "I love you and I don't want to leave you but I'm going to have to if it happens again."

I smile at her. "Everything is going to be o.k." I feel cleared out and I know everything is going to be all right. The despair of the wreck of our apartment stares at me though. I refuse to think about it. I feel the blankness edging up on my mind and I know that my eyes begin to go dull. I fight it back.

"Listen, everything is going to be o.k.," I tell her forcefully. Cathy cannot even smile she just looks at me with love and exhaustion. I keep her up late in the night with my spoken fears and I weep and go mad begging for love when I am incapable of sex. In the week she must go off to her job with few hours sleep and she falls into silent rages against me and I cannot understand what is wrong.

"I'll get a job," I say. Even as I say it I do not believe it. And I do believe it too. I believe it utterly. Later I imagine myself dazed and blanked standing in fear and self-consciousness asking for a job.

Cathy does not look at me.

In the night at the end of the madness we made love. If I reach a certain point . . . if I break . . . if I cry and weep . . . if I crash through some armor of my spirit then I can allow myself the force that love requires.

The baby comes around the corner and peeps into the room.

"Daddy break everything . . ." she says.

I feel like I am swelling and drifting. If it is true that there is no such thing as time and that my visions are right how does all this matter? Surely by act of will I can supersede all of this and bring us glory . . .

I know I must kill myself. I can't feel a thing. I feel nothing! NOTHING! I feel nothing . . . There's only the clumpy aching dullness in the front of my head. My eyes glass over and my thoughts go elsewhere and I am not sure where they are.—I believe that I am seeing horrible things. Pictures, distorted pictures, out of Norse mythology come into my mind—I see the human gods torturing each other—beams of light pour from their long ugly faces and . . .

Behind all the nothingness locked in the physical body that I am, the small boy slips through halls smelling of castor oil used to polish the floors, and down the dimly-lighted corridor. At the end of the hallway a pair of door-like windows beam a glare of silvery light into the end of the corridor. I push open a door to my right and turn inside. I walk up the three stairs and into the room with walls lined by books . . . I dart straight to the wall with the books of history and mythology . . . My eyes dulled, I see what was once a wonder in distorted horror . . . The gods tear and rip at each other. The fey beings spread—their eyes and organs become farther and farther apart and they dissipate into space and I am one of them . . . I wish to make an opera of bellowings in the emptiness of eternity . . . I am empty . . . Even the tips of my fingers are numb . . . I should kill myself but I will not not kill myself . . . I know the reason that I want to kill myself has been put on me somehow by someone else . . . I will not do it! I will not kill myself . . . I know that I will be o.k. Isn't there somebody somewhere to help me? I am not sure what I am feeling.

I watch my own hand do things . . . It means nothing to me. My own square, almost plump but thin-fingered hand, reaches for a cigarette . . . It shakes it from the pack . . . I do not even care—I look away. What is wrong with my hand now? Once it looked more honest . . . The wrist was more squarish then and more boylike . . . There was a kind of simplicity that I had then . . . I felt things . . . But yes, I remember now . . . there was the beginning of this blankness even then . . . The lovely baby—my child—lay on the rich brown velvet. She glistened in the sun radiating back the light of the sun . . . Her pink pads of flesh were a glory in the light . . . Her smile is the smile of all living creatures telling of utter happiness and joy . . . And as I watch my eyes dim out so long ago at the rage that I must be tied, that I may not be free, that I am not utterly a seeker of pleasure but now a father in a Hell of Heaven . . .

I must kill myself . . . it drifts up to me from somewhere . . .

I will not do it . . .

I will not do it . . .

[. . . ] Some days I am Captain Nowhere. I awake with blindness and stupidity in my eyes and the feeling of dullness in my head that gradually expands to a painless pain that fills my forehead and droops down to my eyes and glazes them. I am forcing myself. Forcing myself to feel something. Now I stick myself with a pin. I stop but it does not mean much. I am not so far gone that I will stick myself with pins. I want to see what it will feel like—I want to see myself react to it. I stick the fine gleaming blue point down to my skin and I prick the flesh . . . No! that doesn't do any good. I stop, I just sit here feeling nothing. Everything is out there but I see nothing. It begins to occur to me that the whole universe is meaningless—and I force that away and try to reject the thought. I know there are elements of life in it . . . I know we are meant to pass over and be transcendent of the pettiness of all we are doing. I envy the wild beautiful creatures who are not out of place—the shining huge and furious fish in the seas and the wild animals on the tops of mountains waiting to become extinct.

"OH!" I say out loud into the air. "AHHHHH!!" I groan. I try to make myself feel something. There is nothing to feel. Only another day to pass as all days have passed. Everything is hideous. Everything radiates a light that is frightening to me because it is meaningless and cold. The space between objects frightens me because it shows me that there is space and space is cold. I do not want there to be space between things. I do not want things to be close together. I hate everything that is made out of physical matter and I hate everything else too.

And there is nothing but what is made out of physical matter and there is no time. Visions of horror begin to come before my eyes. No, they do not come before my eyes—they happen on the inside of my body . . . In my head? No, I surely cannot believe it for we think with our whole body. But do we think with our whole body? I can't feel anything. I can't feel love or hate. I can only feel fear and something else. Everything luminesces. Everything gives off light. This is too hideous! I am nowhere, nowhere, and I am on the verge of dissipation into the air. I feel my eyes grow farther and farther apart and my ears . . . I am expanding into space . . . I fight to stop myself before I expand and become only my component gobs of flesh and atoms. I can't feel anything . . . I can't talk . . . I am by myself . . . I am filled with fears . . . I see things that I cannot see and it is horrible . . . I can't stand it, I will kill myself . . I am numb . . .

[. . . ] Racing along over the freeways, the night is blackish-pink and very cool. The car heater makes warmth all the way to the knees. There are no stars only the mile-high blanket of fog reflecting darkness and neon. Huge beer signs have lighted foam rising and dropping in the giant glass. The time and temperature blink off and on at the tops of concrete towers. Food and toothpaste blare on lighted billboards . . . Sodium lights make yellow glare for a stretch then high street lights give off blue-white light . . .

I am high—driving into a mysterious eternity. I pull the wheel and roll my body turning the sharp bends. Instruction signs about turns never make sense. I am alone in a world of lights and blackness. The smell in the car is the smell of air pipes and gasoline and oil . . . I blank out just a little. It's beautiful but too much to cope with . . . The lumpy dullness in the center of my forehead and the back of my head begins . . . I force it away . . . I flick on the radio knob. Music begins—it is a rich opulent and three-dimensional carpet of sound that fills the car floating and drifting in waves. The car becomes a red four-wheeled chariot in a modern fairy story. I drive into a technicolor infinity. Cars should be honored and made into creatures with their sides hammered into patterns of feathers and wings and fur or rich abstract patterns of texture and each one should be unique and loved . . .

Cathy drives in the dusk. She smiles enjoying the freedom of cars. Her face leans forward as she drives. She smiles into the road ahead. In profile she is a sweet little girl. I am totally devoid of feeling except for fear rising in me. The knolls and hills are covered with fields of grass and copses of dark trees. There is something that seems like evil in the plants and rounded hills—they threaten. The trees are green but there's a blackness that shines out of the leaves—a genuine mysterious evil. The hills are threatening . . . Nothing makes any sense to me. I am afraid I will be liberated into time and space and no longer be myself but be the drifting meaningless bundle of molecules and atoms and cells of my being.

"Cathy . . . I . . ."

She doesn't hear. She shifts to a lower gear for the grade. Her arm is a fine beautiful arm in the tight sweater.

"Cathy, I feel bad . . . I . . . I don't know . . ."

She looks at me questioningly and angrily . . .

I can't tell her about the threat of the hills and trees or what it would be like to suddenly be a free, loose, meaningless being without thought or feeling—and be everywhere at once.

"I want to . . . uhh," I can't say it because I do not know what I want. I know I don't want to go where we are going or see the people we are going to see. Ragner will turn me off and put me down . . . There will be a mockery of friendship . . . Really I know somewhere inside I must hate him and I am filled with rage that I can't feel and it blanks my mind. How do I express ambition or hatred?

[. . .] I can't talk to anybody . . . I can't even answer simple questions. When somebody asks me something I feel a constriction in my chest and I forget to breathe in . . . I quit breathing . . . I look at them stupidly and helplessly . . . They can say anything to me . . . They can insult me, or put me down, or mock me . . . Everybody is a little afraid of me so that is my last defense . . . otherwise I would be torn to pieces by the world . . .

I begin writing down everything I can't say.

I carry a notebook with me and I write whatever answer I could not give in the notebook. I do it the first chance I get but I do not let anyone see me do it. Each time I try to write down what scared me and why I could not answer. I refuse to be afraid of anything!

This is taking the edge off the anguish. I begin to understand more things from biology and the facts that I know begin to explain my problems. I am afraid sometimes, when I look with a clear head at what I am saying, that I am totally mad. Things have never been so bad as they are right now . . . I am having visions of rapine and destruction that are not describable because they are not images and I am having brain-movies still from the peyote and I cannot speak to people and I feel the constriction in my chest. All I can do is write in my notebook and sit with dull eye and masturbate.

I do not want to die and I will fight dying like I will fight madness—but I can't speak to anyone or tell them . . . I can't ask for help and I do not know what I could say or ask for if I could speak. I am overcome with urges to hurl myself into death. I try to keep the desires abstract without pictures of how I might kill myself springing into mind.

The blocks go by . . . block after block of absolute meaninglessness—building fronts and dead or lifeless people existing and walking and breathing like robots or funguses . . . It all slashes by the bus windows with perfect clarity . . . I start to stand up and scream and I sit back down . . . I have quit breathing . . . I take a deep breath . . . I close my eyes and I think about the meaninglessness and what is going by the bus windows . . . I have to remember to breathe. I open my eyes and see more buildings just like the others flashing by . . . More fungoid robot people walk the streets or stand on the corners . . . Nothing makes sense to me . . . I do not belong here . . . I stand up and get ready to run the length of the bus screaming . . . I stop myself . . . If I do that I will be locked up.

I sit down again . . . I am going to scream anyway . . . I open my eyes . . . Nothing I see makes sense to me or has any meaning . . . I have no human feelings for anything I see . . . I know if I scream and hurl myself the length of the bus I will be locked up . . . I hold myself back . . . I've got to do something . . . I feel nothing but terror and the fear that I am dissolving into meaninglessness.

I pull the cord and run and jump out the door of the bus as it stops. I start running down the streets . . . I need some wine. That will help! Some wine! I will knock myself out with wine. I will daze myself with something to drink.

I dash into a liquor store. "Gimme that," I want to say but I can't speak . . . I point at the little pint bottle of wine I want . . . The man looks at me and sees my face . . . He hands the bottle to me . . . I reach into my pocket . . .

"That's forty-seven cents," he says.

I still can't talk. I show the man what I have in my hand. I have thirty-seven cents.

The man looks at my face again.

"Take it," he says . . .

I run out into the streets and begin running for block after block. I open the bottle and take swigs as I run . . . I have never been so close to the edge before.

I run a mile to the little print shop where a friend works . . . I try to tell him what happened. I still can't talk very well but he is patient . . . and he touches me on the shoulder and it helps. I wonder if the man in the liquor store knows he saved a life . . . at least for a while.

## JOSEPH HELLER

*is the author of* Catch-22, *some of whose characters figure in the story below. He has also written the play* We Bombed in New Haven *and is completing his second novel,* Something Happened. *He uses the mode of black humor to bring home the madness of war—even "just" wars like the one against Hitler and the Axis. In this short story, originally written as a chapter for* Catch-22, *the generation gap is ironically portrayed as it takes form in a wealthy American family. The rapid social changes American society is undergoing seemingly make such a gap inevitable—often with tragic consequences for both youth and parents. But even more important, such a gap contains within it symptoms and causes of the interpersonal alienation that is so widespread in our society.*

# LOVE, DAD

Second Lieutenant Edward J. Nately III was really a good kid. He was a slender, shy, rather handsome young man with fine brown hair, delicate cheekbones, large, intent eyes and a sharp pain in the small of his back when he woke up alone on a couch in the parlor of a whorehouse in Rome one morning and began wondering who and where he was and how in the world he had ever got there. He had no real difficulty remembering *who* he was. He was Second Lieutenant Edward J. Nately III, a bomber pilot in Italy in World War Two, and he would be 20 years old in January, if he lived.

Nately had always been a good kid from a Philadelphia family that was even better. He was always pleasant, considerate, trustworthy, loyal, helpful, friendly, courteous, kind, obedient, cheerful, not always so thrifty or wise but invariably brave, clean and reverent. He was without envy, malice, anger, hatred or resentment, which puzzled his good friend Yossarian and kept him aware of how eccentric and naïve Nately really was and how much in need of protection by Yossarian against the wicked ways of the world.

Why, Nately had actually enjoyed his childhood—and was not even ashamed to admit it! Nately *liked* all his brothers and sisters and always had, and he did not mind going home for vacations and furloughs. He got on well with his uncles and his aunts and with all his first, second and third cousins, whom, of course, he numbered by the dozens, with all the friends of the family and with just about everyone else he ever met, except, possibly, the incredibly and unashamedly depraved old man who was always in the whorehouse when Nately and Yossarian arrived and seemed to have spent his entire life living comfortably and happily there. Nately was well bred, well groomed, well mannered and well off.

He was, in fact, immensely wealthy, but no one in his squadron on the island of Pianosa held his good nature or his good family background against him.

Nately had been taught by both parents all through childhood, preadolescence and adolescence to shun and disdain "climbers," "pushers," "*nouveaux*" and "parvenus," but he had never been able to, since no climbers, pushers, *nouveaux* or parvenus had ever been allowed near any of the family homes in Philadelphia, Fifth Avenue, Palm Beach, Bar Harbor, Southampton, Mayfair and Belgravia, the 16th *arrondissement*, the north of France, the south of France and all of the good Greek islands. To the best of his knowledge, the guest lists at all these places had always been composed exclusively of ladies and gentlemen and children of faultless dress and manners and great dignity and aplomb. There were always many bankers, brokers, judges, ambassadors and former ambassadors among them, many sportsmen, cabinet officials, fortune hunters and dividend-collecting widows, divorcees, orphans and spinsters. There were no labor leaders among them and no laborers, and there were never any self-made men. There was one unmarried social worker, who toiled among the underprivileged for fun, and several retired generals and admirals who were dedicating the remaining years of their lives to preserving the American Constitution by destroying it and perpetuating the American way of life by bringing it to an end.

The only one in the entire group who worked hard was Nately's mother; but since she did not work hard at anything constructive, her reputation remained good. Nately's mother worked very hard at opening and closing the family homes in Philadelphia, Fifth Avenue, Palm Beach, Bar Harbor, Southampton, Mayfair and Belgravia, the 16th *arrondissement*, the north of France, the south of France and all of the good Greek islands, and at safeguarding the family traditions, of which she had appointed herself austere custodian.

"You must never forget who and what you are"; Nately's mother had begun drumming it into Nately's head about Natelys long before Nately had any idea what a Nately was. "You are not a Guggenheim, who mined copper for a living, nor a Vanderbilt, whose fortune is descended from a common tugboat captain, nor an Armour, whose ancestors peddled putrefying meat to the gallant Union Army during the heroic War between the States, nor a Harriman, who made his money playing with choo-choo trains. Our family," she always declared with pride, "does *nothing* for our money."

"What your mater means, my boy," interjected his father with the genial, rococo wit Nately found so impressive, "is that people who make new fortunes are not nearly as good as the families who've lost old ones. Ha, ha, ha! Isn't that good, my dear?"

"I wish you would mind your own business when I'm talking to the boy," Nately's mother replied sharply to Nately's father.

"Yes, my dear."

Nately's mother was a stiff-necked, straight-backed, autocratic descendant of the old New England Thorntons. The family tree of the New England Thorntons, as she often remarked, extended back far past the Mayflower, almost to Adam himself. It was a matter of historical record that the Thorntons were lineal descendants of the union of John Alden, a climber, to Priscilla Mullins, a pusher. The genealogy of the Natelys was no less impressive, since one of Nately's father's forebears had distinguished himself conspicuously at the battle of Bosworth Field, on the losing side.

"Mother, what is a regano?" Nately inquired innocently one day while on holiday from Andover after an illicit tour through the Italian section of Philadelphia, before reporting to his home for duty. "Is it anything like a Nately?"

"Oregano," replied his mother with matriarchal distaste, "is a revolting vice indulged in by untitled foreigners in Italy. Don't ever mention it again."

Nately's father chuckled superiorly when Nately's mother had gone. "You mustn't take everything your mother says too literally, son," he advised with a wink. "Your mother is a remarkable woman, as you probably know, but when she deals with such matters as oregano, she's usually full of shit. Now, I've eaten oregano many times, if you know what I mean, and I expect that you will, too, before you marry and settle down. The important thing to remember about eating oregano is never to do it with a girl from your own social station. Do it with salesgirls and waitresses, if you can, or with any of our maids, except Lili, of course, who, as you may have noticed, is something of a favorite of mine. I'm not sending you to women of lower social station out of snobbishness, but simply because they're so much better at it than the daughters and wives of our friends. Nurses and schoolteachers enjoy excellent reputations in this respect. Not a word about this to your mother, of course."

Nately's father overflowed with sanguine advice of that kind. He was a dapper, affable man of great polish and experience whom everybody but Nately's mother respected. Nately was proud of his father's wisdom and sophistication; and the eloquent, brilliant letters he received when away at school were treasured compensation for those bleak and painful separations from his parents. Nately's father, on the other hand, welcomed these separations from his son with ceremonious zeal, for they gave him opportunity to fashion the graceful, aesthetic, metaphysical letters in which he took such epicurean satisfaction.

> Dear Son (he wrote when Nately was away at Andover):
>
> Don't be the first person by whom new things are tried and don't be the last one to set old ones aside. If our family were ever to adopt for itself a brief motto, I would want it to be precisely those words, and not merely because I wrote them myself. (Ha, ha, ha!) I would select them for the wisdom they contain. They urge restraint, and restraint is the quintessence of dignity and taste. It is incumbent upon you as a Nately that dignity and taste are always what you show.
>
> Today you are at Andover. Tomorrow you will be elsewhere. There will be times in later life when you will find yourself with people who attended Exeter, Choate, Hotchkiss, Groton and other institutions of like ilk. These people will address you as equals and speak to you familiarly, as though you share with them a common fund of experience. Do not be deceived. Andover is Andover, and Exeter is not, and neither are any of the others anything that they are not.
>
> Throughout life, you must always choose your friends as discriminately as you choose your clothing, and you must bear in mind constantly that all that glitters is not gold.
>
> Love,
> Dad

Nately had hoarded these letters from his father loyally and was often tempted to fling their elevated contents into the jaded face of the hedonistic old man who seemed to be in charge of the whorehouse in Rome, in lordly refutation of his pernicious, unkempt immorality and as a triumphant illustration of what a cultivated, charming, intelligent and distinguished man of character was really like. What restrained Nately was a confused and intimidating suspicion that the old man would succeed in degrading his father with the same noxious and convincing trickery with which he had succeeded in degrading everything else Nately deemed holy. Nately had a large number of his father's letters to save. Following Andover, he had moved, of course, to Harvard, and his father had proved equal to the occasion.

Dear Son (his father wrote):

Don't be the first person by whom new things are tried and don't be the last person to set the old things aside. This pregnant couplet came to me right out of the blue only a few moments ago, while I was out on the patio listening to your mother and a Mozart concerto and spreading Crosse & Blackwell marmalade on my Melba toast, and I am interrupting my breakfast to communicate it to you while it is still fresh in my mind. Write it down on your brain, inscribe it on your heart, engrave it for all time on your memory centers, for the advice it contains is as sound as any I have ever told you.

Today you are at Harvard, the oldest educational institution in the United States of America, and I am not certain if you are as properly impressed with your situation as you should be. Harvard is more than just a good school; Harvard is also a good place to get an education, should you decide that you do want an education. Columbia University, New York University and the City College of New York in the city of New York are other good places at which to get an education, but they are not good schools. Universities such as Princeton, Yale, Dartmouth and bungalows in the Amherst-Williams complex are, of course, neither good schools nor good places at which to get an education and are never to be compared with Harvard. I hope that you are being as choosy in your choice of acquaintances there as you know your mother and I would like you to be.

Love,
Dad

> P.S. Avoid associating familiarly with Roman Catholics, colored people and Jews, regardless of how accomplished, rich or influential their parents may be, although Chinese, Japanese, Spaniards of royal blood and Moslems of foreign nationality are perfectly all right.
>
> P.P.S. Are you getting much oregano up there? (Ha, ha, ha!)

Nately sampled oregano dutifully his freshman year with a salesgirl, a waitress, a nurse and a schoolteacher, and with three girls in Scranton, Pennsylvania, on two separate occasions, but his appetite for the spice was not hoggish and exposure did not immunize him against falling so unrealistically in love the first moment he laid eyes on the dense, sluggish, yawning, ill-kempt whore lounging stark-naked in a room full of enlisted men ignoring her. Apart from these several formal and rather unexciting excursions into sexuality, Nately's first year at Harvard was empty and dull. He made few close friends, restricted, as he was, to associating only with wealthy Episcopalian and Church of England graduates of Andover whose ancestors had either descended lineally from the union of John Alden with Priscilla Mullins or been conspicuous at Bosworth Field, on the losing side. He spent many solitary hours fondling the expensive vellum bindings of the five books sent to him by his father as the indispensable basis of a sound personal library: *Forges and Furnaces of Pennsylvania; The Catalog of the Porcellian Club of Harvard University, 1941; Burke's Genealogical and Heraldic History of the Peerage, Baronetage and Knightage; Lord Chesterfield's Letters Written to His Son;* and the Francis Palgrave *Golden Treasury* of English verse. The pages themselves did not hold his interest, but the bindings were fascinating. He was often lonely and nagged by vague, incipient longings. He contemplated his sophomore year at Harvard without enthusiasm, without joy. Fortunately, the War broke out in time to save him.

> Dear Son (his father wrote, after Nately had volunteered for the Air Corps, to escape being drafted into the Infantry):
>
> You are now embarked upon the highest calling that Providence ever bestows upon man, the privilege to fight for his country. Play up, play up and play the game! I have every confidence that you will not fail your country, your family

and yourself in the execution of your most noble responsibility, which is to play up, play up and play the game—and to come out ahead.

The news at home is all good. The market is buoyant and the cost-plus-six-percent type of contract now in vogue is the most salutary invention since the international cartel and provides us with an excellent buffer against the excess-profits tax and the outrageous personal income tax. I have it on excellent authority that Russia cannot possibly hold out for more than a week or two and that after communism has been destroyed, Hitler, Roosevelt, Mussolini, Churchill, Mahatma Gandhi and the Emperor of Japan will make peace and operate the world forever on a sound businesslike basis. However, it remains to be seen whether the wish is just being father to the thought. (Ha, ha, ha!)

My spirit is soaring and my optimism knows no bounds. Hitler has provided precisely the right stimulus needed to restore the American economy to that splendid condition of good health it was enjoying on that glorious Thursday just before Black Friday. War, as you undoubtedly appreciate, presents civilization with a great opportunity and a great challenge. It is in time of war that great fortunes are often made. It is between wars that economic conditions tend to deteriorate. If mankind can just discover some means of increasing the duration of wars and decreasing the intervals between wars, we will have found a permanent solution to this most fundamental of all human ills, the business cycle.

What better advice can a devoted parent give you in this grave period of national crisis than to oppose government interference with all the vigor at your command and to fight to the death to preserve free enterprise—provided, of course, that the enterprise in question is one in which you own a considerable number of shares. (Ha, ha, ha!)

Above all this, to your own self be true. Never be a borrower or a lender of money: Never borrow money at more than two percent and never lend money at less than nine percent.

Love,
Dad

P.S. Your mother and I will not go to Cannes this year.

There had been no caviling in the family over Nately's course once war was declared; it was simply taken for granted that he would continue the splendid family tradition of military service that dated all the way back to the battle of Bosworth Field, on the losing side, particularly since Nately's father had it from the most reliable sources in Washington that Russia could not possibly hold out for more than two or three more weeks and that the War would come to an end before Nately could be sent overseas.

It was Nately's mother and Nately's eldest sister's idea that he become an aviation cadet, since Air Corps officers wore no wires in their dress caps and since he would be sheltered in an elaborate training program while the Russians were defeated and the War was brought to a satisfactory end. Furthermore, as a cadet and an officer, he would associate only with gentlemen and frequent only the best places.

As it turned out, there was a catch. In fact, there was a series of catches, and instead of associating only with gentlemen in only the best places, Nately found himself regularly in a whorehouse in Rome, associating with such people as Yossarian and the satanic and depraved mocking old man and, even worse, sadly and hopelessly in love with an indifferent prostitute there who paid no attention to him and always went off to bed without him, because he stayed up late arguing with the evil old man.

Nately was not quite certain how it had all come about, and neither was his father, who was always so certain about everything else. Nately was struck again and again by the stark contrast the seedy, disreputable old man there made with his own father, whose recurring allusions in his letters to oregano and rhapsodic exclamations about war and business were starting to become intensely disturbing. Nately often was tempted to blot these offending lines out of the letters he saved, but was afraid to; and each time he returned to the whorehouse, he wished earnestly that the sinful and corrupt old man there would put on a clean shirt and tie and act like a cultured gentleman, so that Nately would not have to feel such burning and confusing anger each time he looked at him and was reminded of his father.

> Dear Son (wrote his father):
>
> Well, those blasted Communists failed to capitulate as I expected them to, and now you are overseas in combat as an airplane pilot and in danger of being killed.

We have instructed you always to comport yourself with honor and taste and never to be guilty of anything degrading. Death, like hard work, is degrading, and I urge you to do everything possible to remain alive. Resist the temptation to cover yourself with glory, for that would be vanity. Bear in mind that it is one thing to fight for your country and quite another thing to die for it. It is absolutely imperative in this time of national peril that, in the immortal words of Rudyard Kipling, you keep your head while others about you are losing theirs. (Ha, ha, ha! Get it?) In peace, nothing so becomes a man as modest stillness and humility. But, as Shakespeare said, when the blast of war blows loose, then it is time for discretion to be the better part of valor. In short, the times cry out for dignity, balance, caution and restraint.

It is probable that within a few years after we have won, someone like Henry L. Mencken will point out that the number of Americans who suffered from this War were far outnumbered by those who profited by it. We should not like a member of our family to draw attention to himself for being among those relative few who did not profit. I pray daily for your safe return. Could you not feign a liver ailment or something similar and be sent home?

Love,
Dad

P.S. How I envy you your youth, your opportunity and all that sweet Italian pussy! I wish I were with you. (Ha, ha, ha!)

The letter was returned to him, stamped KILLED IN ACTION.

## RICHARD BRAUTIGAN

*was born in 1936 and lives in San Francisco. His works include three novels:* Trout Fishing in America, A Confederate General at Big Sur, *and* In Watermelon Sugar; *and two volumes of poetry,* The Pill Versus the Springhill Mine Disaster *and* Rommel Drives on Deep into Egypt.

## SAN FRANCISCO

*This poem was found written on a paper bag by Richard Brautigan in a laundromat in San Francisco. The author is unknown.*

By accident, you put
Your money in my
Machine (#4)
By accident, I put
My money in another
Machine (#6)
On purpose, I put
Your clothes in the
Empty machine full
Of water and no
Clothes

It was lonely.

## NORMAN MAILER

*is the author of many novels, including* An American Dream, The Naked and the Dead, *and* The Deer Park. *He has also developed a method of combining journalistic and fictional techniques through which the author becomes a part of the historical drama being played out. He has published two recent works using this technique:* Armies of the Night, *dealing with the 1967 march on the Pentagon, and* Miami and the Siege of Chicago, *dealing with the 1968 political party conventions. Among his lesser-known achievements is his campaign for the office of Mayor of New York City. In this selection, Mailer delineates some of the central problems of American alienation. Mailer's characters have empty relationships and lead boring lives, caught between daydreaming and inertia. On both the interpersonal and political levels, these people find themselves wanting to carry through, but somehow always being unable to do so—thus dooming themselves to constantly watch others act in their stead.*

# THE MAN WHO STUDIED YOGA

## 1

I would introduce myself if it were not useless. The name I had last night will not be the same as the name I have tonight. For the moment, then, let me say that I am thinking of Sam Slovoda. Obligatorily, I study him, Sam Slovoda who is neither ordinary nor extraordinary, who is not young nor yet old, not tall nor short. He is sleeping, and it is fit to describe him now, for like most humans he prefers sleeping to not sleeping. He is a mild pleasant-looking man who has just turned forty. If the crown of his head reveals a little bald spot, he has nourished in compensation the vanity of a mustache. He has generally when he is awake an agreeable manner, at least with strangers; he appears friendly, tolerant, and genial. The fact is that like most of us, he is full of envy, full of spite, a gossip, a man who is pleased to find others are as unhappy as he, and yet—this is the worst to be said—he is a decent man. He is better than most. He would prefer to see a more equitable world, he scorns prejudice and privilege, he tries to hurt no one, he wishes to be liked. I will go even further. He has one serious virtue—he is not fond of himself, he wishes he were better. He would like to free himself of envy, of the annoying necessity to talk about his friends, he would like to love people more; specifically, he would like to love his wife more, and to love his two daughters without the tormenting if nonetheless irremediable vexation that they closet his life in the dusty web of domestic responsibilities and drudging for money.

How often he tells himself with contempt that he has the cruelty of a kind weak man.

May I state that I do not dislike Sam Slovoda; it is just that I am disappointed in him. He has tried too many things and never with a whole heart. He has wanted to be a serious novelist and now merely indulges the ambition; he wished to be of consequence in the world, and has ended, temporarily perhaps, as an overworked writer of continuity for comic magazines; when he was young he tried to be a bohemian and instead acquired a wife and family. Of his appetite for a variety of new experience I may say that it is matched only by fear of new people and novel situations.

I will give an instance. Yesterday, Sam was walking along the street and a bum approached him for money. Sam did not see the man until too late; lost in some inconsequential thought, he looked up only in time to see a huge wretch of a fellow with a red twisted face and an outstretched hand. Sam is like so many; each time a derelict asks for a dime, he feels a coward if he pays the money, and is ashamed of himself if he doesn't. This once, Sam happened to think, I will not be bullied, and hurried past. But the bum was not to be lost so easily. "Have a heart, Jack," he called after in a whisky voice, "I need a drink bad." Sam stopped, Sam began to laugh. "Just so it isn't for coffee, here's a quarter," he said; and he laughed, and the bum laughed. "You're a man's man," the bum said. Sam went away pleased with himself, thinking about such things as the community which existed between all people. It was cheap of Sam. He should know better. He should know he was merely relieved the situation had turned out so well. Although he thinks he is sorry for bums, Sam really hates them. Who knows what violence they can offer?

At this time, there is a powerful interest in Sam's life, but many would ridicule it. He is in the process of being psychoanalyzed. Myself, I do not jeer. It has created the most unusual situation between Sam and me. I could go into details but they are perhaps premature. It would be better to watch Sam awaken.

His wife, Eleanor, has been up for an hour, and she has shut the window and neglected to turn off the radiator. The room is stifling. Sam groans in a stupor which is neither sleep nor refreshment, opens one eye, yawns, groans again, and lies twisted, strangled and trussed in pajamas which are too large for him. How painful it is for him to rise. Last night there was a party, and this morning, Sunday morning, he is awakening with a hangover. Invariably, he is depressed in the morning, and it is no different today. He finds himself in the flat and familiar dispirit of nearly all days.

It is snowing outside. Sam finally lurches to the window, and opens it for air. With the oxygen of a winter morning clearing his brain, he looks down six stories into the giant quadrangle of the Queens housing development in which he lives, staring morosely at the inch of slush which covers the monotonous artificial park that separates his apartment building from an identical structure not two hundred feet away. The walks are black where the snow has melted, and in the children's playground, all but deserted, one swing oscillates back and forth, pushed by an irritable little boy who plays by himself among the empty benches, swaddled in galoshes, muffler, and overcoat. The snow falls sluggishly, a wet snow which probably will turn to rain. The little boy in the playground gives one last disgusted shove to the swing and trudges away gloomily, his overshoes leaving a small animal track behind him. Back of Sam, in the four-room apartment he knows like a blind man, there is only the sound of Eleanor making breakfast.

Well, thinks Sam, depression in the morning is a stage of his analysis, Dr. Sergius has said.

This is the way Sam often phrases his thoughts. It is not altogether his fault. Most of the people he knows think that way and talk that way, and Sam is not the strongest of men. His language is doomed to the fashion of the moment. I have heard him remark mildly, almost apologetically, about his daughters: "My relation with them still suffers because I haven't worked through all my feminine identifications." The saddest thing is that the sentence has meaning to Sam even if it will not have meaning to you. A great many ruminations, discoveries, and memories contribute their connotation to Sam. It has the significance of a cherished line of poetry to him.

Although Eleanor is not being analyzed, she talks in a similar way. I have heard her remark in company, "Oh, you know Sam, he not only thinks I'm his mother, he blames me for being born." Like most women, Eleanor can be depended upon to employ the idiom of her husband.

What amuses me is that Sam is critical of the way others speak. At the party last night he was talking to a Hollywood writer, a young man with a great deal of energy and enthusiasm. The young man spoke something like this: "You see, boychick, I can spike any script with yaks, but the thing I can't do is heartbreak. My wife says she's gonna give me heartbreak. The trouble is I've had a real solid-type life. I mean I've had my ups and downs like all of humanity, but there's never been a shriek in my life. I don't know how to write shrieks."

On the trip home, Sam had said to Eleanor, "It was disgraceful. A writer should have some respect for language."

Eleanor answered with a burlesque of Sam's indignation. "Listen, I'm a real artist-type. Culture is for comic-strip writers."

Generally, I find Eleanor attractive. In the ten years they have been married she has grown plump, and her dark hair which once was long is now cropped in a mannish cut of the prevailing mode. But, this is quibbling. She still possesses her best quality, a healthy exuberance which glows in her dark eyes and beams in her smile. She has beautiful teeth. She seems aware of her body and pleased with it. Sam tells himself he would do well to realize how much he needs her. Since he has been in analysis he has come to discover that he remains with Eleanor for more essential reasons than mere responsibility. Even if there were no children, he would probably cleave to her.

Unhappily, it is more complicated than that. She is always—to use their phrase—competing with him. At those times when I do not like Eleanor, I am irritated by her lack of honesty. She is too sharp-tongued, and she does not often give Sam what he needs most, a steady flow of uncritical encouragement to counteract the harshness with which he views himself. Like so many who are articulate on the subject, Eleanor will tell you that she resents being a woman. As Sam is disappointed in life, so is Eleanor. She feels Sam has cheated her from a proper development of her potentialities and talent, even as Sam feels cheated. I call her dishonest because she is not so ready as Sam to put the blame on herself.

Sam, of course, can say all this himself. It is just that he experiences it in a somewhat different way. Like most men who have been married for ten years, Eleanor is not quite real to him. Last night at the party, there were perhaps half a dozen people whom he met for the first time, and he talked animatedly with them, sensing their reactions, feeling their responses, aware of the life in them, as they were aware of the life in him. Eleanor, however, exists in his nerves. She is a rather vague embodiment, he thinks of her as "she" most of the time, someone to conceal things from. Invariably, he feels uneasy with her. It is too bad. No matter how inevitable, I am always sorry when love melts into that pomade of affection, resentment, boredom and occasional compassion which is the best we may expect of a man and woman who have lived together a long time. So often, it is worse, so often no more than hatred.

They are eating breakfast now, and Eleanor is chatting about the party. She is pretending to be jealous about a young girl in a strapless evening gown, and indeed, she does not have to pretend altogether. Sam, with liquor inside him, had been leaning over the girl; obviously he had coveted her. Yet, this morning, when Eleanor begins to talk about her, Sam tries to be puzzled.

"Which girl was it now?" he asks a second time.

"Oh, you know, the hysteric," Eleanor says, "the one who was parading her bazooms in your face." Eleanor has ways of impressing certain notions upon Sam. "She's Charlie's new girl."

"I didn't know that," Sam mutters. "He didn't seem to be near her all evening."

Eleanor spreads marmalade over her toast and takes a bite with evident enjoyment. "Apparently, they're all involved. Charles was funny about it. He said he's come to the conclusion that the great affairs of history are between hysterical women and detached men."

"Charles hates women," Sam says smugly. "If you notice, almost everything he says about them is a discharge of aggression." Sam has the best of reasons for not liking Charles. It takes more than ordinary character for a middle-aged husband to approve of a friend who moves easily from woman to woman.

"At least Charles discharges his aggression," Eleanor remarks. "He's almost a classic example of the Don Juan complex. You notice how masochistic his women are?"

"I know a man or two who's just as masochistic."

Sam sips his coffee. "What made you say the girl was an hysteric?"

Eleanor shrugs. "She's an actress. And I could see she was a tease."

"You can't jump to conclusions," Sam lectures. "I had the impression she was a compulsive. Don't forget you've got to distinguish between the outer defenses, and the more deeply rooted conflicts."

I must confess that this conversation bores me. As a sample it is representative of the way Sam and Eleanor talk to each other. In Sam's defense I can say nothing; he has always been too partial to jargon.

I am often struck by how eager we are to reveal all sorts of supposedly ugly secrets about ourselves. We can explain the hatred we feel for our parents, we are rather pleased with the perversions to which we are prone. We seem determinedly proud to be superior to ourselves. No motive is too terrible for our inspection. Let someone hint, however, that we have bad table manners and we fly into a rage. Sam will agree to anything you may say about him, provided it is sufficiently serious—he will be the first to agree he has fantasies of murdering his wife. But tell him that he is afraid of waiters, or imply to Eleanor that she is a nag, and they will be quite annoyed.

Sam has noticed this himself. There are times when he can hear the jargon in his voice, and it offends him. Yet, he seems powerless to change his habits.

An example: He is sitting in an armchair now, brooding upon his breakfast, while Eleanor does the dishes. The two daughters are not home; they have gone to visit their grandmother for the week-end. Sam had encouraged the visit. He had looked forward to the liberty Eleanor and himself would enjoy. For the past few weeks the children had seemed to make the most impossible demands upon his attention. Yet now they are gone and he misses them, he even misses their noise. Sam, however, cannot accept the notion that many people are dissatisfied with the present, and either dream of the past or anticipate the future. Sam must call this "ambivalence over possessions." Once he even felt obliged to ask his analyst, Dr. Sergius, if ambivalence over possessions did not characterize him almost perfectly, and Sergius whom I always picture with the flat precision of a coin's head—bald skull and horn-rimmed glasses—answered in his German accent, "But, my dear Mr. Slovoda, as I have told you, it would make me happiest if you did not include in your reading, these psychoanalytical text-works."

At such rebukes, Sam can only wince. It is so right, he tells himself, he is exactly the sort of ambitious fool who uses big words when small ones would do.

2

While Sam sits in the armchair, gray winter light is entering the windows, snow falls outside. He sits alone in a modern seat, staring at the gray, green, and beige décor of their living room. Eleanor was a painter before they were married, and she has arranged this room. It is very pleasant, but like many husbands, Sam resents it, resents the reproductions of modern painters upon the wall, the slender coffee table, a free-form poised like a spider on wire legs, its feet set onto a straw rug. In the corner, most odious of all, is the playmate of his children, a hippopotamus of a television-radio-and-phonograph cabinet with the blind monstrous snout of the video tube.

Eleanor has set the Sunday paper near his hand. Soon, Sam intends to go to work. For a year, he has been giving a day once or twice a month to a bit of thought and a little writing on a novel he hopes to begin sometime. Last night, he told himself he would work today. But he has little enthusiasm now. He is tired, he is too depressed. Writing for the comic strips seems to exhaust his imagination.

Sam reads the paper as if he were peeling an enormous banana. Flap after flap of newsprint is stripped away and cast upon the straw rug until only the Magazine Section is left. Sam glances through it with restless irritability. A biography of a political figure runs its flatulent prose into the giant crossword puzzle at the back. An account of a picturesque corner of the city becomes lost in statistics and exhortations on juvenile delinquency, finally to emerge with photographs about the new style of living which desert architecture provides. Sam looks at a wall of windows in rotogravure with a yucca tree framing the pool.

There is an article about a workingman. His wife and his family are described, his apartment, his salary and his budget. Sam reads a description of what the worker has every evening for dinner, and how he spends each night of the week. The essay makes its point; the typical American workingman must watch his pennies, but he is nonetheless secure and serene. He would not exchange his life for another.

Sam is indignant. A year ago he had written a similar article in an attempt to earn some extra money. Subtly, or so he thought, he had suggested that the average workingman was raddled with insecurity. Naturally, the article had been rejected.

Sam throws the Magazine Section away. Moments of such anger torment him frequently. Despite himself, Sam is enraged at editorial dishonesty, at the smooth strifeless world which such articles present. How angry he is—how angry and how helpless. "It is the actions of men and not their sentiments which make history," he thinks to himself, and smiles wryly. In his living room he would go out to tilt the windmills of a vast, powerful, and hypocritical society; in his week of work he labors in an editorial cubicle to create spaceships, violent death, women with golden tresses and wanton breasts, men who act with their fists and speak with patriotic slogans.

I know what Sam feels. As he sits in the armchair, the Sunday papers are strewn around him, carrying their war news, their murders, their parleys, their entertainments, mummery of a real world which no one can grasp. It is terribly frustrating. One does not know where to begin.

Today, Sam considers himself half a fool for having been a radical. There is no longer much consolation in the thought that the majority of men who succeed in a corrupt and acquisitive society are themselves obligatorily corrupt, and one's failure is therefore the price of one's idealism. Sam cannot recapture the pleasurable bitterness which resides in the notion that one has suffered for one's principles. Sergius is too hard on him for that.

They have done a lot of work on the subject. Sergius feels that Sam's concern with world affairs has always been spurious. For example, they have uncovered in analysis that Sam wrote his article about the worker in such a way as to make certain it would be refused. Sam, after all, hates editors; to have such a piece accepted would mean he is no better than they, that he is a mediocrity. So long as he fails he is not obliged to measure himself. Sam, therefore, is being unrealistic. He rejects the world with his intellect, and this enables him not to face the more direct realities of his present life.

Sam will argue with Sergius but it is very difficult. He will say, "Perhaps you sneer at radicals because it is more comfortable to ignore such ideas. Once you became interested it might introduce certain unpleasant changes in your life."

"Why," says Sergius, "do you feel it so necessary to assume that I am a bourgeois interested only in my comfort?"

"How can I discuss these things," says Sam, "if you insist that my opinions are the expression of neurotic needs, and your opinions are merely dispassionate medical advice?"

"You are so anxious to defeat me in an argument," Sergius will reply. "Would you admit it is painful to relinquish the sense of importance which intellectual discussion provides you?"

I believe Sergius has his effect. Sam often has thoughts these days which would have been repellent to him years ago. For instance, at the moment, Sam is thinking it might be better to live the life of a worker, a simple life, to be completely absorbed with such necessities as food and money. Then one could believe that to be happy it was necessary only to have more money, more goods, less worries. It would be nice, Sam thinks wistfully, to believe that the source of one's unhappiness comes not from oneself, but from the fault of the boss, or the world, or bad luck.

Sam has these casual daydreams frequently. He likes to think about other lives he might have led, and he envies the most astonishing variety of occupations. It is easy enough to see why he should wish for the life of an executive with the power and sense of command it may offer, but virtually from the same impulse Sam will wish himself a bohemian living in an unheated loft, his life a catch-as-catch-can from day to day. Once, after reading an article, Sam even wished himself a priest. For about ten minutes it seemed beautiful to him to surrender his life to God. Such fancies are common. I know. It is just that I, far better than Sam, know how serious he really is, how fanciful, how elaborate, his imagination can be.

The phone is ringing. Sam can hear Eleanor shouting at him to answer. He picks up the receiver with a start. It is Marvin Rossman who is an old friend, and Marvin has an unusual request. They talk for several minutes, and Sam squirms a little in his seat. As he is about to hang up, he laughs. "Why, no, Marvin, it gives me a sense of adventure," he says.

Eleanor has come into the room toward the end of this conversation. "What is it all about?" she asks.

Sam is obviously a bit agitated. Whenever he attempts to be most casual, Eleanor can well suspect him. "It seems," he says slowly, "that Marvin has acquired a pornographic movie."

"From whom?" Eleanor asks.

"He said something about an old boy friend of Louise's."

Eleanor laughs. "I can't imagine Louise having an old boy friend with a dirty movie."

"Well, people are full of surprises," Sam says mildly.

"Look, here," says Eleanor suddenly. "Why did he call us?"

"It was about our projector."

"They want to use it?" Eleanor asks.

"That's right." Sam hesitates. "I invited them over."

"Did it ever occur to you I might want to spend my Sunday some other way?" Eleanor asks crossly.

"We're not doing anything," Sam mumbles. Like most men, he feels obliged to act quite nonchalantly about pornography. "I'll tell you, I am sort of curious about the film. I've never seen one, you know."

"Try anything once, is that it?"

"Something of the sort." Sam is trying to conceal his excitement. The truth is that in common with most of us, he is fascinated by pornography. It is a minor preoccupation, but more from lack of opportunity than anything else. Once or twice, Sam has bought the sets of nude photographs which are sold in marginal bookstores, and with guilty excitement has hidden them in the apartment.

"Oh, this is silly," Eleanor says. "You were going to work today."

"I'm just not in the mood."

"I'll have to feed them," Eleanor complains. "Do we have enough liquor?"

"We can get beer." Sam pauses. "Alan Sperber and his wife are coming too."

"Sam, you're a child."

"Look, Eleanor," says Sam, controlling his voice, "if it's too much trouble, I can take the projector over there."

"I ought to make you do that."

"Am I such an idiot that I must consult you before I invite friends to the house?"

Eleanor has the intuition that Sam, if he allowed himself, could well drown in pornography. She is quite annoyed at him, but she would never dream of allowing Sam to take the projector over to Marvin Rossman's where he could view the movie without her—that seems indefinably dangerous. Besides she would like to see it, too. The mother in Eleanor is certain it cannot hurt her.

"All right, Sam," she says, "but you are a child."

More exactly, an adolescent, Sam decides. Ever since Marvin phoned, Sam has felt the nervous glee of an adolescent locking himself in the bathroom. Anal fixation, Sam thinks automatically.

While Eleanor goes down to buy beer and cold cuts in a delicatessen, Sam gets out the projector and begins to clean it. He is far from methodical in this. He knows the machine is all right, he has shown movies of Eleanor and his daughters only a few weeks ago, but from the moment Eleanor left the apartment, Sam has been consumed by an anxiety that the projection bulb is burned out. Once he has examined it, he begins to fret about the motor. He wonders if it needs oiling, he blunders through a drawer of household tools looking for an oilcan. It is ridiculous. Sam knows that what he is trying to keep out of his mind are the reactions Sergius will have. Sergius will want to "work through" all of Sam's reasons for seeing the movie. Well, Sam tells himself, he knows in advance what will be discovered: detachment, not wanting to accept Eleanor as a sexual partner, evasion of responsibility, etc. etc. The devil with Sergius. Sam has never seen a dirty movie, and he certainly wants to.

He feels obliged to laugh at himself. He could not be more nervous, he knows, if he were about to make love to a woman he had never touched before. It is really disgraceful.

When Eleanor comes back, Sam hovers about her. He is uncomfortable with her silence. "I suppose they'll be here soon," Sam says.

"Probably."

Sam does not know if he is angry at Eleanor or apprehensive that she is angry at him. Much to his surprise he catches her by the waist and hears himself saying, "You know, maybe tonight when they're gone . . . I mean, we do have the apartment, to ourselves." Eleanor moves neither toward him nor away from him. "Darling, it's not because of the movie," Sam goes on, "I swear. Don't you think maybe we could . . ."

"Maybe," says Eleanor.

3

The company has arrived, and it may be well to say a word or two about them. Marvin Rossman who has brought the film is a dentist, although it might be more accurate to describe him as a frustrated doctor. Rossman is full of statistics and items of odd information about the malpractice of physicians, and he will tell these things in his habitually gloomy voice, a voice so slow, so sad, that it almost conceals the humor of his remarks. Or, perhaps, that is what creates his humor. In his spare time, he is a sculptor, and if Eleanor may be trusted, he is not without talent. I often picture him working in the studio loft he has rented, his tall bony frame the image of dejection. He will pat a piece of clay to the armature, he will rub it sadly with his thumb, he will shrug, he does not believe that anything of merit could come from him. When he talked to Sam over the phone, he was pessimistic about the film they were to see. "It can't be any good," he said in his melancholy voice. "I know it'll be a disappointment." Like Sam, he has a mustache, but Rossman's will droop at the corners.

Alan Sperber who has come with Rossman is the subject of some curiosity for the Slovodas. He is not precisely womanish; in fact, he is a large plump man, but his voice is too soft, his manners too precise. He is genial, yet he is finicky; waspish, yet bland; he is fond of telling long rather affected stories, he is always prepared with a new one, but to general conversation he contributes little. As a lawyer, he seems miscast. One cannot imagine him inspiring a client to confidence. He is the sort of heavy florid man who seems boyish at forty, and the bow ties and gray flannel suits he wears do not make him appear more mature.

Roslyn Sperber, his wife, used to be a schoolteacher, and she is a quiet nervous woman who talks a great deal when she is drunk. She is normally quite pleasant, and has only one habit which is annoying to any degree. It is a little flaw, but social life is not unlike marriage in that habit determines far more than vice or virtue. This mannerism which has become so offensive to the friends of the Sperbers is Roslyn's social pretension. Perhaps I should say intellectual pretension. She entertains people as if she were conducting a salon, and in her birdlike voice is forever forcing her guests to accept still another intellectual canapé. "You must hear Sam's view of the world market," she will say, or "Has Louise told you her statistics on divorce?" It is quite pathetic for she is so eager to please. I have seen her eyes fill with tears at a sharp word from Alan.

Marvin Rossman's wife, Louise, is a touch grim and definite in her opinions. She is a social welfare worker, and will declare herself with force whenever conversation impinges on those matters where she is expert. She is quite opposed to psychoanalysis, and will say without quarter, "It's all very well for people in the upper-middle area"—she is referring to the upper middle class—"but, it takes more than a couch to solve the problems of . . ." and she will list narcotics, juvenile delinquency, psychosis, relief distribution, slum housing, and other descriptions of our period. She recites these categories with an odd anticipation. One would guess she was ordering a meal.

Sam is fond of Marvin but he cannot abide Louise. "You'd think she discovered poverty," he will complain to Eleanor.

The Slovodas do feel superior to the Rossmans and the Sperbers. If pressed, they could not offer the most convincing explanation why. I suppose what it comes down to is that Sam and Eleanor do not think of themselves as really belonging to a class, and they feel that the Sperbers and Rossmans are petit-bourgeois. I find it hard to explain their attitude. Their company feels as much discomfort and will apologize as often as the Slovodas for the money they have, and the money they hope to earn. They are all of them equally concerned with progressive education and the methods of raising children to be well adjusted—indeed, they are discussing that now—they consider themselves relatively free of sexual taboo, or put more properly, Sam and Eleanor are no less possessive than the others. The Slovodas' culture is not more profound; I should be hard put to say that Sam is more widely read, more seriously informed, than Marvin or Alan, or for that matter, Louise. Probably, it comes to this: Sam, in his heart, thinks himself a rebel, and there are few rebels who do not claim an original mind. Eleanor has been a bohemian and considers herself more sophisticated than her friends who merely went to college and got married. Louise Rossman could express it most soundly. "Artists, writers, and people of the creative layer have in their occupational ideology the belief that they are classless."

One thing I might remark about the company. They are all being the most unconscionable hypocrites. They have rushed across half the city of New York to see a pornographic film, and they are not at all interested in each other at the moment. The women are giggling like tickled children at remarks which cannot possibly be so funny. Yet, they are all determined to talk for a respectable period of time. No less, it must be serious talk. Roslyn has said once, "I feel so funny at the thought of seeing such a movie," and the others have passed her statement by.

At the moment, Sam is talking about value. I might note that Sam loves conversation and thrives when he can expound an idea.

"What are our values today?" he asks. "It's really fantastic when you stop to think of it. Take any bright talented kid who's getting out of college now."

"My kid brother, for example," Marvin interposes morosely. He passes his bony hand over his sad mustache, and somehow the remark has become amusing, much as if Marvin has said, "Oh, yes, you have reminded me of the trials, the worries, and the cares which my fabulous younger brother heaps upon me."

"All right, take him," Sam says. "What does he want to be?"

"He doesn't want to be anything," says Marvin.

"That's my point," Sam says excitedly. "Rather than work at certain occupations, the best of these kids would rather do nothing at all."

"Alan has a cousin," Roslyn says, "who swears he'll wash dishes before he becomes a businessman."

"I wish that were true," Eleanor interrupts. "It seems to me everybody is conforming more and more these days."

They argue about this. Sam and Eleanor claim the country is suffering from hysteria; Alan Sperber disagrees and says it's merely a reflection of the headlines; Louise says no adequate criteria exist to measure hysteria; Marvin says he doesn't know anything at all.

"More solid liberal gains are being made in this period," says Alan, "than you would believe. Consider the Negro—"

"Is the Negro any less maladjusted?" Eleanor shouts with passion.

Sam maneuvers the conversation back to his thesis. "The values of the young today, and by the young I mean the cream of the kids, the ones with ideas, are a reaction of indifference to the culture crisis. It really is despair. All they know is what they don't want to do."

"That is easier," Alan says genially.

"It's not altogether unhealthy," Sam says. "It's a corrective for smugness and the false value of the past, but it has created new false value." He thinks it worth emphasizing. "False value seems always to beget further false value."

"Define your terms," says Louise, the scientist.

"No, look," Sam says, "there's no revolt, there's no acceptance. Kids today don't want to get married, and—"

Eleanor interrupts. "Why should a girl rush to get married? She loses all chance for developing herself."

Sam shrugs. They are all talking at once. "Kids don't want to get married," he repeats, "and they don't want not to get married. They merely drift."

"It's a problem we'll all have to face with our own kids in ten years," Alan says, "although I think you make too much of it, Sam."

"My daughter," Marvin states. "She's embarrassed I'm a dentist. Even more embarrassed than I am." They laugh.

Sam tells a story about his youngest, Carol Ann. It seems he had a fight with her, and she went to her room. Sam followed, he called through the door.

"No answer," Sam says. "I called her again, 'Carol Ann.' I was a little worried you understand, because she seemed so upset, so I said to her, 'Carol Ann, you know I love you.' What do you think she answered?"

"What?" asks Roslyn.

"She said, 'Daddie, why are you so anxious?' "

They all laugh again. There are murmurs about what a clever thing it was to say. In the silence which follows, Roslyn leans forward and says quickly in her high voice, "You must get Alan to tell you his wonderful story about the man who studied yogi."

"Yoga," Alan corrects. "It's too long to tell."

The company prevails on him.

"Well," says Alan, in his genial courtroom voice, "it concerns a friend of mine named Cassius O'Shaugnessy."

"You don't mean Jerry O'Shaugnessy, do you?" asks Sam.

Alan does not know Jerry O'Shaugnessy. "No, no, this is Cassius O'Shaugnessy," he says. "He's really quite an extraordinary fellow." Alan sits plumply in his chair, fingering his bow tie. They are all used to his stories, which are told in a formal style and exhibit the attempt to recapture a certain note of urbanity, wit, and *élan* which Alan has probably copied from someone else. Sam and Eleanor respect his ability to tell these stories, but they resent the fact that he talks *at* them.

"You'd think we were a jury of his inferiors," Eleanor has said. "I hate being talked down to." What she resents is Alan's quiet implication that his antecedents, his social position, in total his life outside the room is superior to the life within. Eleanor now takes the promise from Alan's story by remarking, "Yes, and let's see the movie when Alan has finished."

"Ssh," Roslyn says.

"Cassius was at college a good while before me," says Alan, "but I knew him while I was an undergraduate. He would drop in and visit from time to time. An absolutely extraordinary fellow. The most amazing career. You see, he's done about everything."

"I love the way Alan tells it," Roslyn pipes nervously.

"Cassius was in France with Dos Passos and Cummings, he was even arrested with e.e. After the war, he was one of the founders of the Dadist school, and for a while I understand he was Fitzgerald's guide to the gold of the Côte d' Azur. He knew everybody, he did everything. Do you realize that before the twenties had ended, Cassius had managed his father's business and then entered a monastery? It is said he influenced T. S. Eliot."

"Today, we'd call Cassius a psychopath," Marvin observes.

"Cassius called himself a great dilettante," Alan answers, "although perhaps the nineteenth-century Russian conception of the great sinner would be more appropriate. What do you say if I tell you this was only the beginning of his career?"

"What's the point?" Louise asks.

"Not yet," says Alan, holding up a hand. His manner seems to say that if his audience cannot appreciate the story, he does not feel obliged to continue. "Cassius studied Marx in the monastery. He broke his vows, quit the Church, and became a Communist. All through the thirties he was a figure in the Party, going to Moscow, involved in all the Party struggles. He left only during the Moscow trials."

Alan's manner while he relates such stories is somewhat effeminate. He talks with little caresses of his hand, he mentions names and places with a lingering ease as if to suggest that his audience and he are aware, above all, of nuance. The story as Alan tells it is drawn overlong. Suffice it that the man about whom he is talking, Cassius O'Shaugnessy, becomes a Trotskyist, becomes an anarchist, is a pacifist during the second World War, and suffers it from a prison cell.

"I may say," Alan goes on, "that I worked for his defense, and was successful in getting him acquitted. Imagine my dolor when I learned that he had turned his back on his anarchist friends and was living with gangsters."

"This is weird," Eleanor says.

"Weird, it is," Alan agrees. "Cassius got into some scrape, and disappeared. What could you do with him? I learned only recently that he had gone to India and was studying yoga. In fact, I learned it from Cassius himself. I asked him of his experiences at Brahna-puth-thar, and he told me the following story."

Now Alan's voice alters, he assumes the part of Cassius and speaks in a tone weary of experience, wise and sad in its knowledge. " 'I was sitting on my haunches contemplating my navel,' Cassius said to me, 'when of a sudden I discovered my navel under a different aspect. It seemed to me that if I were to give a counterclockwise twist, my navel would unscrew.' "

Alan looks up, he surveys his audience which is now rapt and uneasy, not certain as yet whether a joke is to come. Alan's thumb and forefinger pluck at the middle of his ample belly, his feet are crossed upon the carpet in symbolic suggestion of Cassius upon his haunches.

" 'Taking a deep breath, I turned, and the abysses of Vishtarni loomed beneath. My navel had begun to unscrew. I knew I was about to accept the reward of three years of contemplation. So,' said Cassius, 'I turned again, and my navel unscrewed a little more. I turned and I turned,' " Alan's fingers now revolving upon his belly, " 'and after a period I knew that with one more turn my navel would unscrew itself forever. At the edge of revelation, I took one sweet breath, and turned my navel free.' "

Alan looks up at his audience.

" 'Damn,' said Cassius, 'if my ass didn't fall off.' "

## 4

The story has left the audience in an exasperated mood. It has been a most untypical story for Alan to tell, a little out of place, not offensive exactly, but irritating and inconsequential. Sam is the only one to laugh with more than bewildered courtesy, and his mirth seems excessive to everyone but Alan, and of course, Roslyn, who feels as if she has been the producer. I suppose what it reduces to, is a lack of taste. Perhaps that is why Alan is not the lawyer one would expect. He does not have that appreciation—as necessary in his trade as for an actor—of what is desired at any moment, of that which will encourage as opposed to that which does not encourage a stimulating but smooth progression of logic and sentiment. Only a fool would tell so long a story when everyone is awaiting the movie.

Now, they are preparing. The men shift armchairs to correspond with the couch, the projector is set up, the screen is unfolded. Sam attempts to talk while he is threading the film, but no one listens. They seem to realize suddenly that a frightful demand has been placed upon them. One does not study pornography in a living room with a beer glass in one's hand, and friends at the elbow. It is the most unsatisfactory of compromises; one can draw neither the benefits of solitary contemplation nor of social exchange. There is, at bottom, the same exasperated fright which one experiences in turning the shower tap and receiving cold water when the flesh has been prepared for heat. Perhaps that is why they are laughing so much now that the movie is begun.

A title, *The Evil Act*, twitches on the screen, shot with scars, holes, and the dust lines of age. A man and woman are sitting on a couch, they are having coffee. They chat. What they say is conveyed by printed words upon an ornately flowered card, interjected between glimpses of their casual gestures, a cup to the mouth, a smile, a cigarette being lit. The man's name, it seems, is Frankie Idell; he is talking to his wife, Magnolia. Frankie is dark, he is sinister, he confides in Magnolia, his dark counterpart, with a grimace of his brows, black from make-up pencil.

This is what the titles read:

FRANKIE She will be here soon.
MAGNOLIA This time the little vixen will not escape.
FRANKIE No, my dear, this time we are prepared.
(*He looks at his watch.*)
FRANKIE Listen, she knocks!

There is a shot of a tall blond woman knocking on the door. She is probably over thirty, but by her short dress and ribboned hat it is suggested that she is a girl of fifteen.

FRANKIE Come in, Eleanor.

As may be expected, the audience laughs hysterically at this. It is so wonderful a coincidence. "How I remember Frankie," says Eleanor Slovoda, and Roslyn Sperber is the only one not amused. In the midst of the others' laughter, she says in a worried tone, obviously adrift upon her own concerns, "Do you think we'll have to stop the film in the middle to let the bulb cool off?" The others hoot, they giggle, they are weak from the combination of their own remarks and the action of the plot.

Frankie and Magnolia have sat down on either side of the heroine, Eleanor. A moment passes. Suddenly, stiffly, they attack. Magnolia from her side kisses Eleanor, and Frankie commits an indecent caress.

ELEANOR How dare you? Stop!
MAGNOLIA Scream, my little one. It will do you no good. The walls are soundproofed.
FRANKIE We've fixed a way to make you come across.
ELEANOR This is hideous. I am hitherto undefiled. Do not touch me!

The captions fade away. A new title takes their place. It says, *But There Is No Escape From The Determined Pair.* On the fade-in, we discover Eleanor in the most distressing situation. Her hands are tied to loops running from the ceiling, and she can only writhe in helpless perturbation before the deliberate and progressive advances of Frankie and Magnolia. Slowly they humiliate her, with relish they probe her.

The audience laughs no longer. A hush has come upon them. Eyes unblinking they devour the images upon Sam Slovoda's screen.

Eleanor is without clothing. As the last piece is pulled away, Frankie and Magnolia circle about her in a grotesque of pantomime, a leering of lips, limbs in a distortion of desire. Eleanor faints. Adroitly, Magnolia cuts her bonds. We see Frankie carrying her inert body.

Now, Eleanor is trussed to a bed, and the husband and wife are tormenting her with feathers. Bodies curl upon the bed in postures so complicated, in combinations so advanced, that the audience leans forward, Sperbers, Rossmans, and Slovodas, as if tempted to embrace the moving images. The hands trace abstract circles upon the screen, passes and recoveries upon a white background so illumined that hollows and swells, limb to belly and mouth to undescribables, tip of a nipple, orb of a navel, swim in giant magnification, flow and slide in a lurching yawing fall, blotting out the camera eye.

A little murmur, all unconscious, passes from their lips. The audience sways, each now finally lost in himself, communing hungrily with shadows, violated or violating, fantasy triumphant.

At picture's end, Eleanor the virgin whore is released from the bed. She kisses Frankie, she kisses Magnolia. "You dears," she says, "let's do it again." The projector lamp burns empty light, the machine keeps turning, the tag of the film goes *slap-tap, slap-tap, slap-tap, slap-tap, slap-tap, slap-tap.*

"Sam, turn it off," says Eleanor.

But when the room lights are on, they cannot look at one another. "Can we see it again?" someone mutters. So, again, Eleanor knocks on the door, is tied, defiled, ravished, and made rapturous. They watch it soberly now, the room hot with the heat of their bodies, the darkness a balm for orgiastic vision. To the Deer Park, Sam is thinking, to the Deer Park of Louis XV were brought the most beautiful maidens of France, and there they stayed, dressed in fabulous silks, perfumed and wigged, the mole drawn upon their cheek, ladies of pleasure awaiting the pleasure of the king. So Louis had stripped an empire, bankrupt a treasury, prepared a deluge, while in his garden on summer evenings the maidens performed their pageants, eighteenth-century tableaux of the evil act, beauteous instruments of one man's desire, lewd translation of a king's power. That century men sought wealth so they might use its fruits; this epoch men lusted for power in order to amass more power, a compounding of power into pyramids of abstraction whose yield are cannon and wire enclosure, pillars of statistics to the men who are the kings of this century and do no more in power's leisure time than go to church, claim to love their wives, and eat vegetables.

Is it possible, Sam wonders, that each of them here, two Rossmans, two Sperbers, two Slovodas, will cast off their clothes when the movie is done and perform the orgy which tickles at the heart of their desire? They will not, he knows, they will make jokes when the projector is put away, they will gorge the plate of delicatessen Eleanor provides, and swallow more beer, he among them. He will be the first to make jokes.

Sam is right. The movie has made him extraordinarily alive to the limits of them all. While they sit with red faces, eyes bugged, glutting sandwiches of ham, salami, and tongue, he begins the teasing.

"Roslyn," he calls out, "is the bulb cooled off yet?"

She cannot answer him. She chokes on beer, her face glazes, she is helpless with self-protecting laughter.

"Why are you so anxious, Daddie?" Eleanor says quickly.

They begin to discuss the film. As intelligent people they must dominate it. Someone wonders about the actors in the piece, and discussion begins afresh. "I fail to see," says Louise, "why they should be hard to classify. Pornography is a job to the criminal and prostitute element."

"No, you won't find an ordinary prostitute doing this," Sam insists. "It requires a particular kind of personality."

"They have to be exhibitionists," says Eleanor.

"It's all economic," Louise maintains.

"I wonder what those girls felt?" Roslyn asks. "I feel sorry for them."

"I'd like to be the cameraman," says Alan.

"I'd like to be Frankie," says Marvin sadly.

There is a limit to how long such a conversation may continue. The jokes lapse into silence. They are all busy eating. When they begin to talk again, it is of other things. Each dollop of food sops the agitation which the movie has spilled. They gossip about the party the night before, they discuss which single men were interested in which women, who got drunk, who got sick, who said the wrong thing, who went home with someone else's date. When this is exhausted, one of them mentions a play the others have not seen. Soon they are talking about books, a concert, a one-man show by an artist who is a friend. Dependably, conversation will voyage its orbit. While the men talk of politics, the women are discussing fashions, progressive schools, and recipes they have attempted. Sam is uncomfortable with the division; he knows Eleanor will resent it, he knows she will complain later of the insularity of men and the basic contempt they feel for women's intelligence.

"But you collaborated," Sam will argue. "No one forced you to be with the women."

"Was I to leave them alone?" Eleanor will answer.

"Well, why do the women always have to go off by themselves?"

"Because the men aren't interested in what we have to say."

Sam sighs. He has been talking with interest, but really he is bored. These are nice pleasant people, he thinks, but they are ordinary people, exactly the sort he has spent so many years with, making little jokes, little gossip, living little everyday events, a close circle where everyone mothers the other by his presence. The womb of middle-class life, Sam decides heavily. He is in a bad mood indeed. Everything is laden with dissatisfaction.

Alan has joined the women. He delights in preparing odd dishes when friends visit the Sperbers, and he is describing to Eleanor how he makes blueberry pancakes. Marvin draws closer to Sam.

"I wanted to tell you," he says, "Alan's story reminded me. I saw Jerry O'Shaugnessy the other day."

"Where was he?"

Marvin is hesitant. "It was a shock, Sam. He's on the Bowery. I guess he's become a wino."

"He always drank a lot," says Sam.

"Yeah." Marvin cracks his bony knuckles. "What a stinking time this is, Sam."

"It's probably like the years after 1905 in Russia," Sam says.

"No revolutionary party will come out of this."

"No," Sam says, "nothing will come."

He is thinking of Jerry O'Shaugnessy. What did he look like? what did he say? Sam asks Marvin, and clucks his tongue at the dispiriting answer. It is a shock to him. He draws closer to Marvin, he feels a bond. They have, after all, been through some years together. In the thirties they have been in the Communist Party, they have quit together, they are both weary of politics today, still radicals out of habit, but without enthusiasm and without a cause. "Jerry was a hero to me," Sam says.

"To all of us," says Marvin.

The fabulous Jerry O'Shaugnessy, thinks Sam. In the old days, in the Party, they had made a legend of him. All of them with their middle-class origins and their desire to know a worker-hero.

I may say that I was never as fond of Jerry O'Shaugnessy as was Sam. I thought him a showman and too pleased with himself. Sam, however, with his timidity, his desire to travel, to have adventure and know many women, was obliged to adore O'Shaugnessy. At least he was enraptured with his career.

Poor Jerry who ends as a bum. He has been everything else. He has been a trapper in Alaska, a chauffeur for gangsters, an officer in the Foreign Legion, a labor organizer. His nose was broken, there were scars on his chin. When he would talk about his years at sea or his experiences in Spain, the stenographers and garment workers, the radio writers and unemployed actors would listen to his speeches as if he were the prophet of new romance, and their blood would be charged with the magic of revolutionary vision. A man with tremendous charm. In those days it had been easy to confuse his love for himself with his love for all underprivileged workingmen.

"I thought he was still in the Party," Sam says.

"No," says Marvin, "I remember they kicked him out a couple of years ago. He was supposed to have piddled some funds, that's what they say."

"I wish he'd taken the treasury," Sam remarks bitterly. "The Party used him for years."

Marvin shrugs. "They used each other." His mustache droops. "Let me tell you about Sonderson. You know he's still in the Party. The most progressive dentist in New York." They laugh.

While Marvin tells the story, Sam is thinking of other things. Since he has quit Party work, he has studied a great deal. He can tell you about prison camps and the secret police, political murders, the Moscow trials, the exploitation of Soviet labor, the privileges of the bureaucracy; it is all painful to him. He is straddled between the loss of a country he has never seen, and his repudiation of the country in which he lives. "Doesn't the Party seem a horror now?" he bursts out.

Marvin nods. They are trying to comprehend the distance between Party members they have known, people by turn pathetic, likable, or annoying—people not unlike themselves—and in contrast the immensity of historic logic which deploys along statistics of the dead.

"It's all schizoid," Sam says. "Modern life is schizoid."

Marvin agrees. They have agreed on this many times, bored with the petulance of their small voices, yet needing the comfort of such complaints. Marvin asks Sam if he has given up his novel, and Sam says, "Temporarily." He cannot find a form, he explains. He does not want to write a realistic novel, because reality is no longer realistic. "I don't know what it is," says Sam. "To tell you the truth, I think I'm kidding myself. I'll never finish this book. I just like to entertain the idea I'll do something good some day." They sit there in friendly depression. Conversation has cooled. Alan and the women are no longer talking.

"Marvin," asks Louise, "what time is it?"

They are ready to go. Sam must say directly what he had hoped to approach by suggestion. "I was wondering," he whispers to Rossman, "would you mind if I held onto the film for a day or two?"

Marvin looks at him. "Oh, why of course, Sam," he says in his morose voice. "I know how it is." He pats Sam on the shoulder as if, symbolically, to convey the exchange of ownership. They are fellow conspirators.

"If you ever want to borrow the projector," Sam suggests.

"Nah," says Marvin, "I don't know that it would make much difference."

It has been, when all is said, a most annoying day. As Sam and Eleanor tidy the apartment, emptying ash trays and washing the few dishes, they are fond neither of themselves nor each other. "What a waste today has been," Eleanor remarks, and Sam can only agree. He has done no writing, he has not been outdoors, and still it is late in the evening, and he has talked too much, eaten too much, is nervous from the movie they have seen. He knows that he will watch it again with Eleanor before they go to sleep; she has given her assent to that. But as is so often the case with Sam these days, he cannot await their embrace with any sure anticipation. Eleanor may be in the mood or Eleanor may not; there is no way he can control the issue. It is depressing; Sam knows that he circles about Eleanor at such times with the guilty maneuvers of a sad hound. Resent her as he must, be furious with himself as he will, there is not very much he can do about it. Often, after they have made love, they will lie beside each other in silence, each offended, each certain the other is to blame. At such times, memory tickles them with a cruel feather. Not always has it been like this. When they were first married, and indeed for the six months they lived together before marriage, everything was quite different.

Their affair was very exciting to them; each told the other with some hyperbole but no real mistruth that no one in the past had ever been comparable as lover.

I suppose I am a romantic. I always feel that this is the best time in people's lives. There is, after all, so little we accomplish, and that short period when we are beloved and triumph as lovers is sweet with power. Rarely are we concerned then with our lack of importance; we are too important. In Sam's case, disillusion means even more. Like so many young men, he entertained the secret conceit that he was an extraordinary lover. One cannot really believe this without supporting at the same time the equally secret conviction that one is fundamentally inept. It is—no matter what Sergius would say—a more dramatic and therefore more attractive view of oneself than the sober notion which Sam now accepts with grudging wisdom, that the man as lover is dependent upon the bounty of the woman. As I say, he accepts the notion, it is one of the lineaments of maturity, but there is a part of him which, no matter how harried by analysis, cannot relinquish the antagonism he feels that Eleanor has respected his private talent so poorly, and has not allowed him to confer its benefits upon more women. I mock Sam, but he would mock himself on this. It hardly matters; mockery cannot accomplish everything, and Sam seethes with that most private and tender pain: even worse than being unattractive to the world is to be unattractive to one's mate; or, what is the same and describes Sam's case more accurately, never to know in advance when he shall be undesirable to Eleanor.

I make perhaps too much of the subject, but that is only because it is so important to Sam. Relations between Eleanor and him are not really that bad—I know other couples who have much less or nothing at all. But comparisons are poor comfort to Sam; his standards are so high. So are Eleanor's. I am convinced the most unfortunate people are those who would make an art of love. It sours other effort. Of all artists, they are certainly the most wretched.

Shall I furnish a model? Sam and Eleanor are on the couch and the projector, adjusted to its slowest speed, is retracing the elaborate pantomime of the three principals. If one could allow these shadows a life . . . but indeed such life has been given them. Sam and Eleanor are no more than an itch, a smart, a threshold of satisfaction; the important share of themselves has steeped itself in

Frankie-, Magnolia-, and Eleanor-of-the-film. Indeed the variations are beyond telling. It is the most outrageous orgy performed by five ghosts.

Self-critical Sam! He makes love in front of a movie, and one cannot say that it is unsatisfactory any more than one can say it is pleasant. It is dirty, downright porno dirty, it is a lewd slop-brush slapped through the middle of domestic exasperations and breakfast eggs. It is so dirty that only half of Sam—he is quite divisible into fractions—can be exercised at all. The part that is his brain worries along like a cuckolded burgher. He is taking the pulse of his anxiety. Will he last long enough to satisfy Eleanor? Will the children come back tonight? He cannot help it. In the midst of the circus, he is suddenly convinced the children will walk through the door. "Why are you so anxious, Daddie?"

So it goes. Sam the lover is conscious of exertion. One moment he is Frankie Idell, destroyer of virgins—take that! you whore!—the next, body moving, hands caressing, he is no more than some lines from a psychoanalytical text. He is thinking about the sensitivity of his scrotum. He has read that this is a portent of femininity in a male. How strong is his latent homosexuality worries Sam, thrusting stiffly, warm sweat running cold. Does he identify with Eleanor-of-the-film?

Technically, the climax is satisfactory. They lie together in the dark, the film ended, the projector humming its lonely revolutions in the quiet room. Sam gets up to turn it off; he comes back and kisses Eleanor upon the mouth. Apparently she has enjoyed herself more than he; she is tender and fondles the tip of his nose.

"You know, Sam," she says from her space beside him, "I think I saw this picture before."

"When?"

"Oh, you know when. That time."

Sam thinks dully that women are always most loving when they can reminisce about infidelity.

"That time!" he repeats.

"I think so."

Racing forward from memory like the approaching star which begins as a point on the mind and swells to explode the eyeball with its odious image, Sam remembers, and is weak in the dark. It is ten years, eleven perhaps, before they were married, yet after they were lovers. Eleanor has told him, but she has always been vague about details. There had been two men, it seemed, and another girl, and all had been drunk. They had seen movie after movie. With reluctant fascination, Sam can conceive the rest. How it had pained him, how excited him. It is years now since he has remembered, but he remembers. In the darkness he wonders at the unreasonableness of jealous pain. That night was impossible to imagine any longer—therefore it is more real; Eleanor his plump wife who presses a pigeon's shape against her housecoat, forgotten heroine of black orgies. It had been meaningless, Eleanor claimed; it was Sam she loved, and the other had been no more than a fancy of which she wished to rid herself. Would it be the same today, thinks Sam, or had Eleanor been loved by Frankie, by Frankie of the other movies, by Frankie of the two men she never saw again on that night so long ago?

The pleasure I get from this pain, Sam thinks furiously.

It is not altogether perverse. If Eleanor causes him pain, it means after all that she is alive for him. I have often observed that the reality of a person depends upon his ability to hurt us; Eleanor as the vague accusing embodiment of the wife is different, altogether different, from Eleanor who lies warmly in Sam's bed, an attractive Eleanor who may wound his flesh. Thus, brother to the pleasure of pain, is the sweeter pleasure which follows pain. Sam, tired, lies in Eleanor's arms, and they talk with the cozy trade words of old professionals, agreeing that they will not make love again before a movie, that it was exciting but also not without detachment, that all in all it has been good but not quite right, that she had loved this action he had done, and was uncertain about another. It is their old familiar critique, a sign that they are intimate and well disposed. They do not talk about the act when it has failed to fire; then they go silently to sleep. But now, Eleanor's enjoyment having mollified Sam's sense of no enjoyment, they talk with the apologetics and encomiums of familiar mates. Eleanor falls asleep, and Sam falls almost asleep, curling next to her warm body, his hand over her round belly with the satisfaction of a sculptor. He is drowsy, and he thinks drowsily that these few moments of creature-pleasure, this brief compassion he can feel for the body that trusts itself to sleep beside him, his comfort in its warmth, is perhaps all the meaning he may ask for his life. That out of disappointment, frustration, and the passage of dreary years come these few moments when he is close to her, and their years together possess a connotation more rewarding than the sum of all which has gone into them.

But then he thinks of the novel he wants to write, and he is wide-awake again. Like the sleeping pill which fails to work and leaves one warped in an exaggeration of the ills which sought the drug, Sam passes through the promise of sex-emptied sleep, and is left with nervous loins, swollen jealousy of an act ten years dead, and sweating irritable resentment of the woman's body which hinders his limbs. He has wasted the day, he tells himself, he has wasted the day as he has wasted so many days of his life, and tomorrow in the office he will be no more than his ten fingers typing plot and words for Bramba the Venusian and Lee-Lee Deeds, Hollywood Star, while that huge work with which he has cheated himself, holding it before him as a covenant of his worth, that enormous novel which would lift him at a bound from the impasse in which he stifles, whose dozens of characters would develop a vision of life in bountiful complexity, lies foundered, rotting on a beach of purposeless effort. Notes here, pages there, it sprawls through a formless wreck of incidental ideas and half-episodes, utterly without shape. He has not even a hero for it.

One could not have a hero today, Sam thinks, a man of action and contemplation, capable of sin, large enough for good, a man immense. There is only a modern hero damned by no more than the ugliness of wishes whose satisfaction he will never know. One needs a man who could walk the stage, someone who—no matter who, not himself. Someone, Sam thinks, who reasonably could not exist.

The novelist, thinks Sam, perspiring beneath blankets, must live in paranoia and seek to be one with the world; he must be terrified of experience and hungry for it; he must think himself nothing and believe he is superior to all. The feminine in his nature cries for proof he is a man; he dreams of power and is without capacity to gain it; he loves himself above all and therefore despises all that he is.

He is that, thinks Sam, he is part of the perfect prescription, and yet he is not a novelist. He lacks energy and belief. It is left for him to write an article some day about the temperament of the ideal novelist.

In the darkness, memories rise, yeast-swells of apprehension. Out of bohemian days so long ago, comes the friend of Eleanor, a girl who had been sick and was committed to an institution. They visited her, Sam and Eleanor, they took the suburban train and sat on the lawn of the asylum grounds while patients circled about intoning a private litany, or shuddering in boob-blundering fright from an insect that crossed their skin. The friend had been silent. She had smiled, she had answered their questions with the fewest words, and had returned again to her study of sunlight and blue sky. As they were about to leave, the girl had taken Sam aside. "They violate me," she said in a whisper. "Every night when the doors are locked, they come to my room and they make the movie. I am the heroine and I am subjected to all variety of sexual viciousness. Tell them to leave me alone so I may enter the convent." And while she talked, in a horror of her body, one arm scrubbed the other. Poor tortured friend. They had seen her again, and she babbled, her face had coarsened into an idiot leer.

Sam sweats. There is so little he knows, and so much to know. Youth of the depression with its economic terms, what can he know of madness or religion? They are both so alien to him. He is the mongrel, Sam thinks, brought up without religion from a mother half Protestant and half Catholic, and a father half Catholic and half Jew. He is the quarter-Jew, and yet he is a Jew, or so he feels himself, knowing nothing of Gospel, tabernacle, or Mass, the Jew through accident, through state of mind. What . . . whatever did he know of penance? self-sacrifice? mortification of the flesh? the love of his fellow man? Am I concerned with my relation to God? ponders Sam, and smiles sourly in the darkness. No, that has never concerned him, he thinks, not for better nor for worse. "They are making the movie," says the girl into the ear of memory, "and so I cannot enter the convent."

How hideous was the mental hospital. A concentration camp, decides Sam. Perhaps it would be the world some day, or was that only his projection of feelings of hopelessness? "Do not try to solve the problems of the world," he hears from Sergius, and pounds a lumpy pillow.

However could he organize his novel? What form to give it? It is so complex. Too loose, thinks Sam, too scattered. Will he ever fall asleep? Wearily, limbs tense, his stomach too keen, he plays again the game of putting himself to sleep. "I do not feel my toes," Sam says to himself, "my toes are dead, my calves are asleep, my calves are sleeping . . ."

In the middle from wakefulness to slumber, in the torpor which floats beneath blankets, I give an idea to Sam. "Destroy time, and chaos may be ordered," I say to him.

"Destroy time, and chaos may be ordered," he repeats after me, and in desperation to seek his coma, mutters back, "I do not feel my nose, my nose is numb, my eyes are heavy, my eyes are heavy."

So Sam enters the universe of sleep, a man who seeks to live in such a way as to avoid pain, and succeeds merely in avoiding pleasure. What a dreary compromise is life!

## ALLEN B. WHEELIS

*is a practicing psychiatrist in San Francisco who has written extensively about interpersonal relationships in contemporary American society. His best-known work on this subject is* Quest for Identity *which deals with problems of identity formation and maintenance. He is also a skilled fiction writer. In this short story Wheelis contrasts the cynic (scientist) and the idealist (romantic), using the maintenance of these two poles of interpersonal orientation as causal factors in creating often illusory and empty relationships. The image society projects of what interpersonal relationships are supposed to be is critically evaluated when those who would live these images see them removed from advertising billboards and television commercials—and juxtaposed instead against the business of real life.*

# THE ILLUSIONLESS MAN AND THE VISIONARY MAID

Once upon a time there was a man who had no illusions about anything. While still in the crib he had learned that his mother was not always kind; at two he had given up fairies; witches and hobgoblins disappeared from his world at three; at four he knew that rabbits at Easter lay no eggs; and at five on a cold night in December, with a bitter little smile, he said goodbye to Santa Claus. At six when he started school, illusions flew from his life like feathers in a windstorm: he discovered that his father was not always brave or even honest, that Presidents are little men, that the Queen of England goes to the bathroom like everybody else, and that his first grade teacher, a pretty round-faced young woman with dimples, did not know everything, as he had thought, but thought only of men and did not know much of anything. At eight he could read, and the printed word was a sorcerer at exorcising illusions—only he knew there were no sorcerers. The abyss of hell disappeared into the even larger abyss into which a clear vision was sweeping his beliefs. Happiness was of course a myth; love a fleeting attachment, a dream of enduring selflessness glued onto the instinct of a rabbit. At twelve he dispatched into the night sky his last unheard prayer. As a young man he realized that the most generous act is self-serving, the most disinterested inquiry serves interest; that lies are told by printed words, even by words carved in stone; that art begins with a small "a" like everything else, and that he could not escape the ruin of value by orchestrating a cry of despair into a song of lasting beauty; for beauty passes and deathless art is quite mortal. Of all those people who lose illusions he lost more than anyone else, taboo and prescription alike; and as everything became permitted nothing was left worthwhile.

He became a carpenter, but could see a house begin to decay in the course of building—perfect pyramid of white sand spreading out irretrievably in the grass, bricks chipping, doors sticking, the first tone of gray appearing on white lumber, the first film of rust on bright nails, the first leaf falling in the shining gutter. He became then a termite inspector, spent his days crawling in darkness under old houses; he lived in a basement room and never raised the blinds, ate canned beans and frozen television dinners, let his hair grow and his beard. On Sundays he walked in the park, threw bread to the ducks—dry French bread, stone-hard/would stamp on it with his heel, gather up the pieces, and walk along the pond, throwing it out to the avid ducks paddling after him, thinking glumly that they would be just as hungry again tomorrow. His name was Henry.

One day in the park he met a girl who believed in everything. In the forest she still glimpsed fairies, heard them whisper; bunnies hopped for her at Easter, laid brilliant eggs; at Christmas hoofbeats shook the roof. She was disillusioned at times and would flounder, gasp desperately, like a fish in sand, but not for long; would quickly, sometimes instantly, find something new, and actually never gave up any illusion, but would lay it aside when necessary, forget it, and whenever it was needed, back it would come. Her name was Lorabelle, and when she saw a bearded young man in the park, alone among couples, stamping on the hard bread, tossing it irritably to the quacking ducks, she exploded into illusions about him like a Roman candle over a desert.

"You are a great and good man," she said.

"I'm petty and self-absorbed," he said.

"You're terribly unhappy."

"I'm morose . . . probably like it that way."

"You have suffered a great deal," she said. "I see it in your face."

"I've been diligent only in self-pity," he said, "have turned away from everything difficult, and what you see are the scars of old acne shining through my beard; I could never give up chocolate and nuts."

"You're very wise," she said.

"No, but intelligent."

They talked about love, beauty, feeling, value, life, work, death—and always she came back to love. They argued about everything, differed on everything, agreed on nothing, and so she fell in love with him. "This partakes of the infinite," she said.

But he, being an illusionless man, was only fond of her. "It partaketh mainly," he said, "of body chemistry," and passed his hand over her roundest curve.

"We have a unique affinity," she said. "You're the only man in the world for me."

"We fit quite nicely," he said. "You are one of no more than five or six girls in the county for me."

"It's a miracle we met," she said.

"I just happened to be feeding the ducks."

"No, no, no, not chance; I couldn't feel this way about anybody else."

"If you'd come down the other side of the hill," he said, "you'd be feeling this way right now about somebody else. And if I had fed squirrels instead of ducks I'd be playing with somebody else's curves."

"You're my dearest darling squirrel," she said, "and most of all you're my silly fuzzy duck, and I don't know why I bother to love you—why are you such a fool? Who dropped you on your head?—come to bed!" On such a note of logic, always, their arguments ended.

She wanted a wedding in church with a dress of white Alençon lace over cream satin, bridesmaids in pink, organ music, and lots of people to weep and be happy and throw rice. "You'll be so handsome in a morning coat," she said, brushing cobwebs from his shoulders, "oh and striped pants, too, and a gray silk cravat, and a white carnation. You'll be divine."

"I'd look a proper fool," he said, "and I'm damned if I'll do it."

"Oh please! It's only once."

"Once a fool, voluntarily, is too often."

"It's a sacrament."

"It's a barbarism."

"Symbols are important."

"Then let's stand by the Washington Monument," he said, "and be honest about it."

"You make fun," she said, "but it's a holy ceremony, a solemn exchange of vows before man and God."

"God won't be there, honey; the women will be weeping for

their own lost youth and innocence, the men wanting to have you in bed; and the priest standing slightly above us will be looking down your cleavage as his mouth goes dry; and the whole thing will be a primitive and preposterous attempt to invest copulation with dignity and permanence, to enforce responsibility for children by the authority of a myth no longer credible even to a child."

So . . . they were married in church: his hands were wet and his knees shook, he frowned and quaked; but looked divine, she said, in morning coat and striped pants; and she was serene and beautiful in Alençon lace; the organ pealed, weeping women watched with joy, vows were said, rice thrown, and then they were alone on the back seat of a taxi, her red lips seeking his, murmuring, "I'm so happy, darling, so terribly happy. Now we'll be together always."

"In our community," he said, "and for our age and economic bracket, we have a 47.3 per cent chance of staying together for twenty years."

She found for them a white house on a hill in a field of orange poppies and white daisies, with three tall maple trees. There they lived in sunlight and wind, and she began to fill their life with fragile feminine deceptions, worked tirelessly at them, and always there was something new. She concealed the monotony of eating by variety, never two meals the same, one morning French toast in the shape of their house, the next a boiled egg with smiling painted face and a tiny straw hat; cut flowers on the table, color and sweetness blooming from a Dutch vase, as if unrelated to manure; Italian posters on the wall as if they had traveled; starched white curtains at the windows, as if made of a brocade too rich and heavy to bend; morning glories covering the outhouse with royal purple. When he came home at night she would brush the cobwebs from his hair, make him bathe and shave and dress—to appear as if he had not worked in dirt. She made wonderful sauces, could cook anything to taste like something else, created a sense of purity by the whiteness of tablecloth, of delicacy by the thinness of crystal, would surround a steak with parsley as if it were not flesh but the bloom of a garden, supported her illusions with candlelight and fine wine, and smiled at him across the table with lips redder than real. In the bedroom candlelight again, and yet another nightgown to suggest a mysterious woman of unknown delights, and a heavy perfume, as if not sweat but sweetness came from her pores.

Being an illusionless man, he knew that he liked these elegant mirages, found them pleasant, that it was good to sleep with her fine curves under his hand, her sweet smells in his nose, that he slept better now than when he lived alone. He became less gloomy, but not much.

One Sunday afternoon, walking hand in hand in sunshine through the poppies and daisies, he noticed her lips moving. "What are you saying?" he said.

"Do you love me?"

"I'm fond of you," he said; "love is an illusion."

"Is there anybody else? I'm terribly jealous."

"Jealousy is the illusion of complete possession."

"Do other women attract you?"

"Yes."

"Some men are not like that."

"Some men are liars," he said.

"Oh . . ."

". . . Don't cry! I won't leave you."

"How can I be sure?"

"I wouldn't hurt you."

She became pregnant, bought baby clothes, tried out names, was always singing. "Please be happy," she said.

"By 1980 the world population will . . ."

"Oh be quiet!" she said.

She prepared a room for the baby, hung curtains, bought a crib, read books, became apprehensive. "Will he be all right? What do you think? Will he be a good baby? He doesn't have to be pretty, you know, that's not so important, but I'd like him to be intelligent. And will he have two eyes and the right number of fingers and toes? I want him to have everything he needs and nothing too much. What do you think?"

"Some minor congenital aberrations are inevitable," he said; "the major malformations are less. . . ."

"Don't say such things," she said. "Why do you scare me?"

"I was just. . . ."

"Oh . . . and will I know what to do?" she said, ". . . how to take care of him? What do you think? Will I be any good at it?"

One night he felt her lips moving in his hair. "Praying?" he said. "Yes." "What did you ask?" "That someday you will say you love me."

She felt weak, became sick; in bed she looked pale and scared. "Will the baby be all right?" she said. "Don't ever leave me. What are you thinking? Tell me." She began to bleed, was terrified, lay very still, but lost the baby anyway.

She was depressed then, her face motionless and dark. "I lost it because you don't love me," she said.

"There is no established correlation," he said, "between the alleged state of love, or lack of it, and the incidence of miscarriage."

"I'm not wanting statistics," she screamed.

"What then?"

"Nothing. Everything. It's not enough . . . just being 'fond.' I hate fondness. What's the matter with you? It wouldn't have happened . . . I want to be loved!"

"You're being hysterical," he said, "and you're not finishing your sentences."

Suddenly, all at once, she looked at him with a level detached gaze and did not like what she saw. "You were right," she said; "you *are* petty and self-absorbed. What's worse, you have a legal mind and there's no poetry in you. You don't give me anything, don't even love me, you're *dull*. You were stuck in a hole in the ground when I found you, and if I hadn't pulled you out you'd be there still. There's no life in you. I give you everything and it's not enough, doesn't make any difference. You can't wait to die, want to bury yourself now and me with you. Well I'm not ready yet and I'm not going to put up with it any longer, and now I'm through with you and I want a divorce."

"You've lost your illusions about me," he said, "but not the having of illusions. . . ."

"While you," she said, "have lost your illusions about everything, and can't get over being sore about it."

". . . they'll focus on someone else. . . ."

"Oh I hope so!" she said; "I can hardly wait."

". . . you waste experience."

"And you waste *life!*"

He wouldn't give her a divorce, but that didn't matter; for she couldn't bear the thought of his moving back to that basement, and anyway, she told herself, he had to have someone to look after him; so they lived together still and she cooked for him when she was home and mended his clothes and darned his socks, and when he asked why, she said, with sweet revenge, "Because I'm fond of you, that's all. Just fond."

She got a job with a theater, typed scripts and programs, worked nights in the box office, let her hair grow into a long silken curtain curled up at the bottom below her shoulders, wore loose chiffon blouses with clown sleeves, trailed filmy scarves from her neck, and fell in love with an actor named Cyrus Anthony de Maronodeck. Hera's broadened and she affected a way of turning her head with so sudden a movement that it could not go unnoticed; no longer did she walk in or out of a room, she strode. Again she demanded a divorce; and when Henry refused she taunted him.

"Cyrus is so *interesting!*" she said, "makes everything an adventure, concentrates energy and passion into a moment until it glows!" She struck a pose: " 'When I die,' he says, 'I may be dead for a long time, but while I'm here I'll live it to the hilt.' "

"A philosopher, too," Henry said.

One Sunday night Cyrus borrowed a thousand dollars from Lorabelle for his sick mother; and the following day it transpired that he had borrowed also the weekend receipts from the box office and had taken his leave of the company. For several days Lorabelle wouldn't believe it, waited for word from him, bit her fingernails—until he was apprehended in Laredo crossing the border with a blonde.

She worked next in a brokerage house operating an enormous and very intelligent machine which tapped and hummed and whirred and rotated, sent its carriage hopping up and down and side to side, performed seventeen mathematical calculations without ever a mistake, took pictures of everything, and had illusions about nothing—but Lorabelle did, and presently fell in love with her boss, Mr. Alexander Orwell Mittelby, a sixty-year-old man who loved her with a great passion, she told Henry, but who was married and unfortunately could not get a divorce because his wife was a schizophrenic, had a private nurse in constant attendance; the shock of divorce, Mr. Mittelby had said, would kill her.

"Alex is unique," Lorabelle told Henry, "simply not like the rest of us . . . not at all. He has no interest in himself, has grown beyond that. I've never met a man so mature, so genuinely wise.

'All my personal goals lie in the past,' he told me; 'the only thing left is to seek the common good.' He has no patience with personal problems, complexes . . . that sort of thing . . . sees the romantic protest for what it is: adolescent complaining. Oh Henry, I wish you could know him. He faces life with so much courage—such a gallant, careless courage. 'Despair is a luxury,' he says, 'the flight of a frightened intelligence, and I can't afford it.' "

Lorabelle wore short tight skirts, high, needle-like heels, jeweled glasses, and her hair bouffant; she read the *Wall Street Journal* and *Barron's Weekly*, studied the new tax legislation, spoke out for laissez faire in discussion groups, and at an Anti-World-Federalist dinner chanced to meet Mrs. Mittelby, who was not schizophrenic at all, but a plain, shrewd woman with a wrinkled face, gray hair, and a very sharp tongue. Lorabelle stared at her with deepening shock. "My husband's secretaries," Mrs. Mittelby said, "always seem stunned by my sanity . . . then seek other employment."

In her depression Lorabelle turned away from people, rented a cabin on an island, left Henry to look after himself, came home only on weekends, spent her days walking on deserted beaches, her nights alone writing an autobiographical novel by lamplight. "It's really a kind of self-analysis," she said, "but maybe I can make it beautiful."

After a few months she fell in love with a fisherman. "His name is Jim," she said to Henry. "That's all, just Jim. And he's like his name, exactly: simple, strong, uncomplicated. I wish you could know each other."

"Bring him to dinner!" Henry shouted. "Let him live here! Give him my clothes, my bed!"

"Don't be angry. You'd like him; you couldn't help it. He's so kind, so gentle, so much a part of the elements: in his eyes the wind and the ocean—you can see them!—in his hand the strength, the toughness . . . the grip on the helm in a storm, in his bearing the straightness of the tall pointed firs, in his character the solid rock of the coast."

"If he had a foundation," Henry said, "he'd be a house with a swimming pool."

Lorabelle cut her hair short, wore boots and a sou'wester, scanned the sky for weather signs, studied navigation charts, hung a tide table on the wall. "I want a divorce," she said. "No."

"Why? You don't love me." "To protect you from your own bad judgment. You'd be married six times before you were forty if you were free." "Then I'll run away with him," she said.

And she would have, but the sheriff got there first, arrested Jim for bigamy: plain Jim had three last names and a wife with each, and while he sat in jail the three of them squabbled for the fishing boat, which was all he owned.

Lorabelle gave up the cabin, burned her manuscript, and moved back home; wept and wailed and could not be consoled. "There's something wrong with *my* sanity," she said. "I can't do it myself. I'd better see a psychoanalyst." "You'll get a whopping transference," Henry said.

She went to a Dr. Milton Tugwell, took to analysis with great facility, worked quickly through her depression, went four times a week, and wished it were more. "I'm so terribly lucky," she said to Henry. "There are so many analysts, you know—good, bad, indifferent—I had no way of knowing . . . and he turns out to be the *one* analyst for me. No one else would be right."

"It really is a kind of miracle, isn't it?" Henry said.

"No, really! I mean it. There's a special affinity between us. I felt it the very first session. We speak the same language; sometimes he knows what I'm thinking before I say it—sometimes even before I know I'm thinking it. It's amazing. And he has the most astonishing memory, remembers *everything*. And the way—Oh Henry! if you could only know him, hear him talk!—the way he fits these things together! things you'd never realize were connected. . . ."

Dr. Tugwell made many excellent interpretations: Lorabelle learned about her orality, anality, penis envy, oedipus complex, and, as a kind of bonus, had many insights also into Henry and shared them with him, surprised at his lack of responsiveness.

One night at the theater she saw Dr. Tugwell in the company of a tall, gray-haired woman with a hard face. His wife, Lorabelle thought, and something clicked for her, an insight all on her own: *Dr. Tugwell was unhappy with this woman.* So this was the source of that sad note in his voice. He deserved better. Lorabelle wanted to make him happy, as a woman; and she could, she knew she could. She looked narrowly at Mrs. Tugwell.

Then it occurred to her (the analysis must be taking effect, she thought; this was her second insight in an hour) that Dr. Tugwell might have some special feeling of this sort for her, and the more she thought about it the more obvious it became.

When in her next hour she talked of these matters: the warmth of his greeting, clearly more than professional; the happy loving way he smiled at her; the little things about her he held in his mind, as if deliberately committing her whole life to memory; the caressing tone of that gentle voice floating out over her on the couch. How could she have failed so long to recognize it? Dr. Tugwell said nothing except "What comes to mind about that?" and she was disappointed, then realized that he could not speak, that he was the prisoner of a professional commitment which required him to stifle his feeling for her. She walked in the meadow on the hill in sunshine and knew in her heart what must be hidden in his; and someday, she thought, when the analysis was over maybe he would get a divorce and Henry would give her a divorce, and she and Dr. Tugwell would meet on a different basis. She picked a daisy, pulled the petals, and it came out right. Softly she tried his name on her lips, "Milton, darling," and blushed, "sweetest Milt . . . honey," felt him walk beside her, his hand slip around her waist, heard his deep beloved voice begin, "Lorabelle, there is something I must tell you. . . ."

The analysis lasted longer than any of her affairs, perhaps because, paying for her sessions, she valued them more than meetings with lovers, or perhaps because her illusions did not encounter anything hard enough in Dr. Tugwell's silence to cause breakage; but after five years Henry came to the end of his resources and tolerance, said he would pay for no more sessions. This proved him cruel and unfeeling, Lorabelle thought, and reported it triumphantly to Dr. Tugwell who, strangely, regarded it as reasonable.

Lorabelle wept through the last hour, tears making lakes in her ears, overflowing on the pillow, dripping from her chin as she stood up, shaking, to face him, her voice quavering as she thanked him for the changes in her, breaking as she said goodbye. Yet at that very moment she had the comfort of a secret vision: now that she was no longer his patient he was free to become her lover. But days passed, and he didn't call, weeks and the vision was shaken, a month and she was desolate. She went back to see him; and this time, sitting in a chair before him, feeling oddly dislocated, really did *see* him. There along the wall was the green couch on which she had lain for so many hours, from which she had looked up at the blank ceiling, had raved, rambled, complained, and wept; and there—shrinking back slightly from the violence of her disappointment—was the man of her dreams who had listened, out of sight, behind the couch: dark suit of expensive cloth and cut, perfectly pressed, dark tie, silk shirt with white-on-white design, high cordovan sheen on calf-skin loafers, shell-rimmed glasses flashing a nervous glare. There was strain in his voice, she thought; he used jargon, was more detached than he need have been: a continuing transference problem, he said . . . not infrequent . . . might require further analysis . . . unresolved father attachment . . . he had committed her hours . . . could do nothing now . . . sorry . . . perhaps later . . . call him in three months.

For weeks Lorabelle stayed home in deep silent gloom, wouldn't eat, wouldn't dress; but bounced back finally, as she always did, got a job selling tickets at a carousel, and there met Adelbert Bassew, big game hunter—"What a man!" she exclaimed to Henry; "six feet six, all fire and brawn. Imagine!"—who asked her on a safari. And so it continued through the days and weeks of their lives, year after year: Catholic Church, Christian Science, yoga; Al, Bob, and Peter; Paris, Rome, and Nairobi; technocracy, mysticism, hypnotism; short hair, long hair, and wig; and whenever she would say, in that rapturous tone of hers, "I realize now . . . ," Henry would know she had abandoned one illusion and was already firmly entrapped by the next. They became poor on her pursuits, lived in a basement; her illusions became sillier, shabbier, until finally she was sending in box-tops from cereal packages. Crow's feet appeared around her eyes, white hair among the gold; her skin became dry and papery. But as she got older something about her stayed young: the springing up of hope, the intoxicating energy, the creation of a new dream from the ruin of the old. From the despair of disillusion always she would find her way back: to a bell-like laughter with the rising note of an unfinished story, to a lilt of voice like the leap of water before rapids, to a wild dancing grace of legs and hips like a horse before a jump, to the happy eyes so easily wet with sympathy or love.

But these same years made Henry older than his actual age, more withdrawn, bitter, morose; his face haggard, lined; his hair gray. Every day he got up and went to work, but did nothing else

—would not read a book or walk in the park or listen to music. In the evenings he would drink; but gin nourished no illusion, brought no pleasure, only numbness and finally sleep. Lorabelle felt anger and pity and contempt, all at the same time, and would rail at him. "Just look at yourself: drunk, dirty, head hanging like a sick cat . . . How can you stand yourself? What are you trying to do? make me feel guilty . . . Well I don't. Playing the martyr? Is that it? What's the matter with you? Why don't you find someone else if you're so unhappy with me?"

Henry would shrug, thinking there are no happy marriages, and it would be no different with anyone else; but sometimes, far at the back of his unhappy mind, he would come upon the truth: he stayed with her because, with all her witless pursuit of illusions, she nevertheless stirred him—like the wren, trapped under a house, that had flown in his face: he had caught it in his hand, felt the terrified struggle, the concentration of heat, the tremolo of heartbeat too faint and fast to count. Lorabelle brought him no comfort; but, holding her, he felt life, and would not give it up. And sometimes in the midst of her railings Lorabelle would know that she stayed with Henry—not simply, as she said, because he wouldn't give her a divorce—but because he was a rock and she leaned on him.

But even rocks may crumble, and one Monday morning Henry did not move when the alarm went off; he lay still, eyes open, looking at the empty face of the clock, thinking numbly of millions of termites burrowing in wood who would suffer no further interference from him.

He stayed in bed most of the day, ate little, drank much, said nothing. The next day was the same, and the next, and so all week; and on Friday it occurred to Lorabelle that—Henry having apparently retired from business—she must earn the living. After her morning coffee, therefore, she sat down at her desk to compose the fourth line of a jingle about soap flakes; first prize would bring a thousand dollars. Next she invented a hatpin that could neither fall out of a hat nor prick a finger; drew a careful sketch of the device, and addressed it to the U.S. Patent Office; this might make a fortune, she thought. Then she collected all her green stamps: not many, she mused, but enough for a present for Henry. She prepared his lunch on a tray, found him lying in bed staring at the ceiling; he would say nothing and would not eat. She put on her best dress, arranged flowers by his bed, and kissed him on the nose. "I'll be back soon," she said.

It was a beautiful day, the sun shining, wind moving here and there among the trees like playful strokes of a great invisible brush. "I know he will be all right," she said to herself, and posted her jingle and her invention, saying a little prayer for each. She went then to a fortune-teller, an old West Indian woman, who told her that someone dear to her was ill and would die. Lorabelle was shocked and left immediately, bought three sweepstakes tickets in Henry's name to fight the prediction, said another prayer, went on to the supply house and got a pipe and slippers for her green stamps. For a dollar she bought jonquils—because they were pretty and would make him happy—then counted her money. With the two dollars that were left she bought a steak to tempt his appetite.

At home she found him in pyjamas sitting at the table drinking gin. "Oh sweetheart!" she said, "you break my heart . . . I won't have it, I just won't have it . . . you understand? Cheer up now. I've got presents for you." She put the pipe in his hand, brought tobacco, put the slippers on his bare feet—"There! You see? Aren't they nice? And so warm. A perfect fit! You like them?"—but he said nothing. She began to sing, trying not to cry, then broke off: "Oh, and I have something else . . . another wonderful surprise, you'll see. Now don't come in the kitchen," she added, unnecessarily. She broiled the steak, put it on a heated plate, garnished it with water cress, put jonquils on the tray, a chef's cap on her head, lighted candles, and brought it in singing the Triumphal March from *Aida,* placed it before him with a flourish and a sweeping low bow. He turned away. "Oh please, do eat it," she cried; "I got it just for you. It's delicious, you'll see! Try it. . . . Would be so good for you."

"Where's the gin?" he said.

"Don't drink any more; you'll get sick. I'm so worried. Eat now. You'll feel better, I know you will, really . . . I just know it. Here, let me feed you."

She cut a bit of steak, waved it under his nose, held it to his mouth, touched his lips; he knocked it away, the fork clattering to the floor, the morsel skittering into a corner. She picked them up, took away the tray. In the kitchen she threw the fork at the calendar, kicked the garbage can, wept, then she composed herself and went back, humming, to the living room; Henry had not moved. Lorabelle put up a card table, took newspaper clippings from her purse, spread out maps of the city: she was working on a treasure hunt. Only three clues had been published, and already she had an idea where the treasure might be. The first prize was five thousand dollars; tomorrow she would take a shovel and go digging.

"Where's the gin?" Henry said.

"There isn't any more, sweetheart. And a good thing because you've had too much. You're drunk; you're ruining your health."

"Give me some money," he said tonelessly.

"We haven't any."

He got up, walked unsteadily to the table where she was sitting, opened her purse and took out her wallet. A few coins fell to the table, rolled on the floor; there were no bills. He turned her handbag upside down: an astrology chart tumbled out, then a Christian Science booklet, a handbill from the Watchtower Society, "Palmistry in Six Easy Lessons," dozens of old sweepstakes tickets and the three new ones, "Love and the Mystic Union," fortunes from Chinese cookies (one of which, saying "He loves you," she snatched away from him), a silver rosary, a daily discipline from the Rosicrucians, the announcement of a book titled *Secret Power from the Unconscious through Hypnosis*—but no money. He shook the bag furiously and threw it in a corner, surveyed the litter before him with unblinking bloodshot eyes, his face expressionless. "Stupid fool!" he said thickly. "Purse full of illusions . . . suitcase full of illusions . . . whole goddamned lousy life full of illusions . . ." He turned away, stumbled back to the table, put the empty gin bottle to his mouth, turned it over his head, broke it on the hearth.

"Oh my dear," Lorabelle cried, her eyes wet, "you keep waiting for the real thing, but this is all there is." He turned ponderously, facing her, eyes like marble; she came to him. "These are the days . . . and nights . . . of our years and they're passing—look at us! We're getting old—and what else is there?"

"Bitch!"

She faltered, raising her arm, but recovered and went on to touch the side of his head where the hair was gray. "Do please come back to life; I don't want you to die; I'd be so lonely. I'd forget all the bad times and remember all the wonderful things

. . . where have they gone? . . . you feeding the ducks, stamping on the bread—so sweet you were!"

"Get out."

The gray stonelike face above her did not move, not even the eyes. A death mask, she thought; the fortune-teller was right. "Oh my dear! I feel so sad." She cried, lowered her head; with a convulsive movement she caught his hand, pressed it to her heart. "It hurts so," she said. "For years you've been cutting yourself off . . . more and more. I'm the only one still holding you, and now you're drifting away. Don't die, sweetheart, let me help you, hold on to me!"

He freed his hand and hit her in the face, sent her crashing into the wall, started after her, thinking, "Where's that broken bottle?" realized with a sense of strangeness that he wanted to kill her . . . paused. She stood looking at him, tears running down her face, then left the room. He turned back to the table, sat heavily, observed the hand that had hit her; the fingers felt numb. Before him on the table was the hatpin she had worked with that morning: long sharp pin, black plastic ball at one end, at the other an odd device of safety pins and scotch tape. "Illusion!" he said, grabbing it up in clenched fist and driving it deep into the table; the plastic ball broke, the base of the pin went through his hand, stuck out three inches on top. There was no blood. His hand hung there in mid-air, quivering slightly, like an insect pinned to a card. He moved his fingers: a white crab without a shell, he thought, impaled on a boy's stick. Blood appeared around the pin; the feeling of numbness crept up his arm; he wanted a drink, didn't want to die yet, wasn't ready. Numbness came now to the other arm. He began tugging at the pin, ten cold crab legs fumbling around a spike.

The next morning he shaved, got dressed, and ate breakfast. He felt restless, wanted to do something but didn't know what. "Will you go for a walk with me?" he said. Lorabelle was tired, her eyes red, hadn't slept, but was never without hope. "Yes," she said.

They walked by rivers, over bridges, through forests, sat in dry grass, and watched a tiny squirrel at the tip of a branch in a fir tree; walked through meadows, by cliffs, over dunes, along the beach, saw two sea stars in a tide pool waving their arms at each other; walked on streets, between high buildings, through crowds, watched a little girl feeding pigeons by a fountain. Lorabelle was silent and dejected, her hair scraggly, her shoulders stooped. Something was moving inside Henry, pressing him; he wanted to say something but didn't know what.

That evening as they sat together in their basement room, silent and unhappy, the phone rang. Henry, having known since childhood that a telephone ring means requests, burdens, and obligations, did not move; and for the first time Lorabelle—to whom the same sound meant love, opportunity, adventure—did not answer. Henry looked up, saw that she was exhausted: "Let it ring," he said. She nodded, but couldn't bear the sense of someone calling unheeded, began to hope as she walked, walked faster as she hoped, was soon running lest she be too late, and a few moments later was exclaiming in astonishment and joy: "What? . . . No! . . . Really? Yes! yes! oh yes, he's right here . . . No, I have it . . . So much! That's wonderful! Marvelous!" then flung herself in Henry's arms, weeping, laughing, "You've won the Irish Sweepstakes! $137,000! Can you imagine! My God . . .!"

Henry was pleased, but confused and vaguely disturbed; said it was hers not his, since she had bought the ticket. "No, no," she said, "I bought it in your name, and it's yours, and I'm so happy I could cry. . . ." She wiped her tears. "You need it, darling, more than I . . . because I've always known about miracles but you haven't known, but now maybe you will, a little, and I'm so glad it happened for you. Isn't it marvelous?"

"It won't be much after taxes."

"Oh, but still a lot," she said, "a very great deal. Just think . . .! We'll go to Paris and live in the Ritz, and you'll have a dark blue suit and a gray silk tie and cufflinks of lapis and maybe a black stick with a little silver. You'll stand very straight and swing the stick lightly, back and forth, as we stroll on the Boulevard St. Germain and the Rue St. Honoré, and I'll be so proud." She sat on his lap, eyes glistening, hugged him, kissed the gray hair by his ear. "Then we'll get a Citroën and drive down the Loire, and come finally to beautiful sand and water. Oh, and Monte Carlo! We'll stand around the casino watching the Texas oilmen and the pretty girls and the diamond bracelets; we'll hold hands and look on at roulette and moisten our lips and be like poor cautious tourists, and nobody will know we're rich. Then you'll toss out a ten thousand dollar bill: 'Red,' you'll say. That's all, just that: 'Red,' in a quiet voice, and people will fall silent and stare, and the croupier's hand will tremble, and the wheel will spin and, oh! . . . it won't matter whether it's red or black because it's just money either way, not love, and we'll go to Rome and rent a villa, and when. . . ."

"We're broke," he said, "long before Rome. In Genoa we couldn't pay the hotel bill. Remember? Had to sell your jewels . . . and my walking stick."

"Oh no!" she said, "there you go, already sad. . . . Then we remembered the *other* bank account—how could you forget?—found we had plenty of money . . . We go on to Rome, rent a villa and in the evening sit on the terrace holding hands, flowers blooming all around us, and to the west on the crest of a hill seven cypress trees in a row, an orange sun sinking between the black trunks, the whole sky a brilliant golden drum; and you'll feel a throbbing of your heart and a kind of singing rapture, and you'll press my hand and say, 'I love you.' "

Henry was touched by her fantasy and felt some lightness of heart: it would be nice to have some money, he thought—how incredible!—and maybe they really would enjoy a trip. That night they slept in each other's arms and the next day the windfall was gone: it had been a mistake, the officials were terribly sorry, it was another man with the same name and almost the same telephone number, who owned a candy store and had five children, weighed three hundred pounds, and was pictured in the newspaper with his family, seven round beaming faces. Lorabelle was in despair, but Henry was tranquil, still felt that lightness of heart. He comforted Lorabelle and stroked her finally to sleep in the evening, her wet face on his shoulder. It was an illusion, he thought, and for a while I believed it, and yet—curious thing—it has left some sweetness. Throughout the night he marveled about this—could it be he had won something after all?—and the next day, crawling under the rotting mansion of a long-dead actor, he looked a termite in the eye and decided to build a house.

He bought land by the sea and built on a cliff by a great madrona tree which grew out horizontally from the rock, a shimmering cloud of red and green; built with massive A-frames, bolted together, stressed, braced, anchored in concrete to withstand five-hundred-mile winds, a house—in the best illusory style, he thought wryly—to last forever. But the cliff crumbled one night in a storm during a twenty-four foot tide; Lorabelle and

Henry stood by hand in hand in the rain and lightning, deafened by crashing surf and thunder, as the house fell slowly into the sea while the great madrona remained, anchored in nothing but dreams. They went then to live in an apartment, and Henry worked as a carpenter, built houses for other people, began planning another house of his own.

One evening after dinner Henry was sitting at the table, smoking a pipe, working on blueprints; across the room Lorabelle, at her desk, bent over a "Who Am I?" contest. ("We might win $3,500," she had said; "just think of it! Wouldn't that be marvelous? Oh the things we will do . . .!") She was humming now, a waltz from *Die Fledermaus*. Henry looked up, observed the happy face bent to the illusory task, the golden hair streaked with gray falling across her cheek, the wrinkles of laughter now indelible around her eyes, the putting of pencil to mouth like a child, puzzled . . . laid down his pipe. "I love you, Lorabelle," he said. She looked up, startled: "What . . . did you say?" "I love you," he said. She blushed, started to rise, the pencil falling from her hand: "But . . . but . . . you said it was an illusion." It is, he thought, because love claims the future and can't hold it; but claims also the present, and we have that. Not wanting to confuse her or start an argument, he said only, "I love you anyway." She ran to him, weeping with joy, "Oh, Henry, I'm so happy, so terribly happy! This is all we lacked . . . all we'll ever need." He took her and the moment in his arms, kissed her, and said nothing.

He built a house on a plateau in a sheltered valley, protected from wind and water; blasted a gigantic hole in solid granite, floated the house on a bubble of pure mercury for earthquakes, built walls of reinforced concrete seven feet thick, doors and cabinets of stainless steel, pipes and lightning rods of copper, roof of inch-thick slate. "Oh, Henry, I'm so proud!" Lorabelle said. "You're a great builder. I'd like to see what could happen to this house." "You'll see," he said darkly. It cost a fortune, and they couldn't meet the payments; the bank took it over, sold it to a university as a seismographic station; Henry and Lorabelle moved to an attic in the city.

One afternoon Lorabelle came home in a rapturous mood. "Oh, Henry, I've met the most wonderful man!" "Sorry to hear that," Henry said. "Oh no!" Lorabelle exclaimed, "you'd like him

. . . really. There's a kind of spiritual quality . . . he's a graduate student of Far Eastern studies and, . . . you know, sort of a mystic himself . . . name is Semelrad Apfelbaum . . . gives seminars on Buddhism." "Sounds like the real thing all right," Henry said bitterly.

That evening after dinner Lorabelle put on a dress of black chiffon, a flowing lavender scarf, a gold chain around her neck, a sapphire on her finger, perfume in her hair. "Where are you going?" Henry said. "To meet Semelrad," she said; he's so wonderfully kind, and so generous . . . is going to tutor me privately till I catch up with the class." "You're not going anywhere," Henry said. "I'm not a child, Henry," Lorabelle said with dignity. "But you *are*—precisely," Henry said. Lorabelle reminded him that theirs was a relationship of equality, with the same rights, that she must live her own life, make her own decisions, her own mistakes if need be; and when this failed to convince him she tossed back her head, affected great hauteur, and marched out of the room. Henry caught her at the door, turned her over his knee, applied the flat of his hand to the bottom of his delight; and it was perhaps that same night—for she did not go out—that Lorabelle got pregnant, and this time didn't lose it: the baby was born on Christmas, blue eyes and golden hair, and they named her Noel.

Henry built a house of solid brick in a meadow of sage and thyme, and there Noel played with flowers and crickets and butterflies and field mice. Most of the time she was a joy to her parents, and some of the time—when she was sick or unkind—she was a sorrow. Lorabelle loved the brick house, painted walls, hung pictures, and polished floors; on hands and knees with a bonnet on her head she dug in the earth and planted flowers, looked up at Henry through a wisp of hair with a happy smile; "We'll never move again," she said. But one day the state sent them away and took over their house to build a freeway. The steel ball crashed through the brick walls, bulldozers sheared away the flower beds, the great shovels swung in, and the house was gone. Henry and Lorabelle and Noel moved back to the city, lived in a tiny flat under a water tank that dripped continuously on the roof and sounded like rain.

Henry and Lorabelle loved each other most of the time, tried to love each other all the time, to create a pure bond, but could not. It was marred by the viciousness, shocking to them, with which they hurt each other. Out of nothing they would create fights, would yell at each other, hate, withdraw finally in bitter silent armistice; then, after a few hours, or sometimes a few days, would come together again, with some final slashes and skirmishes, and try to work things out—to explain, protest, forgive, understand, forget, and above all to compromise. It was a terribly painful and always uncertain process; and even while it was under way Henry would think bleakly, "It won't last, will never last; we'll get through this one maybe, probably, then all will be well for a while—a few hours, days, weeks if we're lucky—then another fight over something—what?—not possible to know or predict, and certainly not to prevent . . . and then all this to go through again; and beyond that still another fight looming in the mist ahead, coming closer . . . and so on without end." But even while thinking these things he still would try to work through the current trouble because, as he would say, "There isn't anything else." And sometimes there occurred to him, uneasily, beyond all this gloomy reflection, an even more sinister thought: that their fights were not only unavoidable but also, perhaps, necessary; for their passages of greatest tenderness followed hard upon their times of greatest bitterness, as if love could be renewed only by gusts of destruction.

Nor could Henry ever build a house that would last forever, no more than anyone else; but he built one finally that lasted quite a while, a white house on a hill with lilac and laurel and three tall trees, a maple, a cedar, and a hemlock. It was an ordinary house of ordinary wood, and the termites caused some trouble, and always it needed painting or a new roof or a faucet dripped or something else needed fixing, and he grew old and gray and finally quite stooped doing these things, but that was all right, he knew, because there wasn't anything else.

Noel grew up in this house—a dreamy, soft-spoken girl, becoming more and more beautiful—wore her long hair in pigtails, practiced the piano, sang in a high, true voice, played in the meadow, caught butterflies among the lilac. At nineteen she fell in love with Falbuck Wheeling who wore a tattered brown leather jacket and roared in on a heavy motorcycle dispelling peace and birds and butterflies, bringing noise and fumes and a misery Henry felt but could not define. Falbuck had a hard bitter face, said little, would sit at the kitchen table sullen and uncomfortable, and Henry could never get him into conversation because whatever the subject—literature, government, justice—Falbuck would sit staring at him, silent and disbelieving, until finally with a few labored and nasty words he would assert some rottenness behind the facade; then, as if exhausted by this excursion into communication, he would get up, taking Noel as if he owned her, and roar away. Noel spent her days with him, and soon her nights, wore jeans and an old army shirt with the tails hanging out, let her hair hang loose and tangled, smoked cigarettes in a long black holder. Henry and Lorabelle talked earnestly to this wild, changed girl, now hardly recognizable as their daughter, advised caution and delay, but to no avail: she married Falbuck and went to live with him in a tiny room over a motorcycle shop. Henry and Lorabelle were left alone in the house on the hill, in peace now, with butterflies and the sound of wind in the three trees and wished she were back.

Every morning Henry took his tools and went to his work of building houses—saw the pyramid of white sand spreading out in the grass, the bricks chipping, the doors beginning to stick, the first tone of gray appearing on white lumber, the first leaf falling in the bright gutter—but kept on hammering and kept on sawing, joining boards and raising rafters; on weekends he swept the driveway and mowed the grass, in the evenings fixed the leaking faucets, tried to straighten out the disagreements with Lorabelle; and in all that he did he could see himself striving toward a condition of beauty or truth or goodness or love that did not exist, but whereas earlier in his life he had always said, "It's an illusion," and turned away, now he said, "There isn't anything else," and stayed with it; and though it cannot be said that they lived happily, exactly, and certainly not ever after, they did live. They lived—for a while—with ups and downs, good days and bad, and when it came time to die Lorabelle said, "Now we'll never be parted," and Henry smiled and kissed her and said to himself "There isn't anything else," and they died.

## TERRENCE MCNALLY

*wrote* And Things That Go Bump in the Night, *produced at the Tyrone Guthrie Theatre in Minnesota and later on Broadway.* Tour *is from* Collision Course, *a review made up of eleven short plays by various authors, first produced in New York in 1968.* Tour *shows an American couple abroad on a pleasure tour observing the "happy natives" of other cultures. McNally's couple is not estranged from the values of American society; and, as a result, when they realize they are not safely isolated from the exploited and totally un-American people of the rest of the world, they panic. Their reaction parallels that of many comfortable middle-class whites sitting in the security of their living rooms watching television to see the "happy natives" in revolt overseas—or in America's ghettoes. The play shows the alarming degree to which most of the world is alienated from American values; American complacency is seen as more than a domestic problem.*

# TOUR

*The scene is in a car. In front sits the* DRIVER. MR. *and* MRS. WILSON *are in the back seat.* MRS. WILSON *is writing a postcard.*

## SCENE ONE

MRS. WILSON Shut up, Woodson. (*He looks at her*) You didn't say anything this time either? (*He slowly shakes his head*) All right, so I'm on edge! I'll take another nerve pill. My fourth since Rome, thanks to you. At least I think it was Rome. I don't even know what country we're in any more. And you call this a vacation. It's a Stations of the Cross!

MR. WILSON Are we still in Italy, driver?
(*The* DRIVER *nods*)

MRS WILSON (*Taking a pill*) It's so bloody hot, and you know how darn sensitive I am to heat. Maybe this just wasn't the summer to travel. Maybe we should have bought that boat instead. I don't know what's right any more.

MR. WILSON We're still in Italy.

MRS WILSON (*Musing, as she looks out the window*) Is the sky that red where Chuck sees it, do you think? Is there sky left in Vietnam? (*She laughs*) Listen to me!

MR. WILSON (*As she resumes writing the postcard*) Poor Cora. (*Pause*) Dear sweet Cora.

MRS. WILSON (*Smiling, relaxing*) That pill works wonders!
(*Blackout*)

## SCENE TWO

MRS. WILSON Shut up, Woodson.
(*Blackout*)

## SCENE THREE

MR. WILSON I guess you people get some pretty strange impressions of us Americans. Whew! I read in the *New York Times*—you know, *giornale*—where this couple from Shreveport asked their driver how old Moses was when he posed for Michelangelo. I've heard dumb questions before but—(*Looking out the window*) Cows, Cora! Look at the cows!

MRS. WILSON They're lying down.

MR. WILSON They're dead. (*Turning her head away*) Don't, dear, you'll only upset yourself. (*Back to the* DRIVER) I read something like that and you know, I'm ashamed to say it: "*Io sono americano.*" (*The* DRIVER *nods*) Cora and I have our faults, but we do know how to travel. We're guests in your country, driver, and we think that's a privilege. So we read up on a place before we get there. We like to mix, meet the people, get off the beaten path . . . that's why we hired you. We drink your water. We eat green vegetables. Why, we even stay in your *pensiones*. (*To* MRS. WILSON) In small towns we do! Rome's different. The bathroom was way the hell down the hall in Lucca. Anyway, the point I'm making, puss—so lay off with the sounds—is that we're not his run-of-the-mill, American Express oriented, enterobioform, boiled-water, bourbon-daiquiris-in-the-Dolomites-type tourist. (*The car swerves suddenly*) Jesus Christ, they can't drive, these wops!

DRIVER *Stronzo!*

MR. WILSON Still, it's a wonderful race. Even the chauffeurs, so volcanic. (*Looking out the window*) Look, Cora, peasants! Oh, that's a sight to tear your heart out. Better roll up your window.

MRS. WILSON They're not waving back.

MR. WILSON Smile at them.

MRS. WILSON Nothing.

MR. WILSON The further south we go, you see, life becomes more primitive. Like in the U.S.

MRS. WILSON Woodson, look, they—!

MR. WILSON (*Turning her head away*) Don't look at them, Cora, you'll only upset yourself.
(*Blackout*)

### SCENE FOUR

MRS. WILSON Shut up, Woodson.
(*Blackout*)

### SCENE FIVE

MRS. WILSON I felt sorry for those people. They were so small and dark and underfed compared to us.

MR. WILSON Sshh! He can hear you, Cora. Italians are called swarthy over here.

MRS. WILSON Why would anyone live in such a wretched place? I'm stifling.

MR. WILSON (*Stopping her from rolling down a window*) Are you crazy, Cora? Plague! You've got to understand, the further we go, life becomes more primitive. The germs out there are centuries old.

MRS. WILSON Like in the U.S.
(*Blackout*)

### SCENE SIX

MRS. WILSON (*Reading a postcard*) "Dear Chuck, greetings from somewhere in Italy."

MR. WILSON Chuck's our oldest. Vietnam.

MRS. WILSON "We are whizzing along, headed for who-knows-where. Daddy wanted to get off the beaten track again. Remember Mexico?"

MR. WILSON Flash flood. The car broke down.

MRS. WILSON "Our driver's a nice young man."

MR. WILSON (*Shushing her*) He can hear you, Cora!

MRS. WILSON "Are you well, darling? I think of you in that jungle, the dangers there, and I worry myself sick. When will this awful trouble be over, and you be home with us? Other people's business should be minded by other people, and not by young men like you. Is that too awful of me? I guess women shouldn't even think about things like that. Ha ha ha!"

MR. WILSON Ha ha ha.

MRS. WILSON "I bought you a gondolier's shirt in Venice. Blue and white stripes. Cute on you. Your father is well and wonders: 'Is there sky left in Vietnam?' Come home soon and safe. Love you. Mom."

(*She is crying*)

MR. WILSON World peace, driver. Maybe you'll see it in your lifetime. The missus and I won't. Still. And there's the agony, in that one word: "still."

MRS. WILSON (*Sniffling*) I know we're lost. He made the wrong turn somewhere. I'm sure of it.

MR. WILSON (*To placate her*) She thinks we're lost, driver. (*The* DRIVER *nods*) We'll be stopping soon, won't we? (*The* DRIVER *nods*) This can't be Italy. Still.

(*No response from the* DRIVER)

(*Blackout*)

## SCENE SEVEN

MRS. WILSON We are too lost! L-a-o-s.

MR. WILSON Pussy!

MRS. WILSON It's like a rain forest, I'm so hot. Just look at that pagoda burning down.

MR. WILSON It's a pyre, Cora. They're burning victims.

MRS. WILSON People.

MR. WILSON Plague victims. Why their plague is as old and inscrutable as Italy itself.

MRS. WILSON Give me the binoculars.

MR. WILSON I've told you, honey, the further south we go, life becomes more primitive. They die today, they don't have to die tomorrow. Primitive races are like that. Right, driver? Say, pull over a minute. I want to get a shot of this. Let's see Dot and Hugh's Nassau slides match these. Talk about your fringe benefits. Driver, I said stop! Not go faster!

MRS. WILSON Use the phrase book on him! (*Craning her neck and looking through the binoculars while he thumbs through the book*) That column of smoke must be five miles high! So black and oily, not your usual puffs. Smells, too; Vietnam must be like that.

MR. WILSON (*Finding the word*) *Fermata!* (*The car screeches to a halt*) Well, never mind now.

MRS. WILSON We can walk back.

MR. WILSON We'll see more further on. Go ahead, driver.

MRS. WILSON Well I'm getting out for some air. He's starting to . . .

(*She pinches her nose*)

MR. WILSON Good thinking.

(*They get out of the car*)

MRS. WILSON Look, natives!

(*She waves to them*)

MR. WILSON On your *P*'s and *Q*'s now, missy. We're ambassadors.

MRS. WILSON Where're our suitcases? Your camera and things? My cosmetic bag?

MR. WILSON In the car.

MRS. WILSON Well get them, Woodson. He might just drive off. You know what they're like, these people.

MR. WILSON We *don't* know what they're like. That's why you're right. (*He goes to the car, but the door is locked*) Open the door. I forgot . . . I said, Open the door. Well, open the window then and I'll reach in . . . OPEN THE DOOR. (*The* DRIVER *doesn't move*) What do you think you're doing? You can't pull something like this with us. Now look, I told you. We're not your typical tourists. We're not your American boobs.

MRS. WILSON (*Indicating the approaching people*) I'll have these men report him to the tourist bureau!

MR. WILSON What's your name, driver? My wife's going to report you. Goddamn it, we love Italy! Now open this door!

(TWO MONKS *appear. They wear orange-brown robes. They are very poor and sickly. They carry wooden begging bowls*)

MRS. WILSON Woodson!

FIRST MONK (*Bowing*) *Prego, signora.*

SECOND MONK (*Pitifully, hands outstretched*) *Pane.*

MR. WILSON No thank you, we . . .

SECOND MONK *Pane.*

MR. WILSON They're begging for bread. (*To the* MONKS) We do not have any bread.

FIRST MONK (*Cheerfully bobbing his head*) *Prego!*

MR. WILSON We are locked out of our car. Will you tell our driver to let us in?

FIRST MONK *Prego!*

MRS. WILSON His face, Woodson. That man . . . he has no nose.

FIRST MONK *Prego, signora.*

MRS. WILSON His nose . . . like a leper's . . . eaten away.

MR. WILSON Now calm yourself, Cora.

MRS. WILSON Or burned . . . yes! . . . napalm.

MR. WILSON Cora, listen to me.

MRS. WILSON I've seen the films.

MR. WILSON We're in difficult straits, Cora, you've got to keep calm.

MRS. WILSON I hate jungle.

MR. WILSON We're on vacation in . . . we're just four hours from . . . hotels!

MRS. WILSON Hate swamp. Smells mud.

MR. WILSON We have passports, Cora, we know who we are and we're going to pull through. Do I make myself clear?

MRS. WILSON Napalm Delta. Where's Chuck!

FIRST MONK *Prego, signore!*

MR. WILSON Now listen—

SECOND MONK *Pane.*

MR. WILSON We are lost. *Telefono.* Is there a—

SECOND MONK *Pane.*

MRS. WILSON I DON'T HAVE ANY BREAD. TELL HIM, WOODSON!

MR. WILSON From Rome, we'll send bread from Rome.

FIRST MONK *Prego!*

MRS. WILSON WE ONLY BOMB THE NORTH! BAD PEOPLE!

SECOND MONK *Pane.*

MR. WILSON We'll send money, drugs, anything you want.

MRS. WILSON WHY DO YOU PEOPLE KEEP BURNING YOURSELVES!

MR. WILSON Airlift. Cargo planes. Just tell us what you need.

SECOND MONK *Pane!*

MR. WILSON We're strangers. We don't live here.

SECOND MONK *Pane!*

MRS. WILSON LEAVE US ALONE!

(MR. WILSON *slaps her. She is calmed*)

MR. WILSON (*To the* MONKS) Now look, buddy, we are tourists. Not your run-of-the-mill tourists, but tourists. We took a wrong turn. We didn't want to come here.

SECOND MONK *Pane!*

MR. WILSON You don't understand! We are Americans, Goddamnit! IO SONO AMERICANO!

FIRST MONK (*A friendly gesture toward them*) *Prego!*

(*Blackout*)

## SCENE EIGHT

MRS WILSON (*They are back in the car, driving along, the three of them again*) Shut up, Woodson.
(*Blackout*)

## SCENE NINE

MR. WILSON What can we do?
(*Blackout*)

## SCENE TEN

MRS. WILSON Shut up, Woodson.
(*Blackout*)

## ALLEN GINSBERG

*graduated from Columbia University in 1948; in 1956 he published* Howl *and began a career as poet, prophet, and public figure that has influenced countless young people. One of his most significant public appearances was at the 1968 Democratic Convention where he led a crowd in the Aum chant for seven hours from the balcony of one of Chicago's larger hotels. In this poem Ginsberg issues a general rebuttal of the "American Way of Life," and a statement of the reasons for his alienation from it.*

## AMERICA

America I've given you all and now I'm nothing.
America two dollars and twentyseven cents January 17, 1956.
I can't stand my own mind.
America when will we end the human war?
Go fuck yourself with your atom bomb.
I don't feel good don't bother me.
I won't write my poem till I'm in my right mind.
America when will you be angelic?
When will you take off your clothes?
When will you look at yourself through the grave?
When will you be worthy of your million Trotskyites?
America why are your libraries full of tears?
America when will you send your eggs to India?
I'm sick of your insane demands.
When can I go into the supermarket and buy what I need with my good looks?
America after all it is you and I who are perfect not the next world.
Your machinery is too much for me.
You made me want to be a saint.
There must be some other way to settle this argument.
Burroughs is in Tangiers I don't think he'll come back it's sinister.
Are you being sinister or is this some form of practical joke?
I'm trying to come to the point.
I refuse to give up my obsession.
America stop pushing I know what I'm doing.
America the plum blossoms are falling.
I haven't read the newspapers for months, everyday somebody goes on trial for murder.
America I feel sentimental about the Wobblies.

America I used to be a communist when I was a kid I'm not sorry.
I smoke marijuana every chance I get.
I sit in my house for days on end and stare at the roses in the closet.
When I go to Chinatown I get drunk and never get laid.
My mind is made up there's going to be trouble.
You should have seen me reading Marx.
My psychoanalyst thinks I'm perfectly right.
I won't say the Lord's Prayer.
I have mystical visions and cosmic vibrations.
America I still haven't told you what you did to Uncle Max after he came over from Russia.

I'm addressing you.
Are you going to let your emotional life be run by Time Magazine?
I'm obsessed by Time Magazine.
I read it every week.
Its cover stares at me every time I slink past the corner candystore.
I read it in the basement of the Berkeley Public Library.
It's always telling me about responsibility. Businessmen are serious. Movie producers are serious. Everybody's serious but me.
It occurs to me that I am America.
I am talking to myself again.

Asia is rising against me.
I haven't got a chinaman's chance.
I'd better consider my national resources.
My national resources consist of two joints of marijuana millions of genitals an unpublished private literature that goes 1400 miles an hour and twentyfive-thousand mental institutions.
I say nothing about my prisons nor the millions of underprivileged who live in my flowerpots under the light of five hundred suns.
I have abolished the whorehouses of France, Tangiers is the next to go.
My ambition is to be President despite the fact that I'm a Catholic.

America how can I write a holy litany in your silly mood?
I will continue like Henry Ford my strophes are as individual as his automobiles more so they're all different sexes.
America I will sell you strophes $2500 apiece $500 down on your old strophe
America free Tom Mooney
America save the Spanish Loyalists
America Sacco & Vanzetti must not die
America I am the Scottsboro boys.
America when I was seven momma took me to Communist Cell meetings they sold us garbanzos a handful per ticket a ticket cost a nickel and the speeches were free everybody was angelic and sentimental about the workers it was all so sincere you have no idea what a good thing the party was in 1835 Scott Nearing was a grand old man a real mensch Mother Bloor made me cry I once saw Israel Amter plain. Everybody must have been a spy.
America you don't really want to go to war.
America it's them bad Russians.
Them Russians them Russians and them Chinamen. And them Russians.
The Russia wants to eat us alive. The Russia's power mad. She wants to take our cars from out our garages.
Her wants to grab Chicago. Her needs a Red Reader's Digest. Her wants our auto plants in Siberia. Him big bureaucracy running our fillingstations.
That no good. Ugh. Him make Indians learn read. Him need big black niggers. Hah. Her make us all work sixteen hours a day. Help.
America this is quite serious.
America this is the impression I get from looking in the television set.
America is this correct?
I'd better get right down to the job.
It's true I don't want to join the Army or turn lathes in precision parts factories, I'm nearsighted and psychopathic anyway.
America I'm putting my queer shoulder to the wheel.

# The Zoo: Education

Contemporary American educational institutions, particularly colleges and universities, while graduating more students every year, are beset with numerous difficulties—as recent campus revolts testify. Not the least of these problems is that the schools, instead of exploring and experimenting with new values, are coming more and more to reflect the general society out of which they grow. While claiming to teach individual initiative and independent study, the *methods* employed—large, overcrowded classes, television lectures, grades, departmental requirements—betray the very goals which the college would try to reach. The result is a kind of mass conformity, the teaching of dependency, and the fear of failure. Grades mean everything, content comes to mean very little. Many students learn to become passive robots, ready to accept classroom gospel as they will later accept advertisements and political speeches. In this way, the otherdirectness of middle-class alienation seeps through the walls of academia, poisoning the often laudatory goals of higher education. Educational institutions become bureaucratic factories turning out student-products, and many professors learn to become "middle-management" executives—administrators rather than teachers. Universities are pervaded by fear of legislative investigations and fear of being fired is reflected in anxious ulcer-ridden faces.

You should have little trouble identifying with the problems articulated in this section, for perhaps here, more than any place else in this reader, *you* are part of the problem. What does graduation mean to you? Do you stop to ask why, or merely memorize answers others supply?

## LIONEL TRILLING

*is Professor of English at Columbia University, and one of our century's most influential literary critics. "Of This Time, of That Place" was written in 1943, and reflects educational problems in a time when the authority of the professor was largely unchallenged. But the relationships between Joseph Howe and his students represent patterns which are still very much with us. Like the narrator in the excerpts from Paul Goodman's* Making Do, *Howe is forced to devise his own way of coping with the conflict between his personal and professional ties with his students. The story provides valuable insight into the psychology of the older generation of academics. The relationship between this story and your own educational situation lies in the fact that Joseph Howe's generation is in power today, inside and outside the universities. 1943s ambitious young teacher is today's full Professor, Chairman, or President.*

# OF THIS TIME, OF THAT PLACE

It was a fine September day. By noon it would be summer again, but now it was true autumn with a touch of chill in the air. As Joseph Howe stood on the porch of the house in which he lodged, ready to leave for his first class of the year, he thought with pleasure of the long indoor days that were coming. It was a moment when he could feel glad of his profession.

On the lawn the peach tree was still in fruit and young Hilda Aiken was taking a picture of it. She held the camera tight against her chest. She wanted the sun behind her, but she did not want her own long morning shadow in the foreground. She raised the camera, but that did not help, and she lowered it, but that made things worse. She twisted her body to the left, then to the right. In the end she had to step out of the direct line of the sun. At last she snapped the shutter and wound the film with intense care.

Howe, watching her from the porch, waited for her to finish and called good morning. She turned, startled, and almost sullenly lowered her glance. In the year Howe had lived at the Aikens', Hilda had accepted him as one of her family, but since his absence of the summer she had grown shy. Then suddenly she lifted her head and smiled at him, and the humorous smile confirmed his pleasure in the day. She picked up her bookbag and set off for school.

The handsome houses on the streets to the college were not yet fully awake, but they looked very friendly. Howe went by the Bradby house where he would be a guest this evening at the first dinner party of the year. When he had gone the length of the picket fence, the whitest in town, he turned back. Along the path there was a fine row of asters and he went through the gate and picked one for his buttonhole. The Bradbys would be pleased if they happened to see him invading their lawn and the knowledge of this made him even more comfortable.

He reached the campus as the hour was striking. The students were hurrying to their classes. He himself was in no hurry. He stopped at his dim cubicle of an office and lit a cigarette. The prospect of facing his class had suddenly presented itself to him and his hands were cold; the lawful seizure of power he was about to make seemed momentous. Waiting did not help. He put out his cigarette, picked up a pad of theme paper, and went to his classroom.

As he entered, the rattle of voices ceased, and the twenty-odd freshmen settled themselves and looked at him appraisingly. Their faces seemed gross, his heart sank at their massed impassivity, but he spoke briskly.

"My name is Howe," he said, and turned and wrote it on the blackboard. The carelessness of the scrawl confirmed his authority. He went on, "My office is 412 Slemp Hall, and my office-hours are Monday, Wednesday and Friday from eleven-thirty to twelve-thirty."

He wrote, "M., W., F., 11:30–12:30." He said, "I'll be very glad to see any of you at that time. Or if you can't come then, you can arrange with me for some other time."

He turned again to the blackboard and spoke over his shoulder. "The text for the course is Jarman's *Modern Plays,* revised edition. The Co-op has it in stock." He wrote the name, underlined "revised edition" and waited for it to be taken down in the new notebooks.

When the bent heads were raised again he began his speech of prospectus. "It is hard to explain—" he said, and paused as they composed themselves. "It is hard to explain what a course like this is intended to do. We are going to try to learn something about modern literature and something about prose composition."

As he spoke, his hands warmed and he was able to look directly at the class. Last year on the first day the faces had seemed just as cloddish, but as the term wore on they became gradually alive and quite likable. It did not seem possible that the same thing could happen again.

"I shall not lecture in this course," he continued. "Our work will be carried on by discussion and we will try to learn by an exchange of opinion. But you will soon recognize that my opinion is worth more than anyone else's here."

He remained grave as he said it, but two boys understood and laughed. The rest took permission from them and laughed too. All Howe's private ironies protested the vulgarity of the joke, but the laughter made him feel benign and powerful.

When the little speech was finished, Howe picked up the pad of paper he had brought. He announced that they would write an extemporaneous theme. Its subject was traditional, "Who I am and why I came to Dwight College." By now the class was more at ease and it gave a ritualistic groan of protest. Then there was a stir as fountain pens were brought out and the writing-arms of the chairs were cleared, and the paper was passed about. At last, all the heads bent to work, and the room became still.

Howe sat idly at his desk. The sun shone through the tall clumsy windows. The cool of the morning was already passing. There was a scent of autumn and of varnish and the stillness of the room was deep and oddly touching. Now and then a student's head was raised and scratched in the old, elaborate students' pantomime that calls the teacher to witness honest intellectual effort.

Suddenly a tall boy stood within the frame of the open door. "Is this," he said, and thrust a large nose into a college catalogue, "is this the meeting place of English 1A? The section instructed by Dr. Joseph Howe?"

He stood on the very sill of the door, as if refusing to enter until he was perfectly sure of all his rights. The class looked up from work, found him absurd and gave a low mocking cheer.

The teacher and the new student, with equal pointedness, ignored the disturbance. Howe nodded to the boy, who pushed his head forward and then jerked it back in a wide elaborate arc to clear his brow of a heavy lock of hair. He advanced into the room and halted before Howe, almost at attention. In a loud, clear voice he announced, "I am Tertan, Ferdinand R., reporting at the direction of Head of Department Vincent."

The heraldic formality of this statement brought forth another cheer. Howe looked at the class with a sternness he could not really feel, for there was indeed something ridiculous about this boy. Under his displeased regard the rows of heads dropped to work again. Then he touched Tertan's elbow, led him up to the desk and stood so as to shield their conversation from the class.

"We are writing an extemporaneous theme," he said. "The subject is, 'Who I am and why I came to Dwight College.' "

He stripped a few sheets from the pad and offered them to the boy. Tertan hesitated and then took the paper, but he held it only tentatively. As if with the effort of making something clear, he gulped, and a slow smile fixed itself on his face. It was at once knowing and shy.

"Professor," he said, "to be perfectly fair to my classmates"—he made a large gesture over the room—"and to you"—he inclined his head to Howe—"this would not be for me an extemporaneous subject."

Howe tried to understand. "You mean you've already thought about it—you've heard we always give the same subject? That doesn't matter."

Again the boy ducked his head and gulped. It was the gesture of one who wishes to make a difficult explanation with perfect candor. "Sir," he said, and made the distinction with great care, "the topic I did not expect, but I have given much ratiocination to the subject."

Howe smiled and said, "I don't think that's an unfair advantage. Just go ahead and write."

Tertan narrowed his eyes and glanced sidewise at Howe. His strange mouth smiled. Then in quizzical acceptance, he ducked his head, threw back the heavy, dank lock, dropped into a seat with a great loose noise and began to write rapidly.

The room fell silent again and Howe resumed his idleness. When the bell rang, the students who had groaned when the task had been set now groaned again because they had not finished. Howe took up the papers, and held the class while he made the first assignment. When he dismissed it, Tertan bore down on him, his slack mouth held ready for speech.

"Some professors," he said, "are pedants. They are Dryasdusts. However, some professors are free souls and creative spirits. Kant, Hegel and Nietzsche were all professors." With this pronouncement he paused. "It is my opinion," he continued, "that you occupy the second category."

Howe looked at the boy in surprise and said with good-natured irony, "With Kant, Hegel and Nietzsche?"

Not only Tertan's hand and head but his whole awkward body waved away the stupidity. "It is the kind and not the quantity of the kind," he said sternly.

Rebuked, Howe said as simply and seriously as he could, "It would be nice to think so." He added, "Of course I am not a professor."

This was clearly a disappointment but Tertan met it. "In the French sense," he said with composure. "Generically, a teacher."

Suddenly he bowed. It was such a bow, Howe fancied, as a stage-director might teach an actor playing a medieval student who takes leave of Abelard—stiff, solemn, with elbows close to the body and feet together. Then, quite as suddenly, he turned and left.

A queer fish, and as soon as Howe reached his office, he sifted through the batch of themes and drew out Tertan's. The boy had filled many sheets with his unformed headlong scrawl. "Who am I?" he had begun. "Here, in a mundane, not to say commercialized academe, is asked the question which from time long immemorably out of mind has accreted doubt and thoughts in the psyche of man to pester him as a nuisance. Whether in St. Augustine (or Austin as sometimes called) or Miss Bashkirtsieff or Frederic Amiel or Empedocles, or in less lights of the intellect than these, this posed question has been ineluctable."

Howe took out his pencil. He circled "academe" and wrote "vocab." in the margin. He underlined "time long immemorably out of mind" and wrote "Diction!" But this seemed inadequate for what was wrong. He put down his pencil and read ahead to discover the principle of error in the theme. "Today as ever, in spite of gloomy prophets of the dismal science (economics) the question is uninvalidated. Out of the starry depths of heaven hurtles this spear of query demanding to be caught on the shield of the mind ere it pierces the skull and the limbs be unstrung."

Baffled but quite caught, Howe read on. "Materialism, by which is meant the philosophic concept and not the moral idea, provides no aegis against the question which lies beyond the tangible (metaphysics). Existence without alloy is the question presented. Environment and heredity relegated aside, the rags and old clothes of practical life discarded, the name and the instrumentality of livelihood do not, as the prophets of the dismal science insist on in this connection, give solution to the interrogation which not from the professor merely but veritably from the cosmos is given. I think, therefore I am (cogito etc.) but who am I? Tertan I am, but what is Tertan? Of this time, of that place, of some parentage, what does it matter?"

Existence without alloy: the phrase established itself. Howe put aside Tertan's paper and at random picked up another. "I am Arthur J. Casebeer, Jr.," he read. "My father is Arthur J. Casebeer and my grandfather was Arthur J. Casebeer before him. My mother is Nina Wimble Casebeer. Both of them are college graduates and my father is in insurance. I was born in St. Louis eighteen years ago and we still make our residence there."

Arthur J. Casebeer, who knew who he was, was less interesting than Tertan, but more coherent. Howe picked up Tertan's paper again. It was clear that none of the routine marginal comments, no "sent. str." or "punct." or "vocab." could cope with this torrential rhetoric. He read ahead, contenting himself with underscoring the errors against the time when he should have the necessary "conference" with Tertan.

It was a busy and official day of cards and sheets, arrangements and small decisions, and it gave Howe pleasure. Even when it was time to attend the first of the weekly Convocations he felt the charm of the beginning of things when intention is still innocent and uncorrupted by effort. He sat among the young instructors on the platform, and joined in their humorous complaints at having to assist at the ceremony, but actually he got a clear satisfaction from the ritual of prayer, and prosy speech, and even from wearing his academic gown. And when the Convocation was over the pleasure continued as he crossed the campus, exchanging greetings with men he had not seen since the spring. They were people who did not yet, and perhaps never would, mean much to him, but in a year they had grown amiably to be part of his life. They were his fellow-townsmen.

The day had cooled again at sunset, and there was a bright chill in the September twilight. Howe carried his voluminous gown over his arm, he swung his doctoral hood by its purple neckpiece, and on his head he wore his mortarboard with its heavy gold tassel bobbing just over his eye. These were the weighty and absurd symbols of his new profession and they pleased him. At twenty-six Joseph Howe had discovered that he was neither so well off nor so bohemian as he had once thought. A small income, adequate when supplemented by a sizable cash legacy, was genteel poverty when the cash was all spent. And the literary life—the room at the Lafayette, or the small apartment without a lease, the long summers on the Cape, the long afternoons and the social evenings—began to weary him. His writing filled his mornings, and should perhaps have filled his life, yet it did not. To the amusement of his friends, and with a certain sense that he was betraying his own freedom, he had used the last of his legacy for a year at Harvard. The small but respectable reputation of his two volumes of verse had proved useful—he continued at Harvard on a fellowship and when he emerged as Doctor Howe he received an excellent appointment, with prospects, at Dwight.

He had his moments of fear when all that had ever been said of the dangers of the academic life had occurred to him. But after a year in which he had tested every possibility of corruption and seduction he was ready to rest easy. His third volume of verse, most of it written in his first years of teaching, was not only ampler but, he thought, better than its predecessors.

There was a clear hour before the Bradby dinner party, and Howe looked forward to it. But he was not to enjoy it, for lying with his mail on the hall table was a copy of this quarter's issue of *Life and Letters,* to which his landlord subscribed. Its severe cover announced that its editor, Frederic Woolley, had this month contributed an essay called "Two Poets," and Howe, picking it up, curious to see who the two poets might be, felt his own name start out at him with cabalistic power—Joseph Howe. As he continued to turn the pages his hand trembled.

Standing in the dark hall, holding the neat little magazine, Howe knew that his literary contempt for Frederic Woolley meant nothing, for he suddenly understood how he respected Woolley in the way of the world. He knew this by the trembling of his hand. And of the little world as well as the great, for although the literary groups of New York might dismiss Woolley, his name carried high authority in the academic world. At Dwight it was even a revered name, for it had been here at the college that Frederic Woolley had made the distinguished scholarly career from which he had gone on to literary journalism. In middle life he had been induced to take the editorship of *Life and Letters,* a literary monthly not widely read but heavily endowed, and in its pages he had carried on the defense of what he sometimes called the older values. He was not without wit, he had great knowledge and considerable taste, and even in the full movement of the "new" literature he had won a certain respect for his refusal to accept it. In France, even in England, he would have been connected with a more robust tradition of conservatism, but America gave him an audience not much better than genteel. It was known in the college that to the subsidy of *Life and Letters* the Bradbys contributed a great part.

As Howe read, he saw that he was involved in nothing less than an event. When the Fifth Series of *Studies in Order and Value* came to be collected, this latest of Frederic Woolley's essays would not be merely another step in the old direction. Clearly and unmistakably, it was a turning point. All his literary life Woolley had been concerned with the relation of literature to morality, religion, and the private and delicate pieties, and he had been unalterably opposed to all that he had called "inhuman humanitarianism." But here, suddenly, dramatically late, he had made an about-face, turning to the public life and to the humanitarian politics he had so long despised. This was the kind of incident the histories of literature make much of. Frederic Woolley was opening for himself a new career and winning a kind of new youth. He contrasted the two poets, Thomas Wormser, who was admirable, Joseph Howe, who was almost dangerous. He spoke of the "precious subjectivism" of Howe's verse. "In times like ours," he wrote, "with millions facing penury and want, one feels that the qualities of the *tour d'ivoire* are well-nigh inhuman, nearly insulting. The *tour d'ivoire* becomes the *tour d'ivresse,* and it is not self-intoxicated poets that our people need." The essay said more: "The problem is one of meaning. I am not ignorant that the creed of the esoteric poets declares that a poem does not and should not *mean* anything, that it *is* something. But poetry is what the poet makes it, and if he is a true poet he makes what his society needs. And what is needed now is the tradition in which Mr. Wormser writes, the true tradition of poetry. The Howes do no harm, but they do no good when positive good is demanded of all responsible men. Or do the Howes indeed do no harm? Perhaps Plato would have said they do, that in some ways theirs is the Phrygian music that turns men's minds from the struggle. Certainly it is true that Thomas Wormser writes in the lucid Dorian mode which sends men into battle with evil."

It was easy to understand why Woolley had chosen to praise Thomas Wormser. The long, lilting lines of *Corn Under Willows* hymned, as Woolley put it, the struggle for wheat in the Iowa fields, and expressed the real lives of real people. But why out of the dozen more notable examples he had chosen Howe's little volume as the example of "precious subjectivism" was hard to guess. In a way it was funny, this multiplication of himself into "the Howes." And yet this becoming the multiform political symbol by whose creation Frederic Woolley gave the sign of a sudden new life, this use of him as a sacrifice whose blood was necessary for the rites of rejuvenation, made him feel oddly unclean.

Nor could Howe get rid of a certain practical resentment. As a poet he had a special and respectable place in the college life. But it might be another thing to be marked as the poet of a wilful and selfish obscurity.

As he walked to the Bradbys', Howe was a little tense and defensive. It seemed to him that all the world knew of the "attack" and agreed with it. And, indeed, the Bradbys had read the essay but Professor Bradby, a kind and pretentious man, said, "I see my old friend knocked you about a bit, my boy," and his wife Eugenia looked at Howe with her childlike blue eyes and said, "I shall *scold* Frederic for the untrue things he wrote about you. You aren't the least obscure." They beamed at him. In their genial snobbery they seemed to feel that he had distinguished himself. He was the leader of Howeism. He enjoyed the dinner party as much as he had thought he would.

And in the following days, as he was more preoccupied with his duties, the incident was forgotten. His classes had ceased to be mere groups. Student after student detached himself from the mass and required or claimed a place in Howe's awareness. Of them all it was Tertan who first and most violently signaled his separate existence. A week after classes had begun Howe saw his silhouette on the frosted glass of his office door. It was motionless for a long time, perhaps stopped by the problem of whether or not to knock before entering. Howe called, "Come in!" and Tertan entered with his shambling stride.

He stood beside the desk, silent and at attention. When Howe asked him to sit down, he responded with a gesture of head and hand, as if to say that such amenities were beside the point. Nevertheless, he did take the chair. He put his ragged, crammed briefcase between his legs. His face, which Howe now observed fully for the first time, was confusing, for it was made up of florid curves, the nose arched in the bone and voluted in the nostril, the mouth loose and soft and rather moist. Yet the face was so thin and narrow as to seem the very type of asceticism. Lashes of unusual length veiled the eyes and, indeed, it seemed as if there were a veil over the whole countenance. Before the words actually came, the face screwed itself into an attitude of preparation for them.

"You can confer with me now?" Tertan said.

"Yes, I'd be glad to. There are several things in your two themes I want to talk to you about." Howe reached for the packet of themes on his desk and sought for Tertan's. But the boy was waving them away.

"These are done perforce," he said. "Under the pressure of your requirement. They are not significant; mere duties." Again his great hand flapped vaguely to dismiss his themes. He leaned forward and gazed at his teacher.

"You are," he said, "a man of letters? You are a poet?" It was more declaration than question.

"I should like to think so," Howe said.

At first Tertan accepted the answer with a show of appreciation, as though the understatement made a secret between himself and Howe. Then he chose to misunderstand. With his shrewd and disconcerting control of expression, he presented to Howe a puzzled grimace. "What does that mean?" he said.

Howe retracted the irony. "Yes. I am a poet." It sounded strange to say.

"That," Tertan said, "is a wonder." He corrected himself with his ducking head. "I mean that is wonderful."

Suddenly, he dived at the miserable briefcase between his legs, put it on his knees, and began to fumble with the catch, all intent on the difficulty it presented. Howe noted that his suit was worn thin, his shirt almost unclean. He became aware, even, of a vague and musty odor of garments worn too long in unaired rooms. Tertan conquered the lock and began to concentrate upon a search into the interior. At last he held in his hand what he was after, a torn and crumpled copy of *Life and Letters*.

"I learned it from here," he said, holding it out.

Howe looked at him sharply, his hackles a little up. But the boy's face was not only perfectly innocent, it even shone with a conscious admiration. Apparently nothing of the import of the essay had touched him except the wonderful fact that his teacher was a "man of letters." Yet this seemed too stupid, and Howe, to test it, said, "The man who wrote that doesn't think it's wonderful."

Tertan made a moist hissing sound as he cleared his mouth of saliva. His head, oddly loose on his neck, wove a pattern of contempt in the air. "A critic," he said, "who admits *prima facie* that he does not understand." Then he said grandly, "It is the inevitable fate."

It was absurd, yet Howe was not only aware of the absurdity but of a tension suddenly and wonderfully relaxed. Now that the "attack" was on the table between himself and this strange boy, and subject to the boy's funny and absolutely certain contempt, the hidden force of his feeling was revealed to him in the very moment that it vanished. All unsuspected, there had been a film over the world, a transparent but discoloring haze of danger. But he had no time to stop over the brightened aspect of things. Tertan was going on. "I also am a man of letters. Putative."

"You have written a good deal?" Howe meant to be no more than polite, and he was surprised at the tenderness he heard in his words.

Solemnly the boy nodded, threw back the dank lock, and sucked in a deep, anticipatory breath. "First, a work of homiletics, which is a defense of the principles of religious optimism against the pessimism of Schopenhauer and the humanism of Nietzsche."

"Humanism? Why do you call it humanism?"

"It is my nomenclature for making a deity of man," Tertan replied negligently. "Then three fictional works, novels. And numerous essays in science, combating materialism. Is it your duty to read these if I bring them to you?"

Howe answered simply, "No, it isn't exactly my duty, but I shall be happy to read them."

Tertan stood up and remained silent. He rested his bag on the chair. With a certain compunction—for it did not seem entirely proper that, of two men of letters, one should have the right to blue-pencil the other, to grade him or to question the quality of his "sentence structure"—Howe reached for Tertan's papers. But before he could take them up, the boy suddenly made his bow-to-Abelard, the stiff inclination of the body with the hands seeming to emerge from the scholar's gown. Then he was gone.

But after his departure something was still left of him. The timbre of his curious sentences, the downright finality of so quaint a phrase as "It is the inevitable fate" still rang in the air. Howe gave the warmth of his feeling to the new visitor who stood at the door announcing himself with a genteel clearing of the throat.

"Doctor Howe, I believe?" the student said. A large hand advanced into the room and grasped Howe's hand. "Blackburn, sir, Theodore Blackburn, vice-president of the Student Council. A great pleasure, sir."

Out of a pair of ruddy cheeks a pair of small eyes twinkled good-naturedly. The large face, the large body were not so much fat as beefy and suggested something "typical"—monk, politician, or innkeeper.

Blackburn took the seat beside Howe's desk. "I may have seemed to introduce myself in my public capacity, sir," he said. "But it is really as an individual that I came to see you. That is to say, as one of your students to be."

He spoke with an English intonation and he went on, "I was once an English major, sir."

For a moment Howe was startled, for the roast-beef look of the boy and the manner of his speech gave a second's credibility to one sense of his statement. Then the collegiate meaning of the phrase asserted itself, but some perversity made Howe say what was not really in good taste even with so forward a student, "Indeed? What regiment?"

Blackburn stared and then gave a little pouf-pouf of laughter. He waved the misapprehension away "*Very* good, sir. It certainly is an ambiguous term." He chuckled in appreciation of Howe's joke, then cleared his throat to put it aside. "I look forward to taking your course in the romantic poets, sir," he said earnestly. "To me the romantic poets are the very crown of English literature."

Howe made a dry sound, and the boy, catching some meaning in it, said, "Little as I know them, of course. But even Shakespeare who is so dear to us of the Anglo-Saxon tradition is in a sense but the preparation for Shelley, Keats and Byron. And Wadsworth."

Almost sorry for him, Howe dropped his eyes. With some embarrassment, for the boy was not actually his student, he said softly, "Wordsworth."

"Sir?"

Wordsworth, not Wadsworth. You said Wadsworth."

"Did I, sir?" Gravely he shook his head to rebuke himself for the error. "Wordsworth, of course—slip of the tongue." Then, quite in command again, he went on. "I have a favor to ask of you, Doctor Howe. You see, I began my college course as an English major,"—he smiled—"as I said."

"Yes?"

"But after my first year I shifted. I shifted to the social sciences. Sociology and government—I find them stimulating and very *real*." He paused, out of respect for reality. "But now I find that perhaps I have neglected the other side."

"The other side?" Howe said.

"Imagination, fancy, culture. A well-rounded man." He trailed off as if there were perfect understanding between them. "And so, sir, I have decided to end my senior year with your course in the romantic poets."

His voice was filled with an indulgence which Howe ignored as he said flatly and gravely, "But that course isn't given until the spring term."

"Yes, sir, and that is where the favor comes in. Would you let me take your romantic prose course? I can't take it for credit, sir, my program is full, but just for background it seems to me that I ought to take it. I do hope," he concluded in a manly way, "that you will consent."

"Well, it's no great favor, Mr. Blackburn. You can come if you wish, though there's not much point in it if you don't do the reading."

The bell rang for the hour and Howe got up.

"May I begin with this class, sir?" Blackburn's smile was candid and boyish.

Howe nodded carelessly and together, silently, they walked to the classroom down the hall. When they reached the door Howe stood back to let his student enter, but Blackburn moved adroitly behind him and grasped him by the arm to urge him over the threshold. They entered together with Blackburn's hand firmly on Howe's biceps, the student inducting the teacher into his own room. Howe felt a surge of temper rise in him and almost violently he disengaged his arm and walked to the desk, while Blackburn found a seat in the front row and smiled at him.

## II

The question was, At whose door must the tragedy be laid?

All night the snow had fallen heavily and only now was abating in sparse little flurries. The windows were valanced high with white. It was very quiet; something of the quiet of the world had reached the class, and Howe found that everyone was glad to talk or listen. In the room there was a comfortable sense of pleasure in being human.

Casebeer believed that the blame for the tragedy rested with heredity. Picking up the book he read, "The sins of the fathers are visited on their children." This opinion was received with general favor. Nevertheless, Johnson ventured to say that the fault was all Pastor Manders' because the Pastor had made Mrs. Alving go back to her husband and was always hiding the truth. To this Hibbard objected with logic enough, "Well then, it was really all her husband's fault. He *did* all the bad things." De Witt, his face bright with an impatient idea, said that the fault was all society's. "By society I don't mean upper-crust society," he said. He looked around a little defiantly, taking in any members of the class who might be members of upper-crust society. "Not in that sense. I mean the social unit."

Howe nodded and said, "Yes, of course."

"If the society of the time had progressed far enough in science," De Witt went on, "then there would be no problem for Mr. Ibsen to write about. Captain Alving plays around a little, gives way to perfectly natural biological urges, and he gets a social disease, a venereal disease. If the disease is cured, no problem. Invent salvarsan and the disease is cured. The problem of heredity disappears and li'l Oswald just doesn't get paresis. No paresis, no problem—no problem, no play."

This was carrying the ark into battle, and the class looked at De Witt with respectful curiosity. It was his usual way and on the whole they were sympathetic with his struggle to prove to Howe that science was better than literature. Still, there was something in his reckless manner that alienated them a little.

"Or take birth-control, for instance," De Witt went on. "If

Mrs. Alving had some knowledge of contraception, she wouldn't have had to have li'l Oswald at all. No li'l Oswald, no play."

The class was suddenly quieter. In the back row Stettenhover swung his great football shoulders in a righteous sulking gesture, first to the right, then to the left. He puckered his mouth ostentatiously. Intellect was always ending up by talking dirty.

Tertan's hand went up, and Howe said, "Mr. Tertan." The boy shambled to his feet and began his long characteristic gulp. Howe made a motion with his fingers, as small as possible, and Tertan ducked his head and smiled in apology. He sat down. The class laughed. With more than half the term gone, Tertan had not been able to remember that one did not rise to speak. He seemed unable to carry on the life of the intellect without this mark of respect for it. To Howe the boy's habit of rising seemed to accord with the formal shabbiness of his dress. He never wore the casual sweaters and jackets of his classmates. Into the free and comfortable air of the college classroom he brought the stuffy sordid strictness of some crowded, metropolitan high school.

"Speaking from one sense," Tertan began slowly, "There is no blame ascribable. From the sense of determinism, who can say where the blame lies? The preordained is the preordained and it cannot be said without rebellion against the universe, a palpable absurdity."

In the back row Stettenhover slumped suddenly in his seat, his heels held out before him, making a loud, dry, disgusted sound. His body sank until his neck rested on the back of his chair. He folded his hands across his belly and looked significantly out of the window, exasperated not only with Tertan, but with Howe, with the class, with the whole system designed to encourage this kind of thing. There was a certain insolence in the movement and Howe flushed. As Tertan continued to speak, Howe stalked casually toward the window and placed himself in the line of Stettenhover's vision. He stared at the great fellow, who pretended not to see him. There was so much power in the big body, so much contempt in the Greek-athlete face under the crisp Greek-athlete curls, that Howe felt almost physical fear. But at last Stettenhover admitted him to focus and under his disapproving gaze sat up with slow indifference. His eyebrows raised high in resignation, he began to examine his hands. Howe relaxed and turned his attention back to Tertan.

"Flux of existence," Tertan was saying, "produces all things, so that judgment wavers. Beyond the phenomena, what? But phenomena are adumbrated and to them we are limited."

Howe saw it for a moment as perhaps it existed in the boy's mind—the world of shadows which are cast by a great light upon a hidden reality as in the old myth of the Cave. But the little brush with Stettenhover had tired him, and he said irritably, "But come to the point, Mr. Tertan."

He said it so sharply that some of the class looked at him curiously. For three months he had gently carried Tertan through his verbosities, to the vaguely respectful surprise of the other students, who seemed to conceive that there existed between this strange classmate and their teacher some special understanding from which they were content to be excluded. Tertan looked at him mildly, and at once came brilliantly to the point. "This is the summation of the play," he said and took up his book and read, " 'Your poor father never found any outlet for the over-mastering joy of life that was in him. And I brought no holiday into his home, either. Everything seemed to turn upon duty and I am afraid I made your poor father's home unbearable to him, Oswald.' Spoken by Mrs. Alving."

Yes that was surely the "summation" of the play and Tertan had hit it, as he hit, deviously and eventually, the literary point of almost everything. But now, as always, he was wrapping it away from sight. "For most mortals," he said, "there are only joys of biological urgings, gross and crass, such as the sensuous Captain Alving. For certain few there are the transmutations beyond these to a contemplation of the utter whole."

Oh, the boy was mad. And suddenly the word, used in hyperbole, intended almost for the expression of exasperated admiration, became literal. Now that the word was used, it became simply apparent to Howe that Tertan was mad.

It was a monstrous word and stood like a bestial thing in the room. Yet it so completely comprehended everything that had puzzled Howe, it so arranged and explained what for three months had been perplexing him that almost at once its horror became domesticated. With this word Howe was able to understand why he had never been able to communicate to Tertan the value of a single criticism or correction of his wild, verbose themes. Their conferences had been frequent and long but had done nothing to reduce to order the splendid confusion of the boy's ideas. Yet, impossible though its expression was, Tertan's incandescent mind could always strike for a moment into some dark corner of thought.

And now it was suddenly apparent that it was not a faulty rhetoric that Howe had to contend with. With his new knowledge he looked at Tertan's face and wondered how he could have so long deceived himself. Tertan was still talking, and the class had lapsed into a kind of patient unconsciousness, a coma of respect for words which, for all that most of them knew, might be profound. Almost with a suffusion of shame, Howe believed that in some dim way the class had long ago had some intimation of Tertan's madness. He reached out as decisively as he could to seized the thread of Tertan's discourse before it should be entangled further.

"Mr. Tertan says that the blame must be put upon whoever kills the joy of living in another. We have been assuming that Captain Alving was a wholly bad man, but what if we assume that he became bad only because Mrs. Alving, when they were first married, acted toward him in the prudish way she says she did?"

It was a ticklish idea to advance to freshmen and perhaps not profitable. Not all of them were following.

"That would put the blame on Mrs. Alving herself, whom most of you admire. And she herself seems to think so." He glanced at his watch. The hour was nearly over. "What do you think, Mr. De Witt?"

De Witt rose to the idea; he wanted to know if society couldn't be blamed for educating Mrs. Alving's temperament in the wrong way. Casebeer was puzzled, Stettenhover continued to look at his hands until the bell rang.

Tertan, his brows louring in thought, was making as always for a private word. Howe gathered his books and papers to leave quickly. At this moment of his discovery and with the knowledge still raw, he could not engage himself with Tertan. Tertan sucked in his breath to prepare for speech and Howe made ready for the pain and confusion. But at that moment Casebeer detached himself from the group with which he had been conferring and which he seemed to represent. His constituency remained at a tactful distance. The mission involved the time of an assigned essay. Casebeer's presentation of the plea—it was based on the freshmen's heavy duties at the fraternities during Carnival Week—cut across Tertan's preparations for speech. "And so some of us fellows thought," Casebeer concluded with heavy solemnity, "that we could do a better job, give our minds to it more, if we had more time."

Tertan regarded Casebeer with mingled curiosity and revulsion. Howe not only said that he would postpone the assignment but went on to talk about the Carnival, and even drew the waiting constituency into the conversation. He was conscious of Tertan's stern and astonished stare, then of his sudden departure.

Now that the fact was clear, Howe knew that he must act on it. His course was simple enough. He must lay the case before the Dean. Yet he hesitated. His feeling for Tertan must now, certainly, be in some way invalidated. Yet could he, because of a word, hurry to assign to official and reasonable solicitude what had been, until this moment, so various and warm? He could at least delay and, by moving slowly, lend a poor grace to the necessary, ugly act of making his report.

It was with some notion of keeping the matter in his own hands that he went to the Dean's office to look up Tertan's records. In the outer office the Dean's secretary greeted him brightly, and at his request brought him the manila folder with the small identifying photograph pasted in the corner. She laughed. "He was looking for the birdie in the wrong place," she said.

Howe leaned over her shoulder to look at the picture. It was as bad as all the Dean's-office photographs were, but it differed from all that Howe had ever seen. Tertan, instead of looking into the camera, as no doubt he had been bidden, had, at the moment of exposure, turned his eyes upward. His mouth, as though conscious of the trick played on the photographer, had the sly superior look that Howe knew.

The secretary was fascinated by the picture. "What a funny boy," she said. "He looks like Tartuffe!"

And so he did, with the absurd piety of the eyes and the conscious slyness of the mouth and the whole face bloated by the bad lens.

"Is he *like* that?" the secretary said.

"Like Tartuffe? No."

From the photograph there was little enough comfort to be had. The records themselves gave no clue to madness, though they suggested sadness enough. Howe read of a father, Stanislaus Tertan, born in Budapest and trained in engineering in Berlin, once employed by the Hercules Chemical Corporation—this was one of the factories that dominated the sound end of the town—but now without employment. He read of a mother Erminie (Youngfellow) Tertan, born in Manchester, educated at a Normal School at Leeds, now housewife by profession. The family lived on Greenbriar Street which Howe knew as a row of once elegant homes near what was now the factory district. The old mansion had long ago been divided into small and primitive apartments. Of Ferdinand himself there was little to learn. He lived with his parents, had attended a Detroit high school and had transferred to the local school in his last year. His rating for intelligence, as expressed in numbers, was high, his scholastic record was remarkable, he held a college scholarship for his tuition.

Howe laid the folder on the secretary's desk. "Did you find what you wanted to know?" she asked.

The phrases from Tertan's momentous first theme came back to him. "Tertan I am, but what is Tertan? Of this time, of that place, of some parentage, what does it matter?"

"No, I didn't find it," he said.

Now that he had consulted the sad, half-meaningless record he knew all the more firmly that he must not give the matter out of his own hands. He must not release Tertan to authority. Not that he anticipated from the Dean anything but the greatest kindness for Tertan. The Dean would have the experience and skill which he himself could not have. One way or another the Dean could answer the question, "What is Tertan?" Yet this was precisely what he feared. He alone could keep alive—not forever but for a somehow important time—the question, "What is Tertan?" He alone could keep it still a question. Some sure instinct told him that he must not surrender the question to a clean official desk in a clear official light to be dealt with, settled and closed.

He heard himself saying, "Is the Dean busy at the moment? I'd like to see him."

His request came thus unbidden, even forbidden, and it was one of the surprising and startling incidents of his life. Later when he reviewed the events, so disconnected in themselves, or so merely odd, of the story that unfolded for him that year, it was over this moment, on its face the least notable, that he paused longest. It was frequently to be with fear and never without a certainty of its meaning in his own knowledge of himself that he would recall this simple, routine request, and the feeling of shame and freedom it gave him as he sent everything down the official chute. In the end, of course, no matter what he did to "protect" Tertan, he would have had to make the same request and lay the matter on the Dean's clean desk. But it would always be a landmark of his life that, at the very moment when he was rejecting the official way, he had been, without will or intention, so gladly drawn to it.

After the storm's last delicate flurry, the sun had come out. Reflected by the new snow, it filled the office with a golden light which was almost musical in the way it made all the commonplace objects of efficiency shine with a sudden sad and noble significance. And the light, now that he noticed it, made the utterance of his perverse and unwanted request even more momentous.

The secretary consulted the engagement pad. "He'll be free any minute. Don't you want to wait in the parlor?"

She threw open the door of the large and pleasant room in which the Dean held his Committee meetings, and in which his visitors waited. It was designed with a homely elegance on the masculine side of the eighteenth-century manner. There was a small coal fire in the grate and the handsome mahogany table was strewn with books and magazines. The large windows gave on the snowy lawn, and there was such a fine width of window that the white casements and walls seemed at this moment but a continuation of the snow, the snow but an extension of casement and walls. The outdoors seemed taken in and made safe, the indoors seemed luxuriously freshened and expanded.

Howe sat down by the fire and lighted a cigarette. The room had its intended effect upon him. He felt comfortable and relaxed, yet nicely organized, some young diplomatic agent of the eighteenth century, the newly fledged Swift carrying out Sir William Temple's business. The rawness of Tertan's case quite vanished. He crossed his legs and reached for a magazine.

It was the famous issue of *Life and Letters* that his idle hand had found and his blood raced as he sifted through it, and the shape of his own name, Joseph Howe, sprang out at him, still cabalistic in its power. He tossed the magazine back on the table as the door of the Dean's office opened and the Dean ushered out Theodore Blackburn.

"Ah, Joseph!" the Dean said.

Blackburn said, "Good morning, Doctor." Howe winced at the title and caught the flicker of amusement over the Dean's face. The Dean stood with his hand high on the door-jamb and Blackburn, still in the doorway, remained standing almost under the long arm.

Howe nodded briefly to Blackburn, snubbing his eager deference. "Can you give me a few minutes?" he said to the Dean.

"All the time you want. Come in." Before the two men could enter the office, Blackburn claimed their attention with a long full "er." As they turned to him, Blackburn said, "Can *you* give *me* a few minutes, Doctor Howe?" His eyes sparkled at the little audacity he had committed, the slightly impudent play with hierarchy. Of the three of them Blackburn kept himself the lowest, but he reminded Howe of his subaltern relation to the Dean.

"I mean, of course," Blackburn went on easily, "when you've finished with the Dean."

"I'll be in my office shortly," Howe said, turned his back on the ready "Thank you, sir," and followed the Dean into the inner room.

"Energetic boy," said the Dean. "A bit beyond himself but very energetic. Sit down."

The Dean lighted a cigarette, leaned back in his chair, sat easy and silent for a moment, giving Howe no signal to go ahead with business. He was a young Dean, not much beyond forty, a tall handsome man with sad, ambitious eyes. He had been a Rhodes scholar. His friends looked for great things from him, and it was generally said that he had notions of education which he was not yet ready to try to put into practice.

His relaxed silence was meant as a compliment to Howe. He smiled and said, "What's the business, Joseph?"

"Do you know Tertan—Ferdinand Tertan, a freshman?"

The Dean's cigarette was in his mouth and his hands were clasped behind his head. He did not seem to search his memory for the name. He said, "What about him?"

Clearly the Dean knew something, and he was waiting for Howe to tell him more. Howe moved only tentatively. Now that he was doing what he had resolved not to do, he felt more guilty at having been so long deceived by Tertan and more need to be loyal to his error.

"He's a strange fellow," he ventured. He said stubbornly, "In a strange way he's very brilliant." He concluded, "But very strange."

The springs of the Dean's swivel chair creaked as he came out of his sprawl and leaned forward to Howe. "Do you mean he's so strange that it's something you could give a name to?"

Howe looked at him stupidly. "What do you mean?" he said.

"What's his trouble?" the Dean said more neutrally.

"He's very brilliant, in a way. I looked him up and he has a top intelligence rating. But somehow, and it's hard to explain just how, what he says is always on the edge of sense and doesn't quite make it."

The Dean looked at him and Howe flushed up. The Dean had surely read Woolley on the subject of "the Howes" and the *tour d'ivresse.* Was that quick glance ironical?

The Dean picked up some papers from his desk, and Howe could see that they were in Tertan's impatient scrawl. Perhaps the little gleam in the Dean's glance had come only from putting facts together.

"He sent me this yesterday," the Dean said. "After an interview I had with him. I haven't been able to do more than glance at it. When you said what you did, I realized there was something wrong."

Twisting his mouth, the Dean looked over the the letter. "You seem to be involved," he said without looking up. "By the way, what did you give him at mid-term?"

Flushing, setting his shoulders, Howe said firmly, "I gave him A-minus."

The Dean chuckled. "Might be a good idea if some of our nicer boys went crazy—just a little." He said, "Well," to conclude the matter and handed the papers to Howe. "See if this is the same thing you've been finding. Then we can go into the matter again."

Before the fire in the parlor, in the chair that Howe had been occupying, sat Blackburn. He sprang to his feet as Howe entered.

"I said my office, Mr. Blackburn." Howe's voice was sharp. Then he was almost sorry for the rebuke, so clearly and naively did Blackburn seem to relish his stay in the parlor, close to authority.

"I'm in a bit of a hurry, sir," he said, "and I did want to be sure to speak to you, sir."

He was really absurd, yet fifteen years from now he would have grown up to himself, to the assurance and mature beefiness. In banks, in consular offices, in brokerage firms, on the bench, more seriously affable, a little sterner, he would make use of his ability to be administered by his job. It was almost reassuring. Now he was exercising his too-great skill on Howe. "I owe you an apology, sir," he said.

Howe knew that he did, but he showed surprise.

"I mean, Doctor, after your having been so kind about letting me attend your class, I stopped coming." He smiled in deprecation. "Extracurricular activities take up so much of my time. I'm afraid I undertook more than I could perform."

Howe had noticed the absence and had been a little irritated by it after Blackburn's elaborate plea. It was an absence that might be interpreted as a comment on the teacher. But there was only one way for him to answer. "You've no need to apologize," he said. "It's wholly your affair."

Blackburn beamed. "I'm so glad you feel that way about it, sir. I was worried you might think I had stayed away because I was influenced by—" he stopped and lowered his eyes.

Astonished, Howe said, "Influenced by what?"

"Well, by—" Blackburn hesitated and for answer pointed to the table on which lay the copy of *Life and Letters*. Without looking at it, he knew where to direct his hand. "By the unfavorable publicity, sir." He hurried on. "And that brings me to another point, sir. I am secretary of Quill and Scroll, sir, the student literary society, and I wonder if you would address us. You could read your own poetry, sir, and defend your own point of view. It would be very interesting."

It was truly amazing. Howe looked long and cruelly into Blackburn's face, trying to catch the secret of the mind that could have conceived this way of manipulating him, this way so daring and inept—but not entirely inept—with its malice so without malignity. The face did not yield its secret. Howe smiled broadly and said, "Of course I don't think you were influenced by the unfavorable publicity."

"I'm still going to take—regularly, for credit—your romantic poets course next term," Blackburn said.

"Don't worry, my dear fellow, don't worry about it."

Howe started to leave and Blackburn stopped him with, "But about Quill, sir?"

"Suppose we wait until next term? I'll be less busy then."

And Blackburn said, "Very good, sir, and thank you."

In his office the little encounter seemed less funny to Howe, was even in some indeterminate way disturbing. He made an effort to put it from his mind by turning to what was sure to disturb him more, the Tertan letter read in the new interpretation. He found what he had always found, the same florid leaps beyond fact and meaning, the same headlong certainty. But as his eye passed over the familiar scrawl it caught his own name, and for the second time that hour he felt the race of his blood.

"The Paraclete," Tertan had written to the Dean, "from a Greek word meaning to stand in place of, but going beyond the primitive idea to mean traditionally the helper, the one who comforts and assists, cannot without fundamental loss be jettisoned. Even if taken no longer in the supernatural sense, the concept remains deeply in the human consciousness inevitably. Humanitarianism is no reply, for not every man stands in the place of every other man for this other comrade's comfort. But certain are chosen out of the human race to be the consoler of some other. Of these, for example, is Joseph Barker Howe, Ph.D. Of intellects not the first yet of true intellect and lambent instructions, given to that which is intuitive and irrational, not to what is logical in the strict word, what is judged by him is of the heart and not the head. Here is one chosen, in that he chooses himself to stand in the place of another for comfort and consolation. To him more than another I give my gratitude, with all respect to our Dean who reads this, a noble man, but merely dedicated, not consecrated. But not in the aspect of the Paraclete only is Dr. Joseph Barker Howe established, for he must be the Paraclete to another aspect of himself, that which is driven and persecuted by the lack of understanding in the world at large, so that he in himself embodies the full history of man's tribulations and, overflowing upon others, notably the present writer, is the ultimate end."

This was love. There was no escape from it. Try as Howe

might to remember that Tertan was mad and all his emotions invalidated, he could not destroy the effect upon him of his student's stern, affectionate regard. He had betrayed not only a power of mind but a power of love. And, however firmly he held before his attention the fact of Tertan's madness, he could do nothing to banish the physical sensation of gratitude he felt. He had never thought of himself as "driven and persecuted" and he did not now. But still he could not make meaningless his sensation of gratitude. The pitiable Tertan sternly pitied him, and comfort came from Tertan's never-to-be-comforted mind.

## III

In an academic community, even an efficient one, official matters move slowly. The term drew to a close with no action in the case of Tertan, and Joseph Howe had to confront a curious problem. How should he grade his strange student, Tertan?

Tertan's final examination had been no different from all his other writing, and what did one "give" such a student? De Witt must have his A, that was clear. Johnson would get a B. With Casebeer it was a question of a B-minus or a C-plus, and Stettenhover, who had been crammed by the team tutor to fill half a blue-book with his thin feminine scrawl, would have his C-minus which he would accept with mingled indifference and resentment. But with Tertan it was not so easy.

The boy was still in the college process and his name could not be omitted from the grade sheet. Yet what should a mind under suspicion of madness be graded? Until the medical verdict was given, it was for Howe to continue as Tertan's teacher and to keep his judgment pedagogical. Impossible to give him an F: he had not failed. B was for Johnson's stolid mediocrity. He could not be put on the edge of passing with Stettenhover, for he exactly did not pass. In energy and richness of intellect he was perhaps even De Witt's superior, and Howe toyed grimly with the notion of giving him an A, but that would lower the value of the A De Witt had won with his beautiful and clear, if still arrogant, mind. There was a notation which the Registrar recognized —Inc., for Incomplete, and in the horrible comedy of the situation, Howe considered that. But really only a mark of M for Mad would serve.

In his perplexity, Howe sought the Dean, but the Dean was

out of town. In the end, he decided to maintain the A-minus he had given Tertan at mid-term. After all, there had been no falling away from that quality. He entered it on the grade sheet with something like bravado.

Academic time moves quickly. A college year is not really a year, lacking as it does three months. And it is endlessly divided into units which, at their beginning, appear larger than they are—terms, half-terms, months, weeks. And the ultimate unit, the hour, is not really an hour, lacking as it does ten minutes. And so the new term advanced rapidly, and one day the fields about the town were all brown, cleared of even the few thin patches of snow which had lingered so long.

Howe, as he lectured on the romantic poets, became conscious of Blackburn emanating wrath. Blackburn did it well, did it with enormous dignity. He did not stir in his seat, he kept his eyes fixed on Howe in perfect attention, but he abstained from using his notebook, there was no mistaking what he proposed to himself as an attitude. His elbow on the writing-wing of the chair, his chin on the curled fingers of his hand, he was the embodiment of intellectual indignation. He was thinking his own thoughts, would give no public offense, yet would claim his due, was not to be intimidated. Howe knew that he would present himself at the end of the hour.

Blackburn entered the office without invitation. He did not smile; there was no cajolery about him. Without invitation he sat down beside Howe's desk. He did not speak until he had taken the blue-book from his pocket. He said, "What does this mean, sir?"

It was a sound and conservative student tactic. Said in the usual way it meant, "How could you have so misunderstood me?" or "What does this mean for my future in the course?" But there were none of the humbler tones in Blackburn's way of saying it.

Howe made the established reply, "I think that's for you to tell me."

Blackburn continued icy. "I'm sure I can't, sir."

There was a silence between them. Both dropped their eyes to the blue-book on the desk. On its cover Howe had penciled: "F. This is very poor work."

Howe picked up the blue-book. There was always the possibility of injustice. The teacher may be bored by the mass of papers and not wholly attentive. A phrase, even the student's handwriting, may irritate him unreasonably. "Well," said Howe, "Let's go through it."

He opened the first page. "Now here: you write, 'In *The Ancient Mariner,* Coleridge lives in and transports us to a honey-sweet world where all is rich and strange, a world of charm to which we can escape from the humdrum existence of our daily lives, the world of romance. Here, in this warm and honey-sweet land of charming dreams we can relax and enjoy ourselves.' "

Howe lowered the paper and waited with a neutral look for Blackburn to speak. Blackburn returned the look boldly, did not speak, sat stolid and lofty. At last Howe said, speaking gently, "Did you mean that, or were you just at a loss for something to say?"

"You imply that I was just 'bluffing'?" The quotation marks hung palpable in the air about the word.

"I'd like to know. I'd prefer believing that you were bluffing to believing that you really thought this."

Blackburn's eyebrows went up. From the height of a great and firm-based idea he looked at his teacher. He clasped the crags for a moment and then pounced, craftily, suavely. "Do you mean, Doctor Howe, that there aren't two opinions possible?"

It was superbly done in its air of putting all of Howe's intellectual life into the balance. Howe remained patient and simple. "Yes, many opinions are possible, but not this one. Whatever anyone believes of *The Ancient Mariner,* no one can in reason believe that it represents a—a honey-sweet world in which we can relax."

"But that is what I *feel,* sir."

This was well-done, too. Howe said, "Look, Mr. Blackburn. Do you really relax with hunger and thirst, the heat and the sea-serpents, the dead men with staring eyes, Life in Death and the skeletons? Come now, Mr. Blackburn."

Blackburn made no answer, and Howe pressed forward. "Now, you say of Wordsworth, 'Of peasant stock himself, he turned from the effete life of the salons and found in the peasant the hope of a flaming revolution which would sweep away all the old ideas. This is the subject of his best poems.' "

Beaming at his teacher with youthful eagerness, Blackburn

said, "Yes, sir, a rebel, a bringer of light to suffering mankind. I see him as a kind of Prothemeus."

"A kind of what?"

"Prothemeus, sir."

"Think, Mr. Blackburn. We were talking about him only today and I mentioned his name a dozen times. You don't mean Prothemeus. You mean—" Howe waited, but there was no response.

"You mean Prometheus."

Blackburn gave no assent, and Howe took the reins. "You've done a bad job here, Mr. Blackburn, about as bad as could be done." He saw Blackburn stiffen and his genial face harden again. "It shows either a lack of preparation or a complete lack of understanding." He saw Blackburn's face begin to go to pieces and he stopped.

"Oh, sir," Blackburn burst out, "I've never had a mark like this before, never anything below a B, never. A thing like this has never happened to me before."

It must be true, it was a statement too easily verified. Could it be that other instructors accepted such flaunting nonsense? Howe wanted to end the interview. "I'll set it down to lack of preparation," he said. "I know you're busy. That's not an excuse, but it's an explanation. Now, suppose you really prepare, and then take another quiz in two weeks. We'll forget this one and count the other."

Blackburn squirmed with pleasure and gratitude. "Thank you, sir. You're really very kind, very kind."

Howe rose to conclude the visit. "All right, then—in two weeks."

It was that day that the Dean imparted to Howe the conclusion of the case of Tertan. It was simple and a little anticlimactic. A physician had been called in, and had said the word, given the name.

"A classic case, he called it," the Dean said. "Not a doubt in the world," he said. His eyes were full of miserable pity, and he clutched at a word. "A classic case, a classic case." To his aid and to Howe's there came the Parthenon and the form of the Greek drama, the Aristotelian logic, Racine and the Well-Tempered Clavichord, the blueness of the Aegean and its clear sky. Classic—that is to say, without a doubt, perfect in its way, a veritable model, and, as the Dean had been told, sure to take a perfectly predictable and inevitable course to a foreknown conclusion.

It was not only pity that stood in the Dean's eyes. For a moment there was fear too. "Terrible," he said, "it is simply terrible."

Then he went on briskly. "Naturally, we've told the boy nothing. And, naturally, we won't. His tuition's paid by his scholarship, and we'll continue him on the rolls until the end of the year. That will be the kindest. After that the matter will be out of our control. We'll see, of course, that he gets into the proper hands. I'm told there will be no change, he'll go on like this, be as good as this, for four to six months. And so we'll just go along as usual."

So Tertan continued to sit in Section 5 of English 1A, to his classmates still a figure of curiously dignified fun, symbol to most of them of the respectable but absurd intellectual life. But to his teacher he was now very different. He had not changed—he was still the greyhound casting for the scent of ideas, and Howe could see that he was still the same Tertan, but he could not feel it. What he felt as he looked at the boy sitting in his accustomed place was the hard blank of a fact. The fact itself was formidable and depressing. But what Howe was chiefly aware of was that he had permitted the metamorphosis of Tertan from person to fact.

As much as possible he avoided seeing Tertan's upraised hand and eager eye. But the fact did not know of its mere factuality, it continued its existence as if it were Tertan, hand up and eye questioning, and one day it appeared in Howe's office with a document.

"Even the spirit who lives egregiously, above the herd, must have its relations with the fellowman," Tertan declared. He laid the document on Howe's desk. It was headed "Quill and Scroll Society of Dwight College. Application for Membership."

"In most ways these are crass minds," Tertan said, touching the paper. "Yet as a whole, bound together in their common love of letters, they transcend their intellectual lacks since it is not a paradox that the whole is greater than the sum of its parts."

"When are the elections?" Howe asked.

"They take place tomorrow."

"I certainly hope you will be successful."

"Thank you. Would you wish to implement that hope?" A

rather dirty finger pointed to the bottom of the sheet. "A faculty recommender is necessary," Tertan said stiffly, and waited.

"And you wish me to recommend you?"

"It would be an honor."

"You may use my name."

Tertan's finger pointed again. "It must be a written sponsorship, signed by the sponsor." There was a large blank space on the form under the heading, "Opinion of Faculty Sponsor."

This was almost another thing and Howe hesitated. Yet there was nothing else to do and he took out his fountain pen. He wrote, "Mr. Ferdinand Tertan is marked by his intense devotion to letters and by his exceptional love of all things of the mind." To this he signed his name, which looked bold and assertive on the white page. It disturbed him, the strange affirming power of a name. With a businesslike air, Tertan whipped up the paper, folding it with decision, and put it into his pocket. He bowed and took his departure, leaving Howe with the sense of having done something oddly momentous.

And so much now seemed odd and momentous to Howe that should not have seemed so. It was odd and momentous, he felt, when he sat with Blackburn's second quiz before him, and wrote in an excessively firm hand the grade of C-minus. The paper was a clear, an indisputable failure. He was carefully and consciously committing a cowardice. Blackburn had told the truth when he had pleaded his past record. Howe had consulted it in the Dean's office. It showed no grade lower than a B-minus. A canvass of some of Blackburn's previous instructors had brought vague attestations to the adequate powers of a student imperfectly remembered, and sometimes surprise that his abilities could be questioned at all.

As he wrote the grade, Howe told himself that his cowardice sprang from an unwillingness to have more dealings with a student he disliked. He knew it was simpler than that. He knew he feared Blackburn; that was the absurd truth. And cowardice did not solve the matter after all. Blackburn, flushed with a first success, attacked at once. The minimal passing grade had not assuaged his feelings and he sat at Howe's desk and again the blue-book lay between them. Blackburn said nothing. With an enormous impudence, he was waiting for Howe to speak and explain himself.

At last Howe said sharply and rudely, "Well?" His throat was tense and the blood was hammering in his head. His mouth was tight with anger at himself for his disturbance.

Blackburn's glance was almost baleful. "This is impossible, sir."

"But there it is," Howe answered.

"Sir?" Blackburn had not caught the meaning but his tone was still haughty.

Impatiently Howe said, "There it is, plain as day. Are you here to complain again?"

"Indeed I am, sir." There was surprise in Blackburn's voice that Howe should ask the question.

"I shouldn't complain if I were you. You did a thoroughly bad job on your first quiz. This one is a little, only a very little, better." This was not true. If anything, it was worse.

"That might be a matter of opinion, sir."

"It is a matter of opinion. Of my opinion."

"Another opinion might be different, sir."

"You really believe that?" Howe said.

"Yes." The omission of the "sir" was monumental.

"Whose, for example?"

"The Dean's, for example." Then the fleshy jaw came forward a little. "Or a certain literary critic's, for example."

It was colossal and almost too much for Blackburn himself to handle. The solidity of his face almost crumpled under it. But he withstood his own audacity and went on. "And the Dean's opinion might be guided by the knowledge that the person who gave me this mark is the man whom a famous critic, the most eminent judge of literature in this country, called a drunken man. The Dean might think twice about whether such a man is fit to teach Dwight students."

Howe said in quiet admonition, "Blackburn, you're mad," meaning no more than to check the boy's extravagance.

But Blackburn paid no heed. He had another shot in the locker. "And the Dean might be guided by the information, of which I have evidence, documentary evidence,"—he slapped his breast pocket twice—"that this same person personally recommended to the college literary society, the oldest in the country, that he personally recommended a student who is crazy, who threw the meeting into an uproar—a psychiatric case. The Dean might take that into account."

Howe was never to learn the details of that "uproar." He had always to content himself with the dim but passionate picture which at that moment sprang into his mind, of Tertan standing on some abstract height and madly denouncing the multitude of Quill and Scroll who howled him down.

He sat quiet a moment and looked at Blackburn. The ferocity had entirely gone from the student's face. He sat regarding his teacher almost benevolently. He had played a good card and now, scarcely at all unfriendly, he was waiting to see the effect. Howe took up the blue-book and negligently sifted through it. He read a page, closed the book, struck out the C-minus and wrote an F.

"Now you may take the paper to the Dean," he said. "You may tell him that after reconsidering it, I lowered the grade."

The gasp was audible. "Oh, sir!" Blackburn cried. "Please!" His face was agonized. "It means my graduation, my livelihood, my future. Don't do this to me."

"It's done already."

Blackburn stood up. "I spoke rashly, sir, hastily. I had no intention, no real intention, of seeing the Dean. It rests with you—entirely, entirely. I *hope* you will restore the first mark."

"Take the matter to the Dean or not, just as you choose. The grade is what you deserve and it stands."

Blackburn's head dropped. "And will I be failed at mid-term, sir?"

"Of course."

From deep out of Blackburn's great chest rose a cry of anguish. "Oh, sir, if you want me to go down on my knees to you, I will, I will."

Howe looked at him in amazement.

"I will, I will. On my knees, sir. This mustn't, mustn't happen."

He spoke so literally, meaning so very truly that his knees and exactly his knees were involved and seeming to think that he was offering something of tangible value to his teacher, that Howe, whose head had become icy clear in the nonsensical drama, thought, "The boy is mad," and began to speculate fantastically whether something in himself attracted or developed aberration. He could see himself standing absurdly before the Dean and saying, "I've found another. This time it's the vice-president of the

Council, the manager of the debating team and secretary of Quill and Scroll."

One more such discovery, he thought, and he himself would be discovered! And there, suddenly, Blackburn was on his knees with a thump, his huge thighs straining his trousers, his hand outstretched in a great gesture of supplication.

With a cry, Howe shoved back his swivel chair and it rolled away on its casters half across the little room. Blackburn knelt for a moment to nothing at all, then got to his feet.

Howe rose abruptly. He said, "Blackburn, you will stop acting like an idiot. Dust your knees off, take your paper and get out. You've behaved like a fool and a malicious person. You have half a term to do a decent job. Keep your silly mouth shut and try to do it. Now get out."

Blackburn's head was low. He raised it and there was a pious light in his eyes. "Will you shake hands, sir?" he said. He thrust out his hand.

"I will not," Howe said.

Head and hand sank together. Blackburn picked up his bluebook and walked to the door. He turned and said, "Thank you, sir." His back, as he departed, was heavy with tragedy and stateliness.

## IV

After years of bad luck with the weather, the College had a perfect day for Commencement. It was wonderfully bright, the air so transparent, the wind so brisk that no one could resist talking about it.

As Howe set out for the campus he heard Hilda calling from the back yard. She called, "Professor, professor," and came running to him.

Howe said, "What's this 'professor' business?"

"Mother told me," Hilda said. "You've been promoted. And I want to take your picture."

"Next year," said Howe. "I won't be a professor until next year. And you know better than to call anybody 'professor.' "

"It was just in fun," Hilda said. She seemed disappointed.

"But you can take my picture if you want. I won't look much different next year." Still, it was frightening. It might mean that he was to stay in this town all his life.

Hilda brightened. "Can I take it in this?" she said, and touched the gown he carried over his arm.

Howe laughed. "Yes, you can take it in this."

"I'll get my things and meet you in front of Otis," Hilda said. "I have the background all picked out."

On the campus the Commencement crowd was already large. It stood about in eager, nervous little family groups. As he crossed, Howe was greeted by a student, capped and gowned, glad of the chance to make an event for his parents by introducing one of his teachers. It was while Howe stood there chatting that he saw Tertan.

He had never seen anyone quite so alone, as though a circle had been woven about him to separate him from the gay crowd on the campus. Not that Tertan was not gay, he was the gayest of all. Three weeks had passed since Howe had last seen him, the weeks of examination, the lazy week before Commencement, and this was now a different Tertan. On his head he wore a panama hat, broad-brimmed and fine, of the shape associated with South American planters. He wore a suit of raw silk, luxurious, but yellowed with age and much too tight, and he sported a whangee cane. He walked sedately, the hat tilted at a devastating angle, the stick coming up and down in time to his measured tread. He had, Howe guessed, outfitted himself to greet the day in the clothes of that ruined father whose existence was on record in the Dean's office. Gravely and arrogantly he surveyed the scene—in it, his whole bearing seemed to say, but not of it. With his haughty step, with his flashing eye, Tertan was coming nearer. Howe did not wish to be seen. He shifted his position slightly. When he looked again, Tertan was not in sight.

The chapel clock struck the quarter hour. Howe detached himself from his chat and hurried to Otis Hall at the far end of the campus. Hilda had not yet come. He went up into the high portico and, using the glass of the door for a mirror, put on his gown, adjusted the hood on his shoulders and set the mortarboard on his head. When he came down the steps, Hilda had arrived.

Nothing could have told him more forcibly that a year had passed than the development of Hilda's photographic possessions from the box camera of the previous fall. By a strap about her neck was hung a leather case, so thick and strong, so carefully stitched and so molded to its contents that it could only hold a costly camera. The appearance was deceptive, Howe knew, for he had been present at the Aikens' pre-Christmas conference about its purchase. It was only a fairly good domestic camera. Still, it looked very impressive. Hilda carried another leather case from which she drew a collapsible tripod. Decisively she extended each of its gleaming legs and set it up on the path. She removed the camera from its case and fixed it to the tripod. In its compact efficiency the camera almost had a life of its own, but Hilda treated it with easy familiarity, looked into its eye, glanced casually at its gauges. Then from a pocket she took still another leather case and drew from it a small instrument through which she looked first at Howe, who began to feel inanimate and lost, and then at the sky. She made some adjustment on the instrument, then some adjustment on the camera. She swept the scene with her eye, found a spot and pointed the camera in its direction. She walked to the spot, stood on it and beckoned to Howe. With each new leather case, with each new instrument, and with each new adjustment she had grown in ease and now she said, "Joe, will you stand here?"

Obediently Howe stood where he was bidden. She had yet another instrument. She took out a tape-measure on a mechanical spool. Kneeling down before Howe, she put the little metal ring of the tape under the tip of his shoe. At her request, Howe pressed it with his toe. When she had measured her distance, she nodded to Howe who released the tape. At a touch, it sprang back into the spool. "You have to be careful if you're going to get what you want," Hilda said. "I don't believe in all this snap-snap-snapping," she remarked loftily. Howe nodded in agreement, although he was beginning to think Hilda's care excessive.

Now at last the moment had come. Hilda squinted into the camera, moved the tripod slightly. She stood to the side, holding the plunger of the shutter-cable. "Ready," she said. "Will you relax, Joseph, please?" Howe realized that he was standing frozen. Hilda stood poised and precise as a setter, one hand holding the little cable, the other extended with curled dainty fingers like a dancer's, as if expressing to her subject the precarious delicacy of the moment. She pressed the plunger and there was the click. At once she stirred to action, got behind the camera, turned a new exposure. "Thank you," she said. "Would you stand under that tree and let me do a character study with light and shade?"

The childish absurdity of the remark restored Howe's ease. He went to the little tree. The pattern the leaves made on his gown was what Hilda was after. He had just taken a satisfactory position when he heard in the unmistakable voice, "Ah, Doctor! Having your picture taken?"

Howe gave up the pose and turned to Blackburn who stood on the walk, his hands behind his back, a little too large for his bachelor's gown. Annoyed that Blackburn should see him posing for a character study in light and shade, Howe said irritably, "Yes, having my picture taken."

Blackburn beamed at Hilda. "And the little photographer?" he said. Hilda fixed her eyes on the ground and stood closer to her brilliant and aggressive camera. Blackburn, teetering on his heels, his hands behind his back, wholly prelatical and benignly patient, was not abashed at the silence. At last Howe said, "If you'll excuse us, Mr. Blackburn, we'll go on with the picture."

"Go right ahead, sir. I'm running along." But he only came closer. "Doctor Howe," he said fervently, "I want to tell you how glad I am that I was able to satisfy your standards at last."

Howe was surprised at the hard, insulting brightness of his own voice, and even Hilda looked up curiously as he said, "Nothing you have ever done has satisfied me, and nothing you could ever do would satisfy me, Blackburn."

With a glance at Hilda, Blackburn made a gesture as if to hush Howe—as though all his former bold malice had taken for granted a kind of understanding between himself and his teacher, a secret which must not be betrayed to a third person. "I only meant, sir," he said, "that I was able to pass your course after all."

Howe said, "You didn't pass my course. I passed you out of my course. I passed you without even reading your paper. I wanted to be sure the college would be rid of you. And when all the grades were in and I did read your paper, I saw I was right not to have read it first."

Blackburn presented a stricken face. "It was very bad, sir?"

But Howe had turned away. The paper had been fantastic. The paper had been, if you wished to see it so, mad. It was at this moment that the Dean came up behind Howe and caught his arm. "Hello, Joseph," he said. "We'd better be getting along, it's almost late."

He was not a familiar man, but when he saw Blackburn, who

approached to greet him, he took Blackburn's arm, too. "Hello, Theodore," he said. Leaning forward on Howe's arm and on Blackburn's, he said, "Hello, Hilda dear." Hilda replied quietly, "Hello, Uncle George."

Still clinging to their arms, still linking Howe and Blackburn, the Dean said, "Another year gone, Joe, and we've turned out another crop. After you've been here a few years, you'll find it reasonably upsetting—you wonder how there can be so many graduating classes while you stay the same. But of course you don't stay the same." Then he said, "Well," sharply, to dismiss the thought. He pulled Blackburn's arm and swung him around to Howe. "Have you heard about Teddy Blackburn?" he asked. "He has a job already, before graduation—the first man of his class to be placed." Expectant of congratulations, Blackburn beamed at Howe. Howe remained silent.

"Isn't that good?" the Dean said. Still Howe did not answer and the Dean, puzzled and put out, turned to Hilda. "That's a very fine-looking camera, Hilda." She touched it with affectionate pride.

"Instruments of precision," said a voice. "Instruments of precision." Of the three with joined arms, Howe was the nearest to Tertan, whose gaze took in all the scene except the smile and the nod which Howe gave him. The boy leaned on his cane. The broad-brimmed hat, canting jauntily over his eye, confused the image of his face that Howe had established, suppressed the rigid lines of the ascetic and brought out the baroque curves. It made an effect of perverse majesty.

"Instruments of precision," said Tertan for the last time, addressing no one, making a casual comment to the universe. And it occurred to Howe that Tertan might not be referring to Hilda's equipment. The sense of the thrice-woven circle of the boy's loneliness smote him fiercely. Tertan stood in majestic jauntiness, superior to all the scene, but his isolation made Howe ache with a pity of which Tertan was more the cause than the object, so general and indiscriminate was it.

Whether in his sorrow he made some unintended movement toward Tertan which the Dean checked, or whether the suddenly tightened grip on his arm was the Dean's own sorrow and fear, he did not know. Tertan watched them in the incurious way people watch a photograph being taken, and suddenly the thought that, to the boy, it must seem that the three were posing for a picture together made Howe detach himself almost rudely from the Dean's grasp.

"I promised Hilda another picture," he announced—needlessly, for Tertan was no longer there, he had vanished in the last sudden flux of visitors who, now that the band had struck up, were rushing nervously to find seats.

"You'd better hurry," the Dean said. "I'll go along, it's getting late for me." He departed and Blackburn walked stately by his side.

Howe again took his position under the little tree which cast its shadow over his face and gown. "Just hurry, Hilda, won't you?" he said. Hilda held the cable at arm's length, her other arm crooked and her fingers crisped. She rose on her toes and said "Ready," and pressed the release. "Thank you," she said gravely and began to dismantle her camera as he hurried off to join the procession.

## MARGE PIERCY

*considers herself a Movement poetess; that is, her poems deal with her experiences as a member of the New Left, portraying interpersonal relationships caught under the glare of contemporary mass society. She has also been active in Women's Liberation.*

## LEARNING EXPERIENCE

The boy sits in the classroom
in Gary, in the United States, in NATO, in SEATO
in the thing-gorged belly of the sociobeast
in fluorescent light in slowly moving time
in boredom thick and greasy as vegetable shortening.
The classroom has green boards and ivory blinds,
the desks are new and the teachers not so old.
I have come out on the train from Chicago to talk
about dangling participles. I am supposed
to teach him to think a little on demand.
The time of tomorrow's draft exam is written on the board.
The boy yawns and does not want to be in the classroom in
    Gary
where the furnaces that consumed his father seethe rusty smoke
and pour cascades of nerve-bright steel
while the slag goes out in little dumpcars smoking,
but even less does he want to be in Today's Action Army
in Vietnam, in the Dominican Republic, in Guatemala,
in death that hurts.
In him are lectures on small groups, Jacksonian democracy,
French irregular verbs, the names of friends
around him in the classroom in Gary in the pillshaped afternoon
where tomorrow he will try and fail his license to live.

## SONIA SANCHEZ

*is a Black poet, playwright, and mother of three. Born in Birmingham, Alabama, she has published a book of poetry,* Homecoming.

## POEM FOR 8TH GRADERS

Look at me 8th
grade.
    i am black
beautiful. i have a
man who looks at
my face and smiles.
on my face
are black warriors
riding in ships
of slavery;
            on my face
                    is malcolm
                            spitting his metal seeds
on a country of sheep;
on my face
            are young eyes
breathing in black crusts.
                    look at us
8th grade
            we are black
beautiful and our black
ness sings out
            while america wanders
dumb with her wet bowels.

## KENNETH KOCH

*teaches at Columbia University and writes poetry remarkable for its humor, fantasy, and surrealist beauty. His works include* Ko *(an epic poem); two volumes of poetry,* Thank You *and* The Pleasures of Peace; *and a book of plays,* Bertha, *from which* The Academic Murders *is taken.*

*This playlet could be viewed as a study in wish fulfillment, exposing the undercurrent of hatred and fear in the universities which is glossed over by the "objective, dispassionate" educational process. Fethering, the young scholar, has something within him that is literally lethal to the university environment. But the ending makes it clear that* The Academic Murders *is about more than academics.*

# THE ACADEMIC MURDERS
## A Play of Detection, with Improvisations

### SCENE 1

*The office of Department Chairman* AUERHEIM, *a stout tweedy man in his late forties. His secretary,* MISS FUND, *sits typing in the office just outside. Enter a tall young man of about twenty-five; not seeing him at first,* MISS FUND *is a little startled.*

MISS FUND: Ah—!?

FETHERING: I'm George Fethering. I have an appointment to see Professor Auerheim.

MISS FUND: Oh—yes—of course. Just a moment. (To AUERHEIM:) Sir, there's a young man to see you—Mr. Fethering.

AUERHEIM: Oh yes—uh—show him in.

MISS FUND: You can go right in, Mr. uh—

FETHERING: Fethering. Yes. Thank you.

AUERHEIM: Well, Mr. Fethering, what can I do for you?

FETHERING: I would like to apply for a job in your department, sir.

AUERHEIM: Yes. I understand from your letter that you are quite a Yeats scholar.

FETHERING: That's right, sir. I don't want to boast, but I dare say there's nothing about W. B. Yeats that I don't know. Nothing except what may be contained in the "secret letters," of course.

AUERHEIM: The "secret letters" . . . ? Hmmm. I don't know anything about those. What are they?

FETHERING: They are a group of letters kept in the possession of the heirs of Lady Gregory, sir. Yeats' will contains a stipulation that they are not to be opened for a thousand years.

AUERHEIM: That seems rather a long time to keep something secret.

FETHERING: Yes, sir. But apparently they contain information which Yeats thought might be harmful in our time. He believed that if the world was hardy enough to last for another thousand years probably nothing could harm it.

AUERHEIM: It seems an ingenious idea . . . Well, let's get down to business. You have your degree, do you not?

FETHERING: Yes, sir, a Ph.D. from the University of Minnesota. I worked there with Hocking T. Nott on my dissertation on A.E., George Russell.

AUERHEIM: The letter from Nott praised you very highly indeed. I vaguely remember reading the abstract of your dissertation, but I don't remember too well what it was about. Could you refresh my memory?

FETHERING: If you put your memory on the table, sir, I may be able to refresh it.

AUERHEIM: Mr. Fethering! What on earth do you mean?

FETHERING: I'm sorry, sir. I—I guess I'm just a little nervous. When I am, I often make clumsy remarks of that kind. I have been reading a lot about Zen Buddhism, sir, and that sort of remark just naturally comes to my mind when I am nervous.

AUERHEIM: I see. I see. Do you know Jung's splendid introduction to Suzuki's *Introduction to Zen Buddhism*?

FETHERING: Yes, sir. I think Jung rather misses the point, sir. He tends to make Zen awfully Jungian.

AUERHEIM: Ummm. Yes. Perhaps. It may be that I simply prefer the thought of Jung to that of Suzuki and the Zen masters.

FETHERING: Sir, you should never say a thing like that!

(AUERHEIM *dies.*)

(*Improvised speech by* FETHERING *on the danger of attacking Zen.*)

## SCENE 2

*The same office, twenty minutes later. Enter Police Officer* STRAITER *and his assistant, Patrolman* BUDGE.

STRAITER: So this is the murderer!

FETHERING: Sir, I didn't touch the victim. Miss Fund can testify to that.

MISS FUND: I didn't see a thing. I was busy here in my office with my typewriter.

FETHERING: Sir, if Miss Fund won't admit that she was spying on us, you are free to examine the body for fingerprints.

MISS FUND: Oh! poor Professor Auerheim! What have you done to him, you horrible person?

STRAITER: Young lady, don't become hysterical. If this man is the murderer, we shall certainly see that he gets what he deserves. As yet, however, we really have no evidence.—Very well, Budge, you stay here and see that no one disturbs the body. I am going to phone our scientific squad to get over here on the double and examine this body for fingerprints.

BUDGE: Yes, sir.

## SCENE 3

*A political hall.*

STRAITER: Since there is no evidence of the body having been touched, it looks as though you're free, Fethering. But don't leave the city. We shall be wanting to have you within reach at all times for questioning.

FETHERING: Sir, is that legal?

STRAITER: You're damn right it is, Fethering. If we wanted to, we could hold you as a material witness indefinitely. In fact, I have half a mind to clap you in jail right now for your improper question.

FETHERING: Oh no, sir. Yes, sir. I understand. I was just asking. You see, I know nothing of the law.

STRAITER: Very well, Fethering. You are dismissed.

## SCENE 4

FETHERING'S *furnished room.*

FETHERING: It would have been foolish to tell the police officer what I think actually killed Auerheim. My own problems, meanwhile, are only redoubled by this whole affair.

(*Improvisation by* FETHERING *on the difficulties of his life, his unpleasant early childhood, his need for a job, etc., and his determination to go to Japan to try to get to the root of the mystery.*)

## SCENE 5

*Japan.*

*Improvisation of a busy day of turmoil in the Tokyo streets.*

*At the end, enter* FETHERING.

## SCENE 6

*The prison room of a ship, sailing to the United States.*
FETHERING *behind bars.*

POLICE OFFICER: We told you not to leave the city, Fethering.

FETHERING: But, sir, I did it only to try to get to the heart of the mystery—

POLICE OFFICER: If you expect us to believe *that,* then you are a greater fool than we thought!

## SCENE 7

*Above, in the ship's bar.* POLICE OFFICER, other policemen, and *other passengers.*

*Improvisation: Discussion of how great a fool* FETHERING *is to expect them to believe such a story. At the end, enter* RADIO MAN.

RADIO MAN: Look! look! listen! There may be some truth in what the boy says after all! The University of Blenheim has just exploded!

POLICE OFFICER: Blenheim!? What in tarnation has Blenheim got to do with this case? Constantia University, where Professor Auerheim was murdered by this boy, is in New York.

RADIO MAN: But wait—wait—listen to this—Blenheim, my dear police officer, is the city in which Dagobert von Auerheim was born!

SAILOR (*rushing up from below*): And listen to this! The ship has been disembowelled, and young Fethering has mysteriously escaped. He can't be found anywhere!

POLICE OFFICER: But then we must be sinking!

ALL: Help! ho! Man the lifeboats! Abandon ship! Ho!

## SCENE 8

*A lovely dusky garden in Japan.* FETHERING *and a beautiful young Japanese girl,* TACOCA.

FETHERING: I hope you don't mind my telling you this tedious story?

TACOCA: I don't find it tedious at all, my darling. I don't find anything that you say tedious.

FETHERING: To think, that I once planned to be a teacher!

TACOCA: Yes—and that now you know what your true destiny is—to be a MAN!

FETHERING: Yes, but I would still like to know who killed Professor Auerheim.

TACOCA: We can ask at the shrine after we have performed our ablutions. But meanwhile, here comes my father, the famous Japanese business man.

(*Enter* TACOCACOM, *a huge burly man.*)

TACOCACOM: Hello, son! Been hearing a lot about y—

(*He drops dead.*)

**Curtain**

(*Improvised* EPILOGUE *by Tacoca.*)

**End**

## PAUL GOODMAN

*has long been a spokesman for the New Left. For the last twenty years he has been a constant critic of American society—particularly of the manner in which this society deals with its youth. Such books as* Growing Up Absurd, Compulsory Miseducation, *and the novel* Making Do *express his concern for the young. His major theme is that youths are growing up into, and being educated for, an ideologically empty and often hypocritical adult society. In the following excerpt from Goodman's novel,* Making Do, *the arbitrary separation of faculty and student roles is examined against the background of large irrelevant classes and educational conferences. What happens when an academic relationship becomes "real" and faculty and students discover* who *they really are behind the academic robes and podiums which can turn men into objects of indifference, rather than subjects of concern?*

*From*

# MAKING DO

## A CONFERENCE ON DELINQUENCY

### 1

Before the first panel began, I knew that Columbus was going to be a beautiful Conference. When the five of us, the section on "Urban Environment and Mental Health," took our places at the table, we were inevitably trapped by the microphones grinning down our throats. (There was a surprisingly large crowd of students.) Nevertheless, before the deep freeze could really set in, the bushy-eyebrowed and moustached man on my left—Warden Howard Green, I figured from the program—implored, "Can't we dispense with these fuckin' machines?" and the white-haired lady—Justice Amy Watkins of Sacramento—favored him with a benign smile.

I myself was not much inhibited by microphones; I never talked into them and was always being admonished by the managers. But I felt heavenly comfort because somebody else was taking some initiative and I didn't have to be the only one to make a pest of himself.

Irving, who was a friend of mine—National Council on Child Labor—leaned over to the student factotum and said something, with his usual sprightly gentleness. The kid responded with the flushed resentment of seventeen years of age, unappreciated in its solipsistically expert arrangements. He pointed out that there was an audience, as if we were blind and deaf.

Judge Watkins—she had a pink face and was still a little girlish—judicially decided, "Let them be," either to spare the boy his embarrassment or because the students were in fact so noisy.

"Let's just shove 'em back," I said, and pushed mine to the

back of the table. I was quick at inventive compromises. "All I need is elbow room and so it don't jump down my throat." I went in more and more for bad grammar.

This put the fifth of us, Dr. Ben B. Blumberg—Associate Superintendent of Junior High Schools—in an awkward position. For four of us had pushed our microphones away, but he was still sitting well behaved, as he had been, with his microphone in front of his mouth. Students in the front let out a laugh. Blumberg was an earnest Pharisee who had developed, in my own big city, with heroic effort and a modicum of success, the Broad Outlook program for the "culturally disadvantaged," as we called them. He believed in the middle-class family, and his eyes were precise and a little hard.

All of us had foreheads worn with worry and perplexity.

Ungraciously, forced to cooperate in deranging his own conception, the seventeen-year-old pulled back Dr. Blumberg's microphone also. "Young man, if you think it's the wrong way to work," said Irving, "why don't you put up more of a fight?" The youth laughed shortly. It was hard for us to remember that we had crashing authority—except in the actual institutions, where we were powerless. (This we remembered exquisitely.)

I turned to look uneasily at the cop, the Warden, who was sitting at my elbow. I saw in his eyes that he was in despair, and I absolved him.

My euphoria was probably relief, after the night before, at being able to carry on a reasonable conversation, with my peers, in a safe academy. For I lived with a good deal of intellectual starvation, and in chronic fear.

## 2

I had little reasonable conversation. I had no office, and when I met my peers at a party, we did not really talk. One man would be looking for somebody more useful than me to talk to, and I would be looking for somebody more attractive than him to look at, gloomy because there was nobody. Under the formal conditions of being on a panel, however, there was nothing *to* do but listen and say one's say. I came to these conferences, as I have said, because they asked me, but once there I often learned something. I was unable to read social science, but here were the authors and right up to date.

Before the serried faces of the students and teachers, we had to talk out loud and clear, and not interrupt too rudely. Yet we spoke to one another and not to the grandstand, except Dr. Blumberg who spoke to the audience, not to upstage us but because he was pedantic.

Irving's current statistics—he started right off—were, as each time, appalling. They confirmed what I saw with my own eyes on the street, yet I wouldn't have believed it. City by city, the youth unemployment was 60 percent, 65 percent, 75 percent.

Then he said, pointedly and quietly as he did: "But employment is not a gimmick. The jobs are mostly no good anyway. And given the disappointment and resentment with which these youngsters finally get them, they are often just as bad off employed." When he said this kind of thing, his Adam's apple moved, swallowing, in his long neck.

"What do you mean by that statement?" interrupted the Associate Superintendent. "The boy with a job can get married." He was suddenly angry and quite human.

"The boy can marry. The husband is an alcoholic," said Irving laconically. "Ben," he said, "I haven't worked thirty years to improved the conditions of child labor in order to feed kids to the present economic machine and call it vocational guidance. That's what I mean."

We looked to Dr. Blumberg to reply. There was a pause. Instead he lit a cigarette, and immediately a hundred of the students lit up. They had been waiting for our permission.

The Warden was next, and started by describing children who up to twelve, thirteen, fourteen years of age had never ventured more than five blocks from home. For some reason Amy was visibly moved by this dreadful information. I refused to be moved, but suddenly cut in, as I do—parenthetically, so to speak—to make a point that, in my opinion, needed saying at once, if we were going to make sense and not waste one another's time. An "urban environment," I said, was *not* a city; "urbanism" was not city planning. If he was going to use words like that we could kiss good-bye to talking about human beings rather than administrative units; but surely that was not his intention—which was why I interrupted him, excuse me.

When I interrupted him, his right hand was outstretched in a broad gesture. He left it there and stopped to think of what I had said. Then abruptly he brought it down and with it skipped two pages of his prepared text that had been founded on an assumption that he no longer accepted. Because of a new thought, he had actually changed not only his mind but his speech, his public image!

Some of the students were visibly electrified. I could see their hair stand up like a dog's ruff in the presence of the uncanny. The students at the State University did not much believe in the existence of the intellect.

He proceeded to describe the panic of hardened diddledybops in the woods, terrified of the dark and small animals—he was the Warden of six forest work camps. He raised a laugh when he told of an encounter with a cow. Many of the students had seen a cow. "But it's not so funny," he said, to their surprise. "These kids are really afraid; but they don't know of what they are afraid." And he showed, in a thrilling example, how a skillful and sympathetic counselor had made use of this exposed nerve of panic to get past hostility and touch a profound castration anxiety.

At this I thought: There were 180 millions of people in the United States. And we poor dears who felt ourselves responsible and acted so—I doubted that we were, from coast to coast, more than a hundred or a hundred and fifty. And fifteen of us were here in Columbus! It was appalling. I was sitting next to the only manly cop in America; and the great State of California had one ordinarily decent judge, Mrs. Watkins there. There we were. The students had come out in large numbers to listen to the visiting grown-ups, as well they might, considering the box that they were in at the University.

It was ten-thirty! We had disregarded the question period. We were too absorbed in the subject and too interested in one another. Oblivious, we got up to go to Amy's room for a drink and carry on. The students crowded round—"Judge Watkins!" "Dr. Blumberg!"—some of them raised their hands as if in class. I kept arguing with Ben and Irving, and we brushed past them and elbowed through the crowd, leaving the young with their mouths half open.

Out of the corner of my eye, as in a picture, I saw a stripling hanging on the fringe. He attracted attention partly because of his flaming scarlet windbreaker, in the style of a juvenile actor of the time named Jimmy Dean, and partly because his face was contorted with unbelief at our unfairness. He was still trembling with the embarrassment of half an hour since he had thought of a sensible question to ask and was working himself up to stammer or blurt it out, while the waves of shame at exhibiting himself engulfed him, and the hostility that he felt at our eminence made him angrier and angrier and more and more unjustified.

3

I couldn't get to sleep even though I masturbated, which is usually an adequate sedative for me. There was too much unfinished business of the day. I oughtn't to have brushed past the students. The scarlet jacket flashed in my mind's eye.

I saw him. He was feverishly rehearsing, rehearsing his revenge —mentally, for he would not be telling it to his roommate. He was walking across the campus, hunched against the drizzle, at 2:00 A.M., and burning up what little energy he had. He was a sick boy. (Mononucleosis, the current style of student blues.)

By now he had quite forgotten the reasonable question that he had meant to ask. He was afraid that he was losing his mind. Indeed, a part of his hostility was that *we* had missed his proper time.

In order to ward off his panic, he attacked. I saw him single out —the Warden. (He was too sentimental to pick on Amy Watkins; and I, so far as I knew, was innocent.) His daydream voice became high-pitched, and suddenly he was accusing the Warden of the execution of Caryl Chessman and throwing in the quotation that he had learned from Camus on capital punishment.

But he was pitilessly self-critical, and he saw (I saw) that what he was saying was incoherent hash. He was ashamed of the name-dropping. Thing was to be more cool. So he started across the campus in another direction and rehearsed it again, and this time he began by asking an insinuating question with a quiet leer: "What did Warden Howard Green think of the student body at State?" And then, the left-hook across, accompanied by an abortive gesture: "What did the Cop think about backhand-slapping my friend Earl and calling him a young punk?" Etcetera, whatever would follow. This had the advantage of establishing the right context, a gang vendetta. Thing was to use the dialect—"fuzz" walking on our "turf." This established the ground rules of conversation in one's own favor.

But using the dialect, the unhappy youth knew he must inevitably slip up and appear ridiculous before his internationalized Model Hipster. He was bound to miss the nuance. And in the meantime the students were angrily shouting at him, "Dry up! Sit down!"

The shouts rang around me in my lonely room, and impulsively I climbed out of bed and pulled up the Venetian blind. The campus was gray in the moonlit drizzle. The illuminated clock on the spire said 2:00 A.M. and Jimmy Dean was frantically striding across the black grass with his head sunk woefully into his depressed chest. Since he could not breathe in that posture, he must have been shivering, drenched. Stoned, I saw his pale face before my mind's eye.

The University hotel, where they had put us up, was absurd, endowed by the Stilton chain to give an M.A. in hotel management. It was used to try things on for size. The bathtub had black safety-stripes that scratched your ass like carborundum. When the bellhop carried up my bag, I did not know whether or not to tip him, since he was only doing his lessons. He took the quarter.

Jimmy Dean was eclipsed by the Memorial Library on whose forehead, incised in stone, were MONTAIGNE SHAKESPEARE CERVANTES. I let the blind drop and went back to bed and to sleep.

## 4

For the next panel they had shuffled us around, though I was still with the Warden. The others were the sociologist who had written the brief for the Integration decision; the great houser who had been dropped by our governor and was now teaching at the Institute of Technology; and Harriet Young, again a friend of mine, the little fire-eater from the Harlem Settlements. In fact, we at this Conference were the star-spangled banner and I might well have been proud of being in the roster. Instead, I had already written us off.

Seduced, no doubt, by the academic surroundings, I now began to hear the voices pouring into the microphones as nothing but the styles of the modern Western world. The microphones were set up exactly as if we had not protested, and this time, naturally, we succumbed. Our fight was spent. The Warden covered my hand with his, in commiseration. (I think he was queer for me—for my type of spirit—but of course we were too old.)

The Negro sociologist was an upright Puritan. One could almost see on him the shining breastplate of Brewster or Bradford, and one could actually hear the mellifluous and law-abiding sexual tones that made it quite impossible to pay attention to his adequate second-rate remarks.—He wasn't any John Milton.—Historically, his righteousness was something like Dr. Blumberg's Pharisaism; but the Jew was more bitter and compassionate, more in contact with his own suffering, more able to tolerate it because he was more supported by community and learning.

During the sermon I had plenty of occasion, while my mind wandered, to look at the student's faces. Scarlet jacket was in the front row on the right, but he was now wearing a handsome chocolate velvet jumper that looked expensive and bespoke a loving mother. The tight black levis were the same.

Suddenly, startlingly, he interrupted the speaker, to point out that if Professor Wesley was going to use words like "delinquent behavior," we could kiss good-bye to talking about real youth, for it was the social context and not the behavior that made the acts delinquent. I flushed red. It was my style, but exactly. And what was remarkable about the imitation was that he had grasped the essence: that the interruption must be important, accurate, and needing to be said as soon as possible, otherwise it was rude.

At once Professor Ellis, who was the moderator, stood up to interrupt the interruption. "There will be plenty of time at the question period," he said. But the sociologist, with an affable wave of his hand to indicate that he was not offended, proceeded with his speech, using the words "delinquent behavior" just as he pleased, stupidly.

I was infinitely distressed. It did not seem to me that the boy was mocking me, because his remark was correct, and nothing comes from nothing. Yet it did not seem to me possible that anybody could introject another so completely, so quickly. My mind clouded over. I went into the past or the future, I don't know where. It was a couple of minutes before I returned, and by now the Warden was on his feet.

The Warden spoke like a Pragmatist, and I was more at home. Good, too; a composite of James and Mead, erotic, communal. I liked his warm touch, his brown face, his blue shirt, his gray moustache. He was more like a forest ranger than a cop!

Slyly I looked at Jimmy Dean, and he was again beginning to be in a panic of embarrassment because he was afraid of Professor Ellis. My heart sank. Again we had missed his proper time. What I should have done, what I should have done was get up, walk around the table, hold him in my arms and say, "Don't be afraid, kid; you spoke well, you made sense. Go on." For what was the decorum of this Conference to me? But instead I pushed back my microphone a couple of inches and wiped my brow.

And next I could hear my own voice speaking. I was not speaking it, but my habits were excellent. I was the Enlightenment —reasonable, outrageous, not without a certain persuasive passion for the reasonable. I hated my voice. I was so tired of making sense! But one cannot be superstitious or a fool if one isn't. And as often, I was offering a practical proposal: to include in the public housing a youth dormitory, a kind of primitive Youth House, where the adolescents could get away from their mothers and their hostility to the frequently changing stepfathers. Where they could lead their own sex lives with freedom. In a trance of the eighteenth century, I heard myself developing the anthropology of the Happy Primitive. I was appalled at my idiocy. I sat down trembling.

In this crisis, the homey and familiar voice of little Harriet saved my life. She was a Quaker—out of Earlham College, by William Biddle—and as she spoke I could read off the description in the catalogue: "Underlying all that Earlham tries to do is the vision of wholeness—both worship and work, both discipline and freedom, respect for the individual and concern for the group. This vision Earlham does not wholly achieve, but there are many among her sons and daughters who strive for it, and at least they know when they have failed because they have a standard by which to judge." And there she was, failing, but with her eyes flashing. She half turned to me, to quote something I had just said, and I had an odd experience: I understood for the first time since I read the words at age fourteen, the relation between Enlightenment and *Illuminatio*. For years it had vaguely disturbed me. Harriet was an *illuminata*, and she assumed, of course, since we both had common sense, that I was too.

Our last speaker, the great houser, was hard to place. He began with the joke, the inside anecdote, of reformist political power, Gladstone, Woodrow Wilson, the New Deal. I could see that many of the students were deeply impressed to hear our message from professional authority, and I prepared to tune out. But how was it, then, that his message was not the law of the land? Why was he politically in such hot water? What took place at that unpublicized meeting at the White House that concluded in his resigning in disgust? Suddenly I began to hear the scornful overtones, throwing caution to the winds, exposing himself naked, the fatal disposition to end up with his head, like Münzer, on the block. Aha, he was an Anabaptist! From time to time there was a little nervous laughter, from those—the teachers—who caught the bearings of what he was saying. By the time he sat down, everybody was uneasy.

We had left plenty of time for questions! A dozen hands shot up.

5

To my surprise, Jimmy Dean was one of the first volunteers. This was not cool of him, to ask for the floor so soon. But he was not able to control himself. His outstretched arm was white out of his rich chocolate blouse.

Professor Ellis said, "Yes, Terry, now you can have your turn."

For ten long seconds, that must have seemed to him like long minutes, he could not get out a word. The attack when it came—I had miscalculated—was not against the Warden but against me. "*You!*" He nodded his head at me to bear the brunt of his respectful inquiry. "Explain how you sit there holding hands and playing footsie with that cop. That's my question. Let me expand it. I can respect him. He comes on like a psychologist, but in the showdown he will act like a cop, so we know where we're at. Last night he tells us how he conned a cat out of his castration complex to make him less of a pain in the ass to IBM. No sweat! He's an artist, I salute him!"—and he sketched a snotty Nazi salute at the Warden. "But what are *you* doing? Here you give us something about balling with jailbait in a Youth House. See? Fuzz. Jailbate. Fuzz. Dig?"

All this was delivered in a throaty intense tone that we could just about hear—he was not giving us the time of day; and only two or three rows back the students began to call, "Louder!" "We can't hear you, Terry!" "Give him the mike!" "Dry up, Terry!" I had the impression that he meant to talk in a more haphazard style, which would have been more narcissistic and insulting, but he was betrayed by the syntax and the logical structure of an intelligent middle-class home. I took it that the Nazi-salute bit came from Norman Mailer. I prepared to answer.

"*Louder!*" they sang at me before I said a word.

"The young man," I said in a loud voice, "wants to ask a question of me. He objects to my playing footsie with Warden Green whom, however, he respects as an authentic cop, although a phony psychologist. But I, he claims, am phony through and through because I talk like an outlaw as a conversation piece. Is that your point, young man?"

It certainly was his point, and yet this résumé entirely missed the point. For his point was that we were an in-group and he was excluded; it was that we had "made" it, and he, in a losing battle with his accumulating woes, was never going to make it; it was, most fatally, that we, whom he looked to, were impotent to accomplish anything, and this threw him into such a panic of insecurity that he defected to the enemy, to any enemy, whether the cops or the robbers. But these things he could not articulate; he knew them too vaguely. The result was that he could not shut up, for he had not really said his say. And so he got up again and launched, now in a loud, leering, and monotonous voice, on his phonograph record. We had to hear about Caryl Chessman and listen to the quotation from Camus. To the Town-Gown fight that neither the dean nor the police could handle, but he, Terry, brought about a truce. Next, by an inner logic, he was bitterly extolling the pimp who peddled him marijuana, although this was certainly an imprudent confession in front of Professor Ellis. Evidently he had to blurt it out to prove his authenticity, as a man tries to demonstrate that he has a sense of humor.

To me all this was new and boring on even the first hearing. It was delivered with an interminable incoherence in a mechanical groove. Pretty soon I had had it and I held out my palm.

"Shut up, Terry," I said. "Let me answer your question."

He sat down. I don't know if he listened.

"My guess is you don't want an answer. Once you turn on that phonograph record, you already have it all figured out. But let me tell you this. The men and women invited to this conference—" and I proceeded to launch on *my* phonograph record, though newly minted only the night before. "There are 180 million people in this country, and we a hundred, we a hundred and fifty, are wearing out our eyes and our hearts trying to do something for it, for you. *And* we expect we aren't going to succeed, but we do it anyway. What do you think about that?"

Unfortunately I spoke this in an earnest and ringing voice that evoked a thunder of handclapping. I was shocked. I had not meant to win a victory. What I had said was honest enough, but so irrelevant as to be almost a lie. For as the case was, nothing was relevant at that moment but to come across and take care of that youth's sick body and soul, preferably beginning with the Infirmary. What was the use of defending against attack? I pointedly cut into the applause. "Look, Terry," I said appealingly, and he did look up.

"Please," said Professor Ellis, rising.

"One moment, Professor. I have not done the young man justice. You're a lousy hipster, Terry, because you don't get anything out of this for yourself. Supposing you're right and you publicly expose us for a lot of crooks and morons. You win the satisfaction of a spiteful victory. Big deal. Wouldn't it be more useful to mourn, because we are no good to you?"

This was fantastic. How to convey to a young person that it is useful to mourn? How can he afford to hear that?

"May I explain something to the young man?" said the Warden, "since I am responsible for the execution of Caryl Chessman. Let me describe my professional activity. It consists in putting on different hats. When the doctor comes and wants a report, I explain what the patient is complaining about. When the boy is in my office, I explain to him what the magistrate thinks the magistrate is doing. When the legislator shows up, I outline what the poor tenant is too speechless to say. I'm what they call an administrator. I'm by no means convinced that this process of communication, as we call it, has any value whatever. But it's the best I know."

Terry courteously waited until the Warden had finished speaking, and then he got up and went rapidly up the aisle and out.

6

I called at the Infirmary and inquired about him. They assured me that they were treating him, or trying to. But when he was supposed to rest, he entered the handball tournament and wore his hands bloody. He missed two meals a day. There was no doubt that he was using marijuana. He couldn't hand in a finished assignment in class, though he worked hard in the library and took pages of notes. In brief, they were going to have to give him a leave of absence, till he got himself in better shape.

"Till he got *himself* in better shape—" I echoed. I wondered what clear and distinct idea was expressed by that form of words. But I said, "How will the other students take his being dropped?"

"The other students?"—Evidently it did not occur to them that there was a community of students.

"Won't they object?"

"You are misinformed," the counselor told me. "He's unpopular with most of the students. They won't miss him."

I doubted it. It was next to impossible not to put up with Terry. But I said, "Thank you," and went to have dinner with Irving, as apart from the rest as could be.

Irving was, as always, cheerful, though not about any foreseeable future.

I asked him for his formula. "How do you keep pitching, Irving, given what you know? You say, Stop! What you're doing is a catastrophe! And you even point out another direction. You see them continue just as before, only worse."

"It won't be in our time!" said Irving cheerfully. "Less than a hundred years ago small children were working in factories fifteen hours a day. There was no workmen's compensation for injuries. Trade unions were illegal. The Socialist platform for 1912 asked for women's suffrage, the forty-four hour week, the conservation of natural resources."

Irving was useful to me at a conference like this, when he touched my arm and cautioned me to bite on my pipe. He said that I was more effective when I kept my temper and behaved like a teacher, which I was, rather than a prophet, which I wasn't.

7

For three days we fifteen conferred and quarreled, framing a body of sentences that we could agree to and publish. It came out that there was only one thing that we knew, but we did know it, and it was this: All these problems—suburban flight and urban housing, narcotics and narcotics laws (as usual the laws were more a problem than the delinquencies), lifeless jobs and a phony standard of living, traffic congestion and bad schools and segregation and the lapse of citizenly initiative—all these were only properties of the kind of community that we had. We came back to the same point. It was a peculiar experience to re-create that community out of statistics and personal frustrations, hour after hour for three days.

And the city sprang alive around us. As when the pigeons in their hundreds suddenly fly down from the eaves. Recollected, but not in tranquillity as in a poem, but in quarreling. Among friends.

8

On Thursday night, seated before the University at a very long table, we knew that we had come to a terrible Conference. We were like the Estates-General with their *cahiers* on the eve of the French Revolution. Every expert among us was convinced that, in his own department, the system of our society was unviable, it did not work, it could not last. And here we came together and it added up: *all* of it did not work, it could not last. This was terrifying. Yet not one person among us believed that we must be on the verge of a mighty revolution. There were no signs of it. Where was the impulse of fraternity that must sweep across the country (if only for a day) on the Fourth of August? and there would be dancing in the streets. Where were the people with their cannon trained on our chamber, demanding a solution of every problem before they would let us rise?

The students and the younger teachers had been conferring too, and they asked us some hard questions that we could not answer. Nevertheless, they bore with us patiently while we floundered. The probability was very high that most of us in Clarence Kellogg Memorial Hall were going to be killed by the blast, fire, or radiation of atomic bombs. Was this the cannon turned on our deliberations?

Some of the young people kept threatening to destroy themselves, even before the bombs. But this kind of blackmail stopped thought; it did *not* invite it.

Terry—this time he was wearing a gray woolen sweater and ordinary loose-cut jeans—they must have been to him like sackcloth and ashes—was sitting in the fourth row. He was close enough to listen intently to what we said in our natural voices, undistorted by the electrical devices. It seemed that he himself did not intend to say anything. Perhaps he no longer felt like an outsider and was not looking for the weak chink in our armor in order to strike. (I did not realize that at supper he had been given notice of his suspension from the University.) But finally, modestly—somewhat awkwardly, for he was not used to modest gestures—he raised his hand.

"Yes, Terry," I recognized him at once, assuming that, of us fifteen, it was my special role to recognize Terry.

He stood up, but even before he could speak, somebody from the back called "Dry up!" He winced, but began anyway in his unvital murmur.

"Louder, Terry," suggested the Warden from the middle of the table.

"Louder? Louder than this?" he asked, his face contorted with pain. He tried, but really could not be heard any better.

"No, no," said Irving, from my side. "You only think you're speaking louder. You're not giving it any breath."

"Try throwing your voice *away*, Terry," suggested the Sociologist, in his trained baritone. "Awaayyy—" he sang, exhausting his breath to the diaphragm.

As for me, I was buzzing with pride of us, of our band, who, although public men, were able to attend to what really mattered. Breathing.

And Terry obediently took a breath and spoke out clear and normally loud, though his voice was drenched with anguish, the following question that he had carefully prepared: "If I—and I don't think I speak only for myself—if I can't make it in this school and have to leave—and this school is not much different from the rest of American society (maybe it's even better)—what do you advise me, us, to do? Is my question clear?"

"Yes, Terry," said the Warden, "it is quite clear. The communication is perfect."

"Would you like to take that one, Judge Watkins?" I called out to Amy at the far end of the table.

"Noooo," she said. "I think I'll let that one pass too."

"Are they dropping you from the University?" asked Dr. Blumberg, surprised. "That's too bad. You're a bright boy."

"Yes, sir," said Terry, and raised a laugh.

"By the way," I asked, a question I was afraid to ask, "how old *are* you, Terry?"

"Twenty," said Terry, and sat down. The unaccustomed breathing, the use of his normally loud voice, had felled him with a wave of vertigo.

His answer hit me in the solar plexus. It was worse than I had feared. This callow youth, so excellently endowed, was not a boy of fifteen as he looked. He knew so much, he had never learned anything.

Yet he *had* asked a good question. And we up front were wise enough to know we did not have a good answer. Perhaps this was a step in the right direction, though it was not exactly dancing in the streets. At least that was Percy Shelley's theory, "If Winter comes, can Spring be far behind?"

## 9

My following, my particular students, crowded around me, to take me downtown for a beer. But I was due at a reception for us at the President's House, a prospect of futility and boredom.

Terry hung on the fringe, pretending to himself that he was observing, but wistfully including himself.

"Let's go," said Shep. "I'd be honored if you come in my Chevy." I loved him, he had strong black hair.

I said, "No. I have to go to the President's reception."

"Oh, no! Not tonight!"

"But you're going away tomorrow, dear!" said the darling girl hanging on my arm. She was, ironically, the daughter of Dynaflow Bombers.

"Don't press me, kids. You know I'd rather go with you."

"Then why don't you?" Immediately I felt the accusing look of them all (I thought) because I was not choosing freely as they expected me to (I thought).

"It's polite; he has to," said the darling, coming to my rescue.

"No, that's not the reason," I said, and I kissed her on the brow and shook her off.

The reason, alas! which I could not tell them, was that in my calamitous picture of myself I had to be their bridge, between them and the World. I was theirs but I was irrevocably a grown-up. I would be their champion; I was not their accomplice. By assuming this thankless role I took the joy out of my life. To myself, my excuse was that thereby I had survived.

Biting his lip, Terry turned away up the aisle. He could not take comfort in his peers.

I pushed past them and called, "Terry!" He stopped. Irving and the Warden were waiting outside for me, to drive me. "Did you want to speak to me?"

"Yes, sir."

"My plane leaves at eleven. I'll meet you at the bookstore at eight-thirty and we can have a couple of hours."

Terry made a circle of approval with his thumb and the tip of his forefinger, like an ad for some beer or other; and this seemed to me so brainwashed, that I assumed he would not show. But he held the door for me politely enough.

## 10

It was only at our last breakfast, when we were taking down addresses and struggling with our bags, that we knew, wistfully, that it had been a beautiful Conference. When we were let down from our rational give-and-take, that came often to agreement—because we respected one another's honesty and wanted to satisfy his reservations—into the absurd mindlessness of the United States of America, the ignorant armies clashing by night. When we faced the bleak prospect of the unnecessary facts.

We clung to one another. We did not know the solution of most of the problems that we had discussed, but they were not such very difficult problems but that we could pretty quickly improve our cities. Except that, in the cold light of Friday morning, we were not going to. We did not have the power, and it was not power that was needed, but public concern, intelligence, willingness to *do* it. We spoke in warm tones and touched one another's bodies.

It was Howard Green who said, "It's been a beautiful Conference," and we could have broken down and wept. I noticed that the despair that was in the back of his eyes when I first met him was in the back of his eyes when I shook his hand good-bye.

Harriet, however, seemed to carry our dismay lightly. When she casually shook my hand—I would soon run across her in New York—she suddenly pressed it, and she said, in a voice that I never forgot, the words, "We shall prevail."

11

I stood around the bookstore for over an hour, but Terry did not show. . . .

## A PHYSICIST

1

"We have tended, as Terry there pointed out last week—" It was as if by accident that Terry had wandered into the Physics lecture. He had decided to flunk out of the University and he had decisively cut the lab section. But after that he had nothing scheduled—he still did not know how to waste the morning, too early for lunch with Joanna. He was again in his accustomed seat in the fourth row on the side, from where his arm used to shoot up when he had a bright idea. He lost what color he had. *Again* Professor Davidson was singling him out for special mention.

He knew that the honor was never quite serious. But the other students envied it and therefore he boasted about it, having so little real to give him confidence.

"We have tended," said Davidson, looking away from him, "to find new particles when we have new apparatus. J. J. Thomson, you remember, took a Crookes tube and redirected the beam, and so he analyzed out the charge and mass."

Terry *had* said it; it was the kind of "germane" idea that struck him. He was bitterly proud that he was again going to disappoint Professor Davidson and disappoint himself. He was distressed that he had come, but if he hadn't come he wouldn't have known this mention, bitterly to mention later.

"The last twenty years," continued the lecturer, "with random bombardment by the atom smashers, we have of course been getting a random proliferation of particles and antiparticles, antiprotons, hypermesons—"

Davidson was a good man as well as a great name. He was really at the University as headman of the research contracted by the University with the Air Force. At $25,000 and no classes to teach. But he felt that there was something indecent in these bogus faculties that did not teach. He had been taught. So he took over the Introductory and was telling them all about the particles. His elementary approach was not so much popular as historical rather than mathematical.

He belonged to the princely line. Thomson taught Rutherford taught Chadwick taught Davidson. He assumed it matter-of-factly, although it was a British line and he was an American Jew. He refused to change the spelling to "Davison." "Analyzed out" was strictly American. His own best was a young, already world-famous, Chinese.

When he singled out Terry, it was only partly as a lecturer's gimmick. He did not much go in for gimmicks; he preferred to hold up the subject in the space before them, and let it shine. But Terry puzzled and disturbed him. Being in a mathematical science, he was used to white faces and borderline-schizophrenic eyes, but he could not understand how this young man could grasp so much so quickly—and even intuitively, mathematically—and yet learn nothing at all. The report from the section leader was "hopeless."

"Good!" he went on. "There is an inventive virtue in the apparatus. We can envisage these men doing. Doing with hands and eyes—men—increasing the energy in the magnet, making a bigger whirlibang. But now let's look at the other side of the process. And that's the subject of my lecture today. Most of these particles, as some of you may know, were *theoretically* predicted long before they showed up—or were produced—whichever way you want to put it. We could not find them without the apparatus, but we did find them because we were looking for them. Take my teacher's neutron. Who remembers from last week what a neutron is? . . . No, not quite. Yes! That's exactly correct. I'm delighted you put in about the cloud chamber."

But Terry, as he sat there—his was not one of the hands that had shot up—no longer knew exactly about neutrons, though he had known. Reminded, he remembered about the cloud chamber, the absence of trace and charge, but he had forgotten it. He knew he had forgotten it. He no longer fooled himself as he had at Columbus. It was not "their" fault; it was somehow his own. His face was white. He loved Professor Davidson—he found it very easy to love. If it didn't require knowing the subject, he could gladly have devoted himself to a career in physics.

He was puzzled and disturbed by Professor Davidson. What was he doing up there? Nobody in this Introductory was going to be a physicist—so Terry had made up his mind for them—and yet Davidson, with obvious affection, and remarkable skill, was earnestly going through a song-and-dance. Why was he?

In spite of himself, Terry was fascinated by the orator of the Western world, the beautiful spirit. "So there it is, a neutron!" said Davidson, at the blackboard, underscoring an equation, his blue suit dusty with chalk. "Picture it! it was partly just on grounds of elegance and symmetry that we demanded, Produce it! It *must* be there! And within two years after the equation, the French *did* produce it!" His voice rang with pleasure at his teacher's triumph. "What are you thinking of now, big eyes?" he suddenly demanded, fourth row on the left. He was curious what that mind thought of *that!*

"Who? Me? Do you want to know what I'm thinking?" said Terry, snottily. "Sure. They're at each other like a gang of bops. The war counselors versus the hippies. Each is one-upping the next to prove he has a hard-on."

"I beg your pardon?" said Davidson, and the crowd cracked up.

"But you can't prove it!" cried Terry hysterically.

The bell rang.

At the bell Davidson had a blinding insight into what it was that disturbed and puzzled him with this generation of youth.

## 2

He caught up to Terry at the door.

"You don't mind my picking on you, do you, young man?" They emerged from Thayer Hall, past the marble Statue of *La Semeuse*, scattering her grain.

"No. The professors always do . . . the good ones," he said, not boasting, but confused.

"Do they? Why do they?"

"I don't know. I used to think it was because I was bright. . . . I'm flunking out again."

"You are bright, it goes without saying. I know you're flunking out. Do *you* know why?"

They walked across the big quadrangle, and past the verdigris statue of *Le Penseur*, with his back, as the joke went, to Philosophy Hall. The campus was crowding up. It was five to twelve.

"*I* know," said Professor Davidson.

Terry looked sidewise at him, with the whites in his eyes showing. He knew that he did know. All these fatherly grown-ups understood him. He said, "Is there something missing?" He almost meant, "Do you think I'm crazy?"

"No, it's not only you!" said Davidson hurriedly, apprehensive. Many of his colleagues *were* pretty crazy. "Tell me, Terry, tell me something. Why do you think the Old Man—or Rutherford or my teacher—*bothered?*" So asked Professor Davidson in the fourth generation. And in the past behind them all loomed, like the fabulous Emperor Chow, Clerk Maxwell. "Do you really think that those men were—what did you say?—hippies? one-upping? And—impotent?" He smiled at the idea and Terry's way of putting it.

Terry said nothing. He was beyond being combative.

"They were in love with her," said Professor Davidson. They walked along in silence. "They wanted to see her better, know her," he said.

It was, in the crowd, as if there were a silence on the campus. He was that sure.

"She favored them," he said.

At this, Terry would have burst into tears. He gave Professor Davidson one look and bolted in another direction. He was not yet ready to burst into tears. That would be later, for the asylum.

Davidson stood, and watched him go. He knew what was wrong, but he did not know how to cope with it. These young people simply did not understand what the enterprise was about. It was not their enterprise—he could not imagine why. They were never going to take it upon themselves. They might go through the University, but they were not going to commence. Some of them—technically the best, morally the worst—imagined that they could *master* the subject. Master it! With others—Terry, vanishing in the crowd—if they were visited by an idea, it was not because of the nature of things, but because of—interpersonal relations. Or to please Professor Davidson.

He felt dirty. Then he became angry at being imposed on.

3

In his haste to have it over with, Terry ran back to catch Professor O'Connor emerging from Philosophy, to tell him that, though he had tried, he could not write the assignment, and he was going to drop the course. He took a pride in himself for this manly statement. He no longer silently ran away, as he used. He watched his behavior like a fever chart and saw good and bad indications.

This professor too walked him across the campus, more and more crowded as the students poured out for lunch. The big bells began to boom noon.

O'Connor was saying: "Get out of this place, it's death. They'll put you in a mold like Jell-o. Like—heh heh—like cold shape, as my English colleagues say."

Terry looked at him sidewise, with narrow eyes, as they passed the black statue of *Le Marteleur*, leaning on his sledgehammer.

"This University is run like a bank!" exclaimed O'Connor with spiteful enthusiasm, demonstrating an unpalatable truth. "Figure it out. I wanted to give a little seminar on Hobbes, to six students. No, it wouldn't pay. The cash take on my afternoon lecture, at $40 a point, 88 students, is $10,560." He had spent the morning calculating. "Now deduct my salary, one-third of a twelve-hour load. . . . Who *gets* all that money? Young man, if you want my advice"—Terry had not asked for it—"escape! Escape while there's time! Go some place where there's sun! Go to Mexico! Travel! See for yourself! I take it that you want to be creative"—this assumption too was uncalled for; Terry would certainly not have put it that way—"then *be* creative! Why do you need lessons? *Make* those poems and stories and pictures, just as they rise up in *you!* Directly!" He jabbed the air with his exclamations. "You kids all say the same thing, you'll start working when you have the equipment. Take a tip from me, you won't get it here. *We*'ll see to that. We'll *kill* your confidence, as dead as we can. And we're stronger than you!" he concluded in triumph, stretching out his arms to embrace—everything.

"Why would you want to kill us, Professor O'Connor?" asked Terry.

"Are you kidding?" said the professor, looking at him in surprise. "Didn't you ever hear of resentment? What do you think that Nietzsche and Scheler are about? Take Scheler—heh heh—Scheler couldn't get a job because he happened to like to screw. The great Husserl—Scheler applied at Marburg—Herr Professor Husserl said, *Nein! niemals Scheler!* So poor Scheler didn't have a job. Did you know that?"

Abruptly Terry left him, and wandered off.

He wandered off, around the gilded seated statue of *Alma Mater,* spreading her offering hands. He had been biting his lips to keep from expressing his contempt. He was glad he had not spoken. What bullshit! If a young man could write down directly those poems, etc., that were apparently teeming in his mind, did Associate Professor O'Connor really think that he wouldn't be able to write a little class assignment on the relation of Husserl and Descartes when he had actually read the two books? A mind strong enough to educate itself would be able to put up even with the University. He'd quit, he wouldn't flunk out. So far as Terry knew, O'Connor had never asked any student a personal question. (Yet there *were* eighty-eight in the class!)

What Terry most resented was that the whole gripe came out of *The New Yorker* magazine. He resented being exploited as a coward's vicarious rebel, age ten, beaten at fourteen, like the adolescent in *The Catcher in the Rye.*

He found himself alone, in a small red-paved quadrangle with a grassy border. From here the lunch-bound crowd had vanished. There was no symbolic statue. Terry himself was standing there—he was self-conscious—like a symbolic statue.

And to his wonder, he was engulfed by an academic nostalgia, a yearning for his fellows, for his fellow students at the University. It expressed itself as another daydream in the biography of Terry. Terry was going, as the champion and ambassador of the students, to the offices of professors, of deans, to plead for the Community of Scholars (which he had also picked up from Goodman). Maybe, after all, people did not understand one another and all really had a common aim. Nobody spoke up. Why not he? He came to the Dean with a proposal to abolish grading. The

Dean looked up at him and asked, "What are *your* grades, Mr. Terry? By what warrant are *you* in the University? Are you part of our Community?" asked the Dean.

In his daydream he flinched, and the depression of the young men of the United States, of England, of the Soviet Union, crept into his breast—

With a start Terry awoke, and looked about at the big unimpressive Georgian buildings surrounding him in the square, of the great University of the greatest city in the Western world, that stood for not much.

And he went back again—this time running—across the quadrangles. Toward the Laboratory, for Professor Davidson had been heading in that direction.

4

He caught him in his lab with the goods, actually putting on his leaden gloves, about to close the door.

Davidson was not annoyed to be interrupted by the breathless young man who called his name. He had plenty of confidence that She would always be there waiting for him to resume their dialogue. He did not think that Teaching interfered with Research.

Terry was pink with indignation, the first time that Davidson had seen any color in his face. "Twenty million of the annual budget," Terry gasped, "comes from government contracts, and most of that—*you* know—is from the National Defense!"

Davidson looked at him blankly.

"That's 40 percent of the running expenses of the University," said Terry.

"Is it really?" asked the professor ingenuously. Forty percent was surprisingly high. "Where'd you get those figures?"

"President's Annual Report, 1961," said Terry, accurate and documented.

"Hm. I shouldn't have thought—that's a big slice of the pie, isn't it, for an academic institution?" Suddenly the implication of Terry's "*you* know" struck him, and he reddened with anger. He was annoyed at the boy's effrontery. He was also a little sad, and disappointed, that Terry had such thoughts of him. "I'm busy," he said roughly. "What do you want?"

Quick as a flash, Terry chose a gambit. "What are the gloves for?" he asked.

Davidson tightened his lips, but he was big enough not simply to dismiss him. Indeed, he did not think that Terry believed that he was there for money or that his research was oriented by a business contract. Nobody was that stupid. But what disappointed him was that Terry, particularly Terry, should need to make such a spiteful attack, and at such a level, just because he could not learn physics. He was always saddened by vindictiveness, yet he understood it—he understood kids—they had to win victories, to retain a little dignity. Yet it was tiresome. He had thought that the boy and he had made a personal contact.

"The gloves?" he said. "Oh, I always put them on because they're stylish on TV. Do you have any other problems?"

"Is the radiation dangerous?" asked Terry.

—Was the boy a moron? "Look," he said, "don't bother me. You're a moron. I have office hours on Thursdays at four, but don't come unless you have a question." This was too harsh. "It doesn't need to be about subatomic particles," he added kindly. What *was* it in Terry's eyes? Was the boy *concerned* for him?

Suddenly the situation had become, inexplicably, extraordinary. Terry was standing there in front of him and suddenly, inexplicably, he thought of the last time that he had seen Niels Bohr. But Terry didn't look anything like Niels Bohr.

"Do you mean I should go away?" said Terry with suppressed fury, but his eyes were blazing with appeal.

What did the boy want to say? Terry was looking at him with doglike respect. He certainly was not accusing him of venality or timeserving. Yet he was accusing him of something. Why the twenty millions? Forty percent *was* a surprising figure; he should have known it. And why the gambit—Davidson understood that it was only a boring gambit—of the gloves?

The physicist felt sick. He was swept by a wave of nausea. For a moment he panicked. Had he been careful in bombarding the lithium? He gripped onto the bench.

Why was human communication so unbelievably confusing, almost as bad as the proliferation of the mesons? In dismay he had seen, year by year, almost month by month, the theory degenerating into a chaos of *ad hoc* explanations that could not possibly be Nature.

Astoundingly young Terry said in a pathetic voice, "Don't you know that you are like a father to them?"

"What is it, young man? What do you want from me?" wailed Professor Davidson, the present heir of J. J. Thomson. He needed to spell everything out, to have it spelled out, simple and clear. "You *don't* think, do you, that I am working on this problem because Washington, D.C., pays me to?" He was ashamed of his question, and he said, "I'm ashamed to ask you such a question. I know you don't."

"I! You!" cried Terry, too amazed to be offended. "Don't you feel well, Professor?" he said with concern, for the man did not look well. His admiration for the great man began to mount so strongly that he was afraid that he would become speechless and not be able to make the direct appeal that he had come for. (He wished, wistfully, that he himself could learn physics.) He was ashamed of his bit and returned to his own skin. And when Terry was alive in the world, and was not cowering or playing roles, he had no passions in his soul so strong as indignation and admiration; and now both these welled up, conflicting and yet reinforcing each other, and he became a very beautiful youth. He had the persuasive force of the future of mankind. It is what moves serious people.

Davidson was a seasoned veteran and quickly recovered from his panic. "Like a father? I see," he said quietly, and even cheerfully, for it was interesting. "Here I have been disappointed in *you* young people, and all the while, it seems, you have had cause to be disappointed in *me*. What can that be? Explain. Sit down. Come into my office." He took off the gloves.

"Not especially in *you*, Professor Davidson—"

"Ah. You mean, in my generation. The mess we have made of the world, and all this?"

"No, sir. I think it's more specific than that."

Davidson sat on his desk and looked at him candidly.

"We are disappointed in science," said Terry.

"Aha! In science," said Davidson.

"If you would stop the war—refuse—all of you from Pugwash, Russians and Americans—it would have a tremendous influence. The students—my fellow students—" He faltered and paused because he was flunking out.

"Go on, Terry, say it."

"They'd be—" He was abashed at the thing that he was going to say. "If the whole Physics Department—"

"The whole Physics Department!" roared Davidson merrily. "Where do you think that is?"

"If the whole Physics Department would take a stand," said Terry, "the students would be very proud of the University!" He paused—and blushed. "Can I be frank?"

Davidson averted his eyes. He was afraid of what the young man was now going to say.

"Last week when you stood there in front of us, joking about the lies of the Civil Defense, smirking and making wise cracks like a junior clerk or a griping sailor—Professor Davidson!—"

For the man started and, to Terry's dismay, blushed a deep scarlet for shame. And he remembered it, the blazing gloomy look of Uncle Niels when they gave him the Peace prize. For a moment he was badly shaken.

His agitation left Terry without support. Automatically the youth tried to retreat into his own callow defenses, except that, precisely when confronted with a boyish shame that responded to his own boyish shame, he could not retreat. So the two were, for a brief spell, in scalding pain, wishing that the earth would open and swallow them up, each by himself, but they were chained together, as they were going to be on another day. Terry cursed the inspiration that had occurred to him in the small quadrangle, to serve as an ambassador for his fellow students. What he had not counted on, in his daydream, was that his intervention would meet a response. He had not believed that the professors were men. He had simply wanted to spite them, by holding up the mirror to their ugliness, because they were powerful. Now he had to take the consequence of human contact. How could it be pleasant in our times?

Again the veteran recovered first. "You've got a point," he said. "I'd have to think about that." He looked at the youth frankly and somewhat humorously. "Thank you, Terry." He held out his hand. "Don't drop the course. You get more out of it than you think. You enjoy the play of mind—better than a movie."

Terry was afraid to take his hand—took it out of politeness—because their touch might be unbearably sensitive. But it was not so bad. Their palms were hot and dry.

"Forget that idea about the whole Physics Department," said Davidson. "There is no Faculty in this factory. Put it this way.

Suppose that among the students you appealed to all the—what do you call them?—*majors* in Physics, the ones who are waiting for Bell and Westinghouse to tap them, the ones who are primed for General Dynamics—"

And because they were his fellows, Terry hung his head.

"Do you happen to know what in fact I am working on these days?"

"Of course," said Terry surprisingly. "You think that something is wrong with the method. You don't like the smashers, but it's deeper than the smashers. Something *must* be wrong, because there are too many particles. It doesn't add up. That's right, isn't it? Naturally you can't *say* this till you've got hold of something, but you're a lousy actor."

"You listen close," said the Professor. "There must be *something* you could learn, son."

By the time he was sitting at the lunch counter with Joanna, he was nearly delirious.

Under the intense bombardment, the particles were flying off in all directions.

The students ate at the counter like pigs at a trough. They jostled his elbow and his coffee was spilling in the saucer.

He envied Joanna. *She* had the philosophy assignment to hand in. What she did was thoughtful and honest, not phony. He did not want to belittle it. He had no right to belittle it.

She had an inner check that enabled her to walk out on the party when she had work to do.

But he was bitterly resentful that she had gone home to her parents over the weekend, and left him to his fate. She did not see that he was taking too much pot. Why didn't she see?

His doughnut was on the floor. He looked at it. She looked at him.

She was in a dilemma. She needed him to be wild and exciting, but if he flunked out again he was going to fall to pieces. He said that he was going to go away to Poland among the communists or to Ghana among the Negroes.

He could not, he would not, tell her about the conversation he had just had with Davidson. Because it was real. He resentfully withheld it, just as he lost his hard-on. Inevitably he was beginning to forget that conversation, like something he had dreamed.

His coffee kept spilling in the saucer because of his own shaking hand. He could not even turn surlily and say, "Watch where you're shoving."

Some One had robbed him of his alibi.

With humility he realized that he was an outlaw not because it was admirable, or good for him, but because he couldn't manage otherwise, just in order to survive. He bent his head.

She took his hand on the counter. She moved against him closer. She was terrified of her lust. Clinging to Terry would be her ruin. But she did not see about her any other young man who was worthwhile.

## JOHN BARTH

*believes the world to be absurd. Accordingly, he attempts to create meaning where there is none, to rearrange history to make it more interesting than the pointless list of facts which supposedly tell us who we are and where we have come from. The selection below is from* Giles Goat-Boy, *a novel in which Barth rewrites the history of the cold war as seen through the life and times of the Goat-Boy, who is a product of the mating of a computer and a woman. The world is seen as divided between two campuses, East and West, which are alternately plagued by various riots. As educational institutions are products and reflections of the society out of which they grow, so too does Barth's metaphor become apparent, and educational problems become a microcosm of the larger community.*

*From*

# GILES GOAT-BOY

He resumed his narrative, shaking his head and fingering his beard ruefully as he spoke. Twenty years ago, he said, a cruel herd of men called Bonifacists, in Siegfrieder College, had attacked the neighboring quads. The Siegfrieders were joined by certain other institutions, and soon every college in the University was involved in the Second Campus Riot. Untold numbers perished on both sides; the populous Moishian community in Siegfried was destroyed. Max himself, born and educated in those famous halls where science, philosophy, and music had flowered in happier semesters, barely escaped with his life to New Tammany College, and though he was by temperament opposed to riot, he'd put his mathematical genius at the service of his new alma mater. He it was who first proposed, in a now-famous memorandum to Chancellor Hector, that WESCAC—which had already assumed control of important non-military operations in the West-Campus colleges—had a destructive potential unlike anything thitherto imagined.

"Oy, Bill, this WESCAC!" he said now with much emotion. "What a creature it is! I didn't make it; nobody did—it's as old as the mind, and you just as well could say it made itself. Its power is the same that keeps the campus going—I don't explain it now, but that's what it is. And the force it gives out with—yi, Bill, it's the first energy of the University: the Mind-force, that we couldn't live a minute without! The thing that tells you there's a *you*, that's different from *me*, and separates the goats from the sheeps . . . Like the life-heat, that it means we aren't dead, but our own house is the fuel of it, and we burn ourselves up to keep warm . . . Ay, ay, Bill!"

So! Well! Max caught hold of his agitation and went on with the tale of WESCAC—which history, owing to my ignorance and my impatience to learn its relevance to myself, I but imperfectly grasped. The beast I gathered had existed as it were in spirit among men from the very founding of the University, especially in West Campus. Only in the last century or so had it acquired a body of the simplest sort—whether flesh and blood or other material I could not quite tell. It was put at first to the simplest tasks: doing sums and verifying certain types of answers. Thereafter, as studentdom's confidence in it grew, so also did its size, complexity, and power; it underwent a series of metamorphoses, like an insect or growing fetus, demanding ever more nourishment and exerting more influence, until in the years just prior to my own birth it cut the last cords to its progenitors and commenced a life of its own. It was not clear to me whether a number of little creatures had merged into one enormous one, for example, or whether like Brickett Ranunculus WESCAC one day had outgrown its docility, kicked over the traces, and turned on its keepers. Nothing about the beast seemed unambiguous; I could imagine it at all only by reference to my own equivocal nature, that had got beyond its own comprehension and injured where it meant to aid. The whole of New Tammany College, I took it, if not the entire campus, had gradually come under WESCAC's hegemony, voluntarily or otherwise: it anticipated its own needs and saw to it they were satisfied; it set its own problems and solved them. It governed every phase of student life, deciding who should marry whom, how many children they should bear, and how they should be reared; itself it taught them, as it saw fit, graded their performance and assigned them lifeworks somewhere in its vast demesne. So wiser grew it than its masters, and more efficient at every task, they had ordered it at some fateful juncture thenceforth to order them, and the keepers became the kept. It was as if, Max said, the Founder Himself should appear to one and declare, "You are to do such-and-so"; one was free in theory to do otherwise, but in fact none but a madman would, in those circumstances. Even the question whether one did right to let WESCAC thus rule him, only WESCAC could reasonably be asked. It was at once the life and death of studentdom: its food was the entire wealth of the college, the whole larder of accumulated lore; in return it disgorged masses of new matter—more, alas, than its subjects ever could digest . . . and so these in turn, like the cud of a cow, became its further nourishment.

As late as Campus Riot II, however, there remained a few men like Max for whom the creature was, if no longer their servant, at least not yet entirely their master, and upon whom it seemed to depend like a giant young brother for the completion of its growth. It was they, under Max's directorship, who taught WESCAC how to EAT . . .

"Imagine a big young buck," Max said: he's got wonderful muscles, and he knows he could jump the fence and kill your enemies if he just knew how. Not only that: he knows who could teach him! So he finds his keeper and says he needs certain lessons. Then he can jump out of his pen to charge anybody he wants to, you see? Including his teacher . . ."

WESCAC's former handlers, it appeared, had already taught it considerable *resourcefulness,* and elements of the college military—the New Tammany ROTC—had long since instructed it to advise them how they might best defend it (and its bailiwick) against all adversaries. Under the pretext therefore of developing a more efficient means of communicating with its extremities, the creature disclosed one day to Max Spielman that a certain sort of energy given off during its normal activity—what Max called "brainwaves"—was theoretically capable of being intensified almost limitlessly, at the same amplitudes and frequencies as human "brainwaves," like a searchlight over tremendous spaces. The military-science application was obvious: in great secret the brute and its handlers perfected a technique they called Electroencephalic Amplification and Transmission—"The better," Professor-General Hector had warned the Bonifacists, "to EAT you with."

"It was an awful race we were in," Max said unhappily. "The WESCAC doesn't just live in NTC, you know: there's some WESCAC in the head of every student that ever was. We had to work fast, and we made two grand mistakes right in the start; we taught it how to teach itself and get smarter without our help, and we showed it how to make its own *policy* out of its knowledge. After that the WESCAC went its own way, and it wasn't till a while we realized a dreadful thing: not one of us could tell for sure any more that its interests were the same as ours!

"So. We were winning the Riot by that time, but it was left yet to make *kaput* the Siegfrieders and their colleagues the Amaterasus, and we knew we'd lose thousands of students before we were done. Then we found out a thing we were already afraid of:

that the Bonifacists were working on an EAT-project of their own. It was their only chance to win the Riot: if we didn't end things in a hurry they'd be sure to EAT us, because all WESCAC wanted was to learn the trick, never mind who taught it or who got killed. We won the race . . ."

I commenced to fidgit. Intriguing though it was, Max's account had no bearing that I could discern upon my pressing interests. But my keeper's face now was altogether rapt with a pained excitement.

"One morning just before daylight we pointed two of WESCAC's antennas at a certain quadrangle in Amaterasu College. There was only a handful of us, in a basement room in Tower Hall. Maurice Stoker turned on the power—he's the new chancellor's half-brother, and I curse him to this day. Eblis Eierkopf set the wavelength: he was just a youngster then, a Siegfrieder himself, that didn't care which side he worked for as long as he could have the best laboratories. I curse him. And I curse Chementinski, the Nikolayan that focused the signal. All was left was the worst thing of all: to turn on the amplifiers and press the *EAT*-button. Not a right-thinking mind in the whole wide campus but curses the hand that pushed that button!" Max's eyes flashed tears; he spread before my face the thumb and three fingers of his right hand. "The Director's hand, Billy; I curse it too! Max Spielman pushed that button!"

Whereupon (he declared after a moment, with dry dispassion) thousands of Amaterasus—men, women, and children—had been instantly EATen alive: which was to say, they suffered "mental burn-out" in varying degrees, like overloaded fuses. For those at the center of the quad, instant death; for the next nearest, complete catalepsy. In the first rings of classrooms, disintegration of personality, loss of identity, and inability to choose, act, or move except on impulse. Throughout the several rings of dormitories beyond the classrooms, madness of various types: suicidal despair, hysteria, vertiginous self-consciousness. And about the periphery of the signal, impotency, nervous collapse, and more or less severe neuroses. All of the damage was functional and therefore "permanent"—terminable, that is, only by the death of the victim, which in thousands of cases followed soon after.

"Think of a college suddenly filled with madmen!" Max cried. "Everybody busy at their work, but all gone mad in the same instant!" Bus-drivers, he declared, had smashed their vehicles into buildings and gibbering pedestrians; infirmary-surgeons had knifed their patients, construction-workers had walked casually off high scaffoldings. The murder and suicide rates shot up a thousandfold, as did the incidence of accidental death. Untended boilers exploded; fires broke out everywhere, while student firemen sat paralyzed in their places or madly wandered the streets, and undergraduates thronged into blazing classrooms, shops, and theaters as if nothing were amiss. Few were capable of eating meals; even fewer of preparing them. Many lost control of bladder and bowels; most neglected common health measures entirely; the few who turned pathologically fastidious washed their faces day and night while perhaps urinating in their wash-water; none was competent to manage the apparatus of public health, minister to the sick, or bury the dead. In consequence, diseases soon raged terribly as the fire. Before rescue forces from other quadrangles brought the situation into hand, a third of the buildings in the target area were more or less destroyed (including an irreplaceable collection of seventeen hundred illustrated manuscripts from the pre-Kamakura period), half at least of the students and faculty were dead or dying, and all but a handful were fit only for custodial asylums. Within the week both Amaterasu and Siegfrieder Colleges had surrendered unconditionally, and the Second Campus Riot was ended.

"But the damage!" Max said woefully. "The damage isn't done yet. Five years ago was the last time I read a newspaper—that was ten years since I pushed the button. There was a story in it about one of the Amaterasus that survived, and everybody thought he was well, till one day he runs wild on his motorbike and kills four little schoolgirls. And the kids themselves, that was born from the survivors: two percent are idiots; one out of three is retarded, and they all got things like enuresis and nightmares. How many generations it will go on, nobody knows." He struck his forehead with his fist. "That's what it means to be EATen, Billy! The goats, now: they'll eat almost anything you feed them; but only us humans is smart enough to EAT one another!"

Full of wonder, I shook my head. The idea of madness was not easy for me to appreciate: I had for examples only the booksweep himself and the character of Carpo the Fool from *Tales of the Trustees*, both of whom appeared more formidable than pathetic. I asked whether George the booksweep had been among the victims of this first attack. My motive was not primarily to learn more about the terrors of WESCAC, but if possible to lead Max discreetly towards the matter he'd first essayed; and I was so far successful, that he left off fisting his brow and wound up his history:

"Yes, well, it wasn't the Riot George was hurt in, but the peace." He explained that terrible as the two Campus Riots had been, they were in one sense almost trifling, the result not of basic contradictions between the belligerents but of old-fashioned collegiate pride (what he called *militant alma-materism*) and unfavorable balances in the informational economy between Siegfried, for example, and its fellow West-Campus colleges. All the while, however, as it were in the background of the two riots, a farther-reaching conflict had developed: a contradiction of first principles that cut across college boundaries and touched upon all the departments of campus life—not only economics and political science, but philosophy, literature, pedagogy; even agriculture and religion.

"What I mean," he said soberly, "is Student-Unionism versus Informationalism. You'll learn about it as you go along: it's the biggest varsity fact the campus has got to live with these days, and nobody can explain it all at once." For the present I had to content myself with understanding that many semesters ago, in what history professors called the Rematriculation Period, the old West-Campus faith in such things as an all-powerful Founder and a Final Examination that sent one forever to Commencement Gate or the Dean o' Flunks had declined (even as Chickie's lover had declared in the pasture) from an intellectual force to a kind of decorous folk-belief. Students still crowded once a week into Founder's Hall to petition an invisible "Examiner" for leniency; schoolchildren still were taught the moral principles of Moishe's Code and the Seminar-on-the-Hill; but in practice only the superstitious really felt any more that the beliefs *they* ran their lives by had any ultimate validity. The new evidence of the sciences was most disturbing: there had been, it appeared, no Foundation-Day: the University had always existed; men's acts, which had been thought to be freely willed and thus responsible, seemed instead to spring in large measure from dark urgings, unreasoning and always guileful; moral principles were regarded by the Psychology Department as symptoms on the order of dreams, by the Anthropology Department as historical relics on the order of potsherds, by the Philosophy Department variously as cadavers for logical dissection or necessary absurdities. The result (especially for thoughtful students) was confusion, anxiety, frustration, despair, and a fitful search for something to fill the moral vacuum in their quads. Thus the proliferation of new religions, secular and otherwise, in the last half-dozen generations: the Pre-Schoolers, with their decadent primitivism and their morbid regard for emotion, dark fancy, and deep sleep; the Curricularists, with their pedagogic nostrums and naïve faith in "the infinite educability of studentdom"; the Evolutionaries; the quasi-mystical Ismists; the neo-Enochians with their tender-minded retreat to the old fraternities—emasculated, however, into aestheticism and intellectual myth-worship; the Bonifacists, frantically sublimating their libidos to the administrative level and revering their *Kanzler* as if he were a founder; the Secular-studentists (called by their detractors Mid-Percentile or Bourgeois-Liberal Baccalaureates) for whom Max himself declared affinity, with their dogged trust in the self-sufficiency of student reason; the Ethical Quadranglists, who subscribed to a doctrine of absolute relativity; the Sexual Programmatists, the Tragicists and New Quixotics, the "Angry Young Freshmen," the "Beist Generation," and all the rest.

Among these new beliefs, Max said, was Student-Unionism, a political-religious philosophy that flowered among the lowest percentiles after the Informational Revolution. As men had turned from post-graduate dreams to the things of this campus, they set off the great explosion of knowledge that still reverberated in our time. Students rose against masters, masters against chairmen; departments banded together into the college-units we know today, drawing their strength from heavy engineering and applied-science laboratories and vast reference libraries. But the "Petty Informationalists" were as lawless in their way as the old department heads had been, and on a far grander scale: where before an occasional sizar had been flogged, or a co-ed ravished by the *droit de Fauteuil*, now thousands and millions of the ignorant were exploited by the learned. Mere kindergarteners were sent down into the Coal-Research diggings; pregnant sophomore girls toiled in sweat-labs and rat-infested carrels. Such were the abuses that drove the Pre-Schoolist poets to cry, "The Campus is realer than the Classroom!" while their counterparts in Philosophy asserted that all the ills of studentdom were effects of formal education. But however productive of great art, the Pre-Schoolist philosophy offered little consolation—and no hope—to the masses of illiterates in their sooty dorms and squalid auditoriums. These it was who commenced to turn, in desperation, to the *Confraternité Administratif des Etudiants*, from beneath whose scarlet pennant a new Grand Tutor, fierce-bearded and sour of visage, cried: "Students of the quads, unite!"

The Student-Unionist Prospectus (Max went on) was not in itself inimical to the spirit of the "Open College" or "Free Research" way of student life: only to its unregulated excesses. Its pacific doctrine was that wherever studentdom is divided into the erudite and ignorant, masters and pupils, a synthesis must inevitably take place; thus Informationalism, based as it was on the concept of private knowledge, must succumb of its own contradictions as did Departmentalism before it. All information and physical plant would become the property of the Student Union; rank and tenure would be abolished, erudition and illiteracy done away with; since Founder and Finals were lies invented by professors to keep students in check, there were in reality no Answers: instead of toiling fearfully for the selfish goal of personal Commencement, a perfectly disciplined student body would live communally in well-regulated academies, studying together at prescribed hours a prescribed curriculum that taught them to subordinate their individual minds to the Mind of the Group. Stated thus, the movement won a host of converts not only among the stupid and oppressed but among the intelligent as well, who saw in its selflessness an alternative to the tawdry hucksterism of the "open college" at its worst—where Logic Departments exhorted one in red neon to *Syllogize One's Weight Away*, and metaphysicians advertised by wireless that *The Chap Who Can Philosophize Never Ossifies*. Max confessed that he himself, as a freshman, had belonged like many intellectual Moishians to a Student-Unionist organization—a fact which was to plague him in later life—and had sympathized whole-heartedly with the Curricularists in Nikolay College who, during Campus Riot I, had overthrown their despotic chancellor and established the first Student-Unionist regime.

"It wasn't till later," he declared sadly, "we saw that the

'Sovereignty of the Bottom Percentile' was just another absolute chancellorship, with some pastry-cook or industrial-arts teacher in charge. The great failing of Informationalism is selfishness; but what the Student-Unionists do, they exchange the selfish student for a selfish college. This *College Self* they're always lecturing about—it's just as greedy and grasping as Ira Hector, the richest Informationalist in New Tammany." He shook his head. "You know what, Billy, I don't agree with old Professor Marcus: I think the mind of a group is always inferior to the minds of its best members—*ach,* to *any* of its members, if it's a committee. And the *passion* of a college—that's a frightening thing! I tell you, the College Self is a great spoilt child; it's a bully and a beast!"

But notwithstanding the many defectors from Nikolay College, the influence of Student-Unionism spread rapidly between the Riots, especially on East Campus. The colleges there were without exception overenrolled and grindingly ignorant; their tradition was essentially spiritualistic, transcendental, passivist, and supra-personal—in a word, Ismist. The *Footnotes to Sakhyan*—their General Prospectus, one might say—taught that the "True Graduate" is the student who can say with understanding: "I and the Founder are one; I am the University; I am not." From this doctrine of self-transcension it was an easy step to the self-suppression of Student-Unionism, and after Campus Riot II—in the teeming quadrangles of Siddartha and the vast monastic reaches of T'ang—they took that step by the millions.

"Mind now, my boy," Max interjected; "this is where you come in."

I confess I had been lulled into a half-drowse by his quiet chronicle and the hum of George's sweeper in the darkling passages; I was worn out by the morning's disasters, and reclined on a table not much harder than the barn-floor I was used to. But these welcome words reroused me.

"I told you already," Max said, "about the Siegfrieders was learning how to EAT just before the Second Riot ended. So the Nikolayans snatch all the Siegfrieder scientists they can find, and the New Tammanies do the same thing, and then Chementinski, that was my best and oldest friend—Chementinski takes it into his head how the campus isn't safe while one side can EAT and the other can't. What he thinks, if there was just an EASCAC to match against the WESCAC, then nobody dares to EAT anybody! So he steals off to Nikolay College with everything he knows, and one evening a year later WESCAC tells us how two thousand political-science flunkees was just EATen alive in a Nikolayan reform school, and not by WESCAC . . ."

There, he maintained, began the so-called "Quiet Riot" between East and West Campus. Each of the two armed campuses strove by every means short of actual rioting to extend its hegemony; neither dared EAT the other, just as the traitor Chementinski had hoped, but each toiled with its whole intelligence to better its weaponry. Thoughtful students everywhere trembled lest some rash folly or inadvertence trigger a third Campus Riot, which must be the end of studentdom; but any who protested were called "fellow-learners" or "pink-pennant pedagogues." Student-Unionist "wizard hunts" became a chief intramural sport from which no liberal was safe. Under the first post-riot Chancellor of NTC, Professor-General Reginald Hector, security measures were carried to unheard-of lengths, and Max Spielman—hero of the scientific fraternity, discoverer of the great laws of the University, the campus-wide image of disinterested genius—Max Spielman was sacked without notice or benefits, on the ground that his loyalty was questionable.

"They should be EATen themselves!" I cried.

Max clucked reproachfully. "Na, Bill, it wasn't Chancellor Hector or the College Senators; they were just scared, like people get. Besides, my friend Chementinski was a Moishian too . . ."

"Whose fault was it, then? I'll eat him myself!" I had known before then, of course, that my dear keeper had been shabbily used by his colleagues, but not until this cram-course in the history of the campus was I able to appreciate the magnitude of their injustice.

Max smiled. "You know, they used to call me 'the father of WESCAC': well, so, then just before you were born, the Son turned against his own Poppa. Just like you did out in the barn."

He explained that whereas EASCAC (larger but cruder than its West-Campus brother) was employed almost solely in the cause of military science and heavy engineering, WESCAC had been trained to do virtually the whole brainwork of the "Free Campus": most importantly, teaching every course of study in the NTC catalogue, while at the same time inventing and implementing extensions of its own power and influence. When asked by its keepers to name its most vulnerable aspects, to the end of strengthening them, its memorable reply had been, "Flunkèd men who tamper with my EATing program"; and it had prescribed two corrective measures: "Program me to program my own Diet" [that is, to decide for itself who was to be EATen, and when], and "Program me to EAT anyone who tries to alter that same Diet." In vain Max protested that already WESCAC's interests had grown multifarious beyond anyone's certain knowledge—perhaps even duplicitous. Of necessity, WESCAC and EASCAC shared the common power source on Founder's Hill, and a certain communication—ostensibly for espionage—went on between them; from a special point of view it might be argued that they were brothers, or even the hemispheres of a single brain. Moreover, it was suspected that Chementinski had already "tampered with the Diet" in subtle ways before his defection: if he was in truth a Student-Unionist traitor, who knew but what WESCAC, given its head, might itself defect, join forces with EASCAC, and destroy the "Free Campus"? Or if Chementinski was merely an overzealous pacifist, as Max had argued, he could well have instructed WESCAC to make just such a plea for programming its own Diet and then to EAT no one at all—in which case, unless he had similarly programmed EASCAC, West Campus would be left helpless against attack. But the professor-generals had no patience with speculation of this sort, nor any substitute for WESCAC's weaponry, however double-edged. And finally, it was just possible that the "flunked persons" on the staff were not the Chementinskis at all. Suppose the Nikolayans decided to EAT us by surprise, they argued, so that no one survived who could authorize WESCAC to retaliate? What a formidable deterrent it would be, what a blow for campus peace would be struck, if WESCAC not only could retaliate automatically but could actually decide when attack was imminent and strike first—as it claimed it could program itself to do!

In fine, Max had been overruled. "All my objections did," he said, "they reminded Chancellor Hector the students shouldn't think WESCAC was out of our control, even if it was. So the generals told it, 'Program your own Diet—except don't destroy NTC—and EAT anybody that comes near your Belly except he's a Grand Tutor.' What that means, the Belly, it's a cave in the basement of Tower Hall where WESCAC's Diet-storage is. Where all the counter-intelligence and EATing programs are kept. It never needs servicing and nobody was allowed to go in there already, but now nobody dared to go anywhere near it. The business about the Grand Tutor means nothing: it was a sop to the *goyim,* that say Enos Enoch will come back to campus someday and put an end to riots."

It was also duly reported to WESCAC which of its keepers had favored and which opposed this augmentation of its power—a practice instituted by the Senate after the Chementinski affair.

The Diet controversy had been followed at once by one more profound, which proved to be Max's last. For all its might and versatility, WESCAC's brain-power was still essentially of one sort: what was called MALI, for Manipulative Analysis and Logical Inference. In Max's words: "All WESCAC does is say *One goat plus one goat is two goats,* or *If Billy is stronger than Tommy, and Brickett is stronger than Billy, then Brickett is stronger than Tommy,* you see? Now, it does this in fancy ways, and quick as a flash; but what it comes down to is millions of little pulses, like the gates between the buck-pens: and all a gate can be is open or shut. The only questions it can answer are the kind we can reduce to a lot of little *yesses* and *nos,* and it answers in the same language."

This elementary capacity WESCAC shared with its crudest ancestors, though it had been refined enormously over the years. To it Max Spielman and his colleagues had made only one fateful addition: the ability to form rudimentary concepts from its information and to sharpen them by trial and error. ("Like when you were a baby kid, you hardly knew you were you and the herd was the herd. Then you learned there was a *you* that was hungry, and a Mary Appenzeller's teat that wasn't you, but filled you up. Next thing, you got a name and a history, and could tell apart seven hundred plants.") Thus it was that their creature's original name had been CACAC, for Campus Analyzer, Conceptualizer, and Computer; thus too it became possible for the beast to educate itself beyond any human scope, conceive and execute its own projects, and display what could only be called resourcefulness, ingenuity, and cunning. Yet though it possessed the power not only to EAT all studentdom but to choose to do so, there were respects in which the callowest new freshman was still its better:

mighty WESCAC was not able to *enjoy*, for example, as I enjoyed frisking through the furze; nor could it contemplate or dream. It could excogitate, extrapolate, generalize, and infer, after its fashion; it could compose an arithmetical music and a sort of accidental literature (not often interesting); it could assess half a hundred variables and make the most sophisticated prognostications. But it could not act on hunch or brilliant impulse; it had no intuitions or exaltations; it could request, but not yearn; indicate, but not insinuate or exhort; command, but not care. It had no sense of style or grasp of the ineffable: its correlations were exact, but its metaphors wrenched; it could play chess, but not poker. The fantastically complex algebra of Max's Cyclology it could manage in minutes, but it never made a joke in its life.

It was young Dr. Eblis Eierkopf, the former Bonifacist, who first proposed that WESCAC be provided with a supplementary intelligence which he called NOCTIS (for Non-Conceptual Thinking and Intuitional Synthesis): this capacity, he maintained, if integrated with the formidable MALI system, would give WESCAC a truly miraculous potential, setting it as far above studentdom in every psychic particular as studentdom was above the insects. *Wescacus malinoctis*, as he called his projected creature, would pose and solve the subtlest problems not alone of scientists, mathematicians, and production managers, but as well of philosophers, poets, and professors of theology. Max himself had found the notion intriguing and had invited Eierkopf to pursue it further, though he cordially questioned both its wisdom and its feasibility: the crippled young Siegfrieder was regarded for all his brilliance as something of an unpleasant visionary, and at the time—Campus Riot II just having ended—everyone was busy finding peaceful employments for *Wescacus mali*. The debate, therefore, between the "Eierkopfians" and the "Spielman faction" had remained academic and good-humored. But when the Nikolayans fed EASCAC its first meal, proving their military equivalence to West Campus, Eierkopf pressed most vigorously for a crash program of the highest priority to develop NOCTIS, carrying his plea over Max's head directly to the Chancellor's office. It was our one hope, he had maintained, of regaining the electroencephalic advantage for West Campus: a malinoctial WESCAC not only would out-general its merely rational opponent in time of riot, but would be of inestimable value in the

Quiet Riot too, possessed of a hundred times the art of Nikolay's whole Propaganda Institute. Indeed he went so far as to suggest it might prove the Commencement of all studentdom, a Grand Tutor such as this campus had never seen. What had been Enos Enoch's special quality, after all, and Sakhyan's, if not an extraordinary psychic endowment of the non-conceptual sort, combined with tremendously influential personality? But the WESCAC he envisioned would be as superior to those Grand Tutors in every such respect as it was already in, say mathematical prowess; *founderlike* was the only word for it, and like the Founder Himself it could well resolve, for good and all, the disharmonies that threatened studentdom.

High officers in the Hector administration grew interested—more in the military than in the moral promise—and supported the NOCTIS project: but Max and several others fought it with all their strength. "Noctility," they agreed with Eierkopf, was exactly the difference between WESCAC's mind and student's; but the limitations of malistic thinking, however many problems they occasioned, were what stood at last between a student body served by WESCAC and the reverse. To thoughtful believers, the notion of a student-made Founder must be utterly blasphemous; to high-minded secular studentists, on the other hand, even a campus ruled by Student-Unionists—who at least were men and as such might be appealed to, outwitted, and in time overthrown—was preferable to eternal and absolute submission to a supra-human power. In an impassioned speech—his last—to the College Senate, Max had declared: "Me, I don't want any Supermind, *danke:* just your mind and my mind. You want to make WESCAC your Founder and everybody get to Commencement Gate? Well, what I think, my friends, that's all poetry, and life is what I like better. The Riot's down here on campus, not up in the Belfry, and the enemy isn't Student-Unionism, but ignorance and suffering, that the WESCAC we got right now can help us fight. If you ask me, the medical student that invented ether did more for studentdom than Sakhyan and Enos Enoch together."

To these perhaps impolitic remarks a well-known senator from the Political Science Department had objected that they sounded to him neither reverent nor alma-matriotic. It was no secret that his distinguished colleague—for what cause, the senator would not presume to guess—had opposed every measure to insure the defense of the Free Campus against Founderless Student-Unionism by strengthening WESCAC's deterrent capacity; that he had moreover "stood up" for the traitor Chementinski and sympathized openly with a number of organizations on the Attorney-Dean's List. But could not even an ivy-tower eccentric (who had better have stuck to his logarithms and left political science to professors of that specialty) see that pain and ignorance were but passing afflictions, mere diversions if he might say so from the true end of life on this campus? Had it not always been, and would it not be again, that when pain and ignorance were vanquished, studentdom turned ever to the Founder in hope of Commencement? And as it was the New Tammany Way to lead the fight against ignorance and pain, so must not our college lead too the Holy Riot against a-founderism and disbelief, with every weapon in its Armory?

# Born under a Bad Sign: Minorities

The middle-class production-and-consumption oriented value system which produces the anxieties and hangups described by the works in the previous two sections dominates American society today. This is the system. Outside the system, in America as well as in the other bureaucratic, over-industrialized nation-states, racial and cultural minorities have developed alternative value systems, some primarily negative and defensive, others positive and creative. This section includes works which express the tensions between majority and minority values. Few of these works espouse concrete solutions. Rather, they involve you in these tensions in a way which intellectual theorizing alone cannot.

The Black man in America has experienced a long history of racial discrimination and oppression. There are many aspects of the problem, but in large measure it revolves around who is and who is not considered a legitimate member of American society, and the criterion is often determined by the color of one's skin. There are, however, other criteria—gainful employment, decent well-kept housing, and willful acknowledgment of the dominant value system—refusing to "rock the boat." Yet, the very things which make one a "legitimate" citizen are denied to a substantial minority of the American people by those who already have these things. This system of exploitation perpetrated (sometimes inadvertently) by middle- and upper-class whites upon lower-class whites, Blacks, Chicanos, and Indians thus symbolizes much more than racial prejudice, although it is felt the most by those who cannot escape the color of their skin, and who thereby are easily identifiable as social, political, and economic outcasts.

The debate on how to resolve this issue has centered largely on whether to integrate or not to integrate, how fast, and in what way. Integration has posed a particular problem for minority-group members who are often thereby forced to give up specific aspects of their culture in order to be accepted into the all-pervasive middle-class value system. Integration, its critics claim, has presumed that the middle-class culture and value framework is "superior" to that of other value frameworks, and that minority-group cultures, in effect, have nothing to offer. This is, of course, not the case. The following selections are arranged in chronological order in terms of which group first suffered discrimination at the hands of a dominant white society—Indians, Blacks, Chicanos, and lower-class whites.

## SMOHALLA

*The long history of white racism in America begins with the Indians, regarded by the European colonizers as barbaric savages to be massacred, or at best to be herded into concentration camps called "reservations," where most of them remain today.* SMOHALLA *was a leader of the Nez Percé Indians and a founder of the Ghost Dance religion. His words have a new relevance to the present struggle against the destruction of our environment; for the restoration of ecological balance can hardly be achieved until we adopt a nonexploitative attitude toward the ground we walk on.*

# SMOHALLA SPEAKS

My young men shall never work. Men who work cannot dream, and wisdom comes in dreams.

You ask me to plow the ground. Shall I take a knife and tear my mother's breast? Then when I die she will not take me to her bosom to rest.

You ask me to dig for stone. Shall I dig under her skin for bones? Then when I die I cannot enter her body to be born again.

You ask me to cut grass and make hay and sell it, and be rich like white men. But how dare I cut off my mother's hair?

It is a bad law, and my people cannot obey it. I want my people to stay with me here. All the dead men will come to life again. We must wait here in the house of our fathers and be ready to meet them in the body of our mother.

From *The Nez Percé Indians* by Herbert J. Spinden, The American Anthropological Association, *Memoirs,* Vol. 2, Part 3. Lancaster, 1908.

## JAMES BALDWIN

*is one of the best-known and highly acclaimed Black authors writing in the United States today. His novels include* Giovanni's Room, Go Tell It on the Mountain *and* Another Country. *Perhaps his most famous work is the autobiographical essay,* The Fire Next Time, *in which he relates how it feels to grow up in a land in which blacks are still far from emancipated. Baldwin has won numerous writing awards and grants, including a Guggenheim Fellowship. In this short story, Baldwin captures the feel of a lynching, and through it, the deepest hostility between blacks and whites unleashed in a myriad of forms and relationships in a quiet Southern town.*

# GOING TO MEET THE MAN

"What's the matter?" she asked.

"I don't know," he said, trying to laugh, "I guess I'm tired."

"You've been working too hard," she said. "I keep telling you."

"Well, goddammit, woman," he said, "it's not my fault!" He tried again; he wretchedly failed again. Then he just lay there, silent, angry, and helpless. Excitement filled him just like a toothache, but it refused to enter his flesh. He stroked her breast. This was his wife. He could not ask her to do just a little thing for him, just to help him out, just for a little while, the way he could ask a nigger girl to do it. He lay there, and he sighed. The image of a black girl caused a distant excitement in him, like a far-away light; but, again, the excitement was more like pain; instead of forcing him to act, it made action impossible.

"Go to sleep," she said, gently, "you got a hard day tomorrow."

"Yeah," he said, and rolled over on his side, facing her, one hand still on one breast. "Goddamn the niggers. The black stinking coons. You'd think they'd learn. Wouldn't you think they'd learn? I mean, *wouldn't* you?"

"They going to be out there tomorrow," she said, and took his hand away, "get some sleep."

He lay there, one hand between his legs, staring at the frail sanctuary of his wife. A faint light came from the shutters; the moon was full. Two dogs, far away, were barking at each other, back and forth, insistently, as though they were agreeing to make an appointment. He heard a car coming north on the road and he half sat up, his hand reaching for his holster, which was on a chair near the bed, on top of his pants. The lights hit the shutters and seemed to travel across the room and then went out. The sound of the car slipped away, he heard it hit gravel, then heard it no more. Some liver-lipped students, probably, heading back to that college—but coming from where? His watch said it was two in the morning. They could be coming from anywhere, from out of state most likely, and they would be at the court-house tomorrow. The niggers were getting ready. Well, they would be ready, too.

He moaned. He wanted to let whatever was in him out; but it wouldn't come out. Goddamn! he said aloud, and turned again, on his side, away from Grace, staring at the shutters. He was a big, healthy man and he had never had any trouble sleeping. And he wasn't old enough yet to have any trouble getting it up—he was only forty-two. And he was a good man, a God-fearing man, he had tried to do his duty all his life, and he had been a deputy sheriff for several years. Nothing had ever bothered him before, certainly not getting it up. Sometimes, sure, like any other man, he knew that he wanted a little more spice than Grace could give him and he would drive over yonder and pick up a black piece or arrest her, it came to the same thing, but he couldn't do that now, no more. There was no telling what might happen once your ass was in the air. And they were low enough to kill a man then, too, everyone of them, or the girl herself might do it, right while she was making believe you made her feel so good. The niggers. What had the good Lord Almighty had in mind when he made the niggers? Well. They were pretty good at that, all right. Damn. Damn. Goddamn.

This wasn't helping him to sleep. He turned again, toward Grace again, and moved close to her warm body. He felt something he had never felt before. He felt that he would like to hold her, hold her, hold her, and be buried in her like a child and never have to get up in the morning again and go downtown to face those faces, good Christ, they were ugly! and never have to enter that jail house again and smell that smell and hear that singing; never again feel that filthy, kinky, greasy hair under his hand, never again watch those black breasts leap against the leaping cattle prod, never hear those moans again or watch that blood run down or the fat lips split or the sealed eyes struggle open. They were animals, they were no better than animals, what could be done with people like that? Here they had been in a civilized country for years and they still lived like animals. Their houses were dark, with oil cloth or cardboard in the windows, the smell was enough to make you puke your guts out, and there they sat, a whole tribe, pumping out kids, it looked like, every damn five minutes, and laughing and talking and playing music like they didn't have a care in the world, and he reckoned they didn't, neither, and coming to the door, into the sunlight, just standing there, just looking foolish, not thinking of anything but just getting back to what they were doing, saying, Yes suh, Mr. Jesse. I surely will, Mr. Jesse. Fine weather, Mr. Jesse. Why, I thank you, Mr. Jesse. He had worked for a mail-order house for a while and it had been his job to collect the payments for the stuff they bought. They were too dumb to know that they were being cheated blind, but that was no skin off his ass—he was just supposed to do his job. They would be late—they didn't have the sense to put money aside; but it was easy to scare them, and he never really had any trouble. Hell, they all liked him, the kids used to smile when he came to the door. He gave them candy, sometimes, or chewing gum, and rubbed their rough bullet heads—maybe the candy should have been poisoned. Those kids were grown now. He had had trouble with one of them today.

"There was this nigger today," he said; and stopped; his voice sounded peculiar. He touched Grace. "You awake?" he asked. She mumbled something, impatiently, she was probably telling him to go to sleep. It was all right. He knew that he was not alone.

"What a funny time," he said, "to be thinking about a thing like that—you listening?" She mumbled something again. He rolled over on his back. "This nigger's one of the ringleaders. We had trouble with him before. We must have had him out there at the work farm three or four times. Well, Big Jim C. and some of the boys really had to whip that nigger's ass today." He looked over at Grace; he could not tell whether she was listening or not; and he was afraid to ask again. "They had this line you know, to register"—he laughed, but she did not—"and they wouldn't stay where Big Jim C. wanted them, no, they had to start blocking traffic all around the court house so couldn't nothing or nobody get through, and Big Jim C. told them to disperse and they wouldn't move, they just kept up that singing, and Big Jim C. figured that the others would move if this nigger would move, him being the ring-leader, but he wouldn't move and he wouldn't let the others move, so they had to beat him and a couple of the others and they threw them in the wagon—but *I* didn't see this nigger till I got to the jail. They were still singing and I was supposed to make them stop. Well, I couldn't make them stop for me but I knew he could make them stop. He was lying on the ground jerking and moaning, they had threw him in a cell by himself, and blood was coming out his ears from where Big Jim C. and his boys had whipped him. Wouldn't you think they'd learn? I put the prod to him and he jerked some more and he kind of screamed—but he didn't have much voice left. "You make them stop that singing," I said to him, "you hear me? You make them stop that singing." He acted like he didn't hear me and I put it to him again, under his arms, and he just rolled around on the floor and blood started coming from his mouth. He'd pissed his pants already." He paused. His mouth felt dry and his throat was as rough as sandpaper; as he talked, he began to hurt all over with that peculiar excitement which refused to be released. "You all are going to stop your singing, I said to him, and you are going to stop coming down to the court house and disrupting traffic and molesting the people and keeping us from our duties and keeping doctors from getting to sick white women and getting all them Northerners in this town to give our town a bad name—!" As he said this, he kept prodding the boy, sweat pouring from beneath the helmet he had not yet taken off. The boy rolled around in his own dirt and water and blood and tried to scream again as the prod hit his testicles, but the scream did not come out, only a kind of rattle and a moan. He stopped. He was not supposed to kill the nigger. The cell was filled with a terrible odor. The boy was still. "You hear me?" he called. "You had enough?" The singing went on. "You had enough?" His foot leapt out, he had not known it was going to, and caught the boy flush on the jaw. *Jesus,* he thought, *this ain't no nigger, this is a goddamn bull,* and he screamed again, "You had enough? You going to make them stop that singing now?"

But the boy was out. And now he was shaking worse than the boy had been shaking. He was glad no one could see him. At the same time, he felt very close to a very peculiar, particular joy; something deep in him and deep in his memory was stirred, but whatever was in his memory eluded him. He took off his helmet. He walked to the cell door.

"White man," said the boy, from the floor, behind him.

He stopped. For some reason, he grabbed his privates.

"You remember Old Julia?"

The boy said, from the floor, with his mouth full of blood, and one eye, barely open, glaring like the eye of a cat in the dark, "My grandmother's name was Mrs. Julia Blossom. *Mrs.* Julia Blossom.

You going to call our women by their right names yet.—And those kids ain't going to stop singing. We going to keep on singing until every one of you miserable white mothers go stark raving out of your minds." Then he closed the one eye; he spat blood; his head fell back against the floor.

He looked down at the boy, whom he had been seeing, off and on, for more than a year, and suddenly remembered him: Old Julia had been one of his mail-order customers, a nice old woman. He had not seen her for years, he supposed that she must be dead.

He had walked into the yard, the boy had been sitting in a swing. He had smiled at the boy, and asked, "Old Julia home?"

The boy looked at him for a long time before he answered. "Don't no Old Julia live here."

"This is her house. I know her. She's lived here for years."

The boy shook his head. "You might know a Old Julia someplace else, white man. But don't nobody by that name live here."

He watched the boy; the boy watched him. The boy certainly wasn't more than ten. *White man.* He didn't have time to be fooling around with some crazy kid. He yelled, "Hey! Old Julia!"

But only silence answered him. The expression on the boy's face did not change. The sun beat down on them both, still and silent; he had the feeling that he had been caught up in a nightmare, a nightmare dreamed by a child; perhaps one of the nightmares he himself had dreamed as a child. It had that feeling—everything familiar, without undergoing any other change, had been subtly and hideously displaced: the trees, the sun, the patches of grass in the yard, the leaning porch and the weary porch steps and the cardboard in the windows and the black hole of the door which looked like the entrance to a cave, and the eyes of the pickaninny, all, all, were charged with malevolence. *White man.* He looked at the boy. "She's gone out?"

The boy said nothing.

"Well," he said, "tell her I passed by and I'll pass by next week." He started to go; he stopped. "You want some chewing gum?"

The boy got down from the swing and started for the house. He said, "I don't want nothing you got, white man." He walked into the house and closed the door behind him.

Now the boy looked as though he were dead. Jesse wanted to go over to him and pick him up and pistol whip him until the boy's head burst open like a melon. He began to tremble with what he believed was rage, sweat, both cold and hot, raced down his body, the singing filled him as though it were a weird, uncontrollable, monstrous howling rumbling up from the depths of his own belly, he felt an icy fear rise in him and raise him up, and he shouted, he howled, "You lucky we *pump* some white blood into you every once in a while—your women! Here's what I got for all the black bitches in the world—!" Then he was, abruptly, almost too weak to stand; to his bewilderment, his horror, beneath his own fingers, he felt himself violently stiffen—with no warning at all; he dropped his hands and he stared at the boy and he left the cell.

"All that singing they do," he said. "All that singing." He could not remember the first time he had heard it; he had been hearing it all his life. It was the sound with which he was most familiar—though it was also the sound of which he had been least conscious—and it had always contained an obscure comfort. They were singing to God. They were singing for mercy and they hoped to go to heaven, and he had even sometimes felt, when looking into the eyes of some of the old women, a few of the very old men, that they were singing for mercy for his soul, too. Of course he had never thought of their heaven or of what God was, or could be, for them; God was the same for everyone, he supposed, and heaven was where good people went—he supposed. He had never thought much about what it meant to be a good person. He tried to be a good person and treat everybody right: it wasn't his fault if the niggers had taken it into their heads to fight against God and go against the rules laid down in the Bible for everyone to read! Any preacher would tell you that. He was only doing his duty: protecting white people from the niggers and the niggers from themselves. And there were still lots of good niggers around—he had to remember that; they weren't all like that boy this afternoon; and the good niggers must be mighty sad to see what was happening to their people. They would thank him when this was over. In that way they had, the best of them, not quite looking him in the eye, in a low voice, with a little smile: We surely thanks you, Mr. Jesse. From the bottom of our hearts, we thanks you. He smiled. They hadn't all gone crazy. This trouble would pass.—He knew that the young people had changed some of the words to the songs. He had scarcely listened to the words before and he did not listen to them now; but he knew that the words were different; he could hear that much. He did not know if the faces were different, he had never, before this trouble began, watched them as they sang, but he certainly did not like what he saw now. They hated him, and this hatred was blacker than their hearts, blacker than their skins, redder than their blood, and harder, by far, than his club. Each day, each night, he felt worn out, aching, with their smell in his nostrils and filling his lungs, as though he were drowning—drowning in niggers; and it was all to be done again when he awoke. It would never end. It would never end. Perhaps this was what the singing had meant all along. They had not been singing black folks into heaven, they had been singing white folks into hell.

Everyone felt this black suspicion in many ways, but no one knew how to express it. Men much older than he, who had been responsible for law and order much longer than he, were now much quieter than they had been, and the tone of their jokes, in a way that he could not quite put his finger on, had changed. These men were his models, they had been friends to his father, and they had taught him what it meant to be a man. He looked to them for courage now. It wasn't that he didn't know that what he was doing was right—he knew that, nobody had to tell him that; it was only that he missed the ease of former years. But they didn't have much time to hang out with each other these days. They tended to stay close to their families every free minute because nobody knew what might happen next. Explosions rocked the night of their tranquil town. Each time each man wondered silently if perhaps this time the dynamite had not fallen into the wrong hands. They thought that they knew where all the guns were; but they could not possibly know every move that was made in that secret place where the darkies lived. From time to time it was suggested that they form a posse and search the home of every nigger, but they hadn't done it yet. For one thing, this might have brought the bastards from the North down on their backs; for another, although the niggers were scattered throughout the town—down in the hollow near the railroad tracks, way west near the mills, up on the hill, the well-off ones, and some out near the college—nothing seemed to happen in one part of town without the niggers immediately knowing it in the other. This meant that they could not take them by surprise. They rarely mentioned it, but they *knew* that some of the niggers had guns. It stood to reason, as they said, since, after all, some of them had been in the Army. There were niggers in the Army right now and God knows they wouldn't have had any trouble stealing this half-assed government blind—the whole world was doing it, look at the European countries and all those countries in Africa. They made jokes about it—bitter jokes; and they cursed the government in Washington, which had betrayed them; but they had not yet formed a posse. Now, if their town had been laid out like some towns in the North, where all the niggers lived together in one locality, they could have gone down and set fire to the houses and brought about peace that way. If the niggers had all lived in one place, they could have kept the fire in one place. But the way this town was laid out, the fire could hardly be controlled. It would spread all over town—and the niggers would probably be helping it to spread. Still, from time to time, they spoke of doing it, anyway; so that now there was a real fear among them that somebody might go crazy and light the match.

They rarely mentioned anything not directly related to the war that they were fighting, but this had failed to establish between them the unspoken communication of soldiers during a war. Each man, in the thrilling silence which sped outward from their exchanges, their laughter, and their anecdotes, seemed wrestling, in various degrees of darkness, with a secret which he could not articulate to himself, and which, however directly it related to the war, related yet more surely to his privacy and his past. They could no longer be sure, after all, that they had all done the same things. They had never dreamed that their privacy could contain any element of terror, could threaten, that is, to reveal itself, to the scrutiny of a judgment day, while remaining unreadable and inaccessible to themselves; nor had they dreamed that the past, while certainly refusing to be forgotten, could yet so stubbornly refuse to be remembered. They felt themselves mysteriously set at naught, as no longer entering into the real concerns of other people—while here they were, outnumbered, fighting to save the civilized world. They had thought that people would care—people didn't care; not enough, anyway, to help them. It would have been a help, really, or at least a relief, even to have been forced to surrender. Thus they had lost, probably forever, their old and easy connection with each other. They were forced to depend on each other more and, at the same time, to trust each other less. Who could tell when one of them might not betray them all, for money, or for the ease of confession? But no one dared imagine what there might be to confess. They were soldiers fighting a war, but their relationship to each other was that of accomplices in a crime. They all had to keep their mouths shut.

*I stepped in the river at Jordan.*

Out of the darkness of the room, out of nowhere, the line came flying up at him, with the melody and the beat. He turned wordlessly toward his sleeping wife.

*I stepped in the river at Jordan.*

Where had he heard that song?

"Grace," he whispered. "You awake?"

She did not answer. If she was awake, she wanted him to sleep. Her breathing was slow and easy, her body slowly rose and fell.

*I stepped in the river at Jordan.*
*The water came to my knees.*

He began to sweat. He felt an overwhelming fear, which yet contained a curious and dreadful pleasure.

*I stepped in the river at Jordan.*
*The water came to my waist.*

It had been night, as it was now, he was in the car between his mother and his father, sleepy, his head in his mother's lap, sleepy, and yet full of excitement. The singing came from far away, across the dark fields. There were no lights anywhere. They had said good-bye to all the others and turned off on this dark dirt road. They were almost home.

*I stepped in the river at Jordan,*
*The water came over my head,*
*I looked way over to the other side,*
*He was making up my dying bed!*

"I guess they singing for him," his father said, seeming very weary and subdued now. "Even when they're sad, they sound like they just about to go and tear off a piece." He yawned and leaned across the boy and slapped his wife lightly on the shoulder, allowing his hand to rest there for a moment. "Don't they?"

"Don't talk that way," she said.

"Well, that's what we going to do," he said, "you can make up your mind to that." He started whistling. "You see? When I begin to feel it, I gets kind of musical, too."

*Oh, Lord! Come on and ease my troubling mind!*

He had a black friend, his age, eight, who lived nearby. His name was Otis. They wrestled together in the dirt. Now the thought of Otis made him sick. He began to shiver. His mother put her arm around him.

"He's tired," she said.

"We'll be home soon," said his father. He began to whistle again.

"We didn't see Otis this morning," Jesse said. He did not know why he said this. His voice, in the darkness of the car, sounded small and accusing.

"You haven't seen Otis for a couple of mornings," his mother said.

That was true. But he was only concerned about *this* morning.

"No," said his father, "I reckon Otis's folks was afraid to let him show himself this morning."

"But Otis didn't do nothing!" Now his voice sounded questioning.

"Otis *can't* do nothing," said his father, "he's too little." The car lights picked up their wooden house, which now solemnly approached them, the lights falling around it like yellow dust. Their dog, chained to a tree, began to bark.

"We just want to make sure Otis *don't* do nothing," said his father, and stopped the car. He looked down at Jesse. "And you tell him what your Daddy said, you hear?"

"Yes sir," he said.

His father switched off the lights. The dog moaned and pranced, but they ignored him and went inside. He could not sleep. He lay awake, hearing the night sounds, the dog yawning and moaning outside, the sawing of the crickets, the cry of the owl, dogs barking far away, then no sounds at all, just the heavy, endless buzzing of the night. The darkness pressed on his eyelids like a scratchy blanket. He turned, he turned again. He wanted to call his mother, but he knew his father would not like this. He was terribly afraid. Then he heard his father's voice in the other room, low, with a joke in it; but this did not help him, it frightened him more, he knew what was going to happen. He put his head under the blanket, then pushed his head out again, for fear, staring at the dark window. He heard his mother's moan, his father's sigh; he gritted his teeth. Then their bed began to rock. His father's breathing seemed to fill the world.

That morning, before the sun had gathered all its strength, men and women, some flushed and some pale with excitement, came with news. Jesse's father seemed to know what the news was before the first jalopy stopped in the yard, and he ran out, crying, "They got him, then? They got him?"

The first jalopy held eight people, three men and two women and three children. The children were sitting on the laps of the grown-ups. Jesse knew two of them, the two boys; they shyly and uncomfortably greeted each other. He did not know the girl.

"Yes, they got him," said one of the women, the older one, who wore a wide hat and a fancy, faded blue dress. "They found him early this morning."

"How far had he got?" Jesse's father asked.

"He hadn't got no further than Harkness," one of the men said. "Look like he got lost up there in all them trees—or maybe he just got so scared he couldn't move." They all laughed.

"Yes, and you know it's near a graveyard, too," said the younger woman, and they laughed again.

"Is that where they got him now?" asked Jesse's father.

By this time there were three cars piled behind the first one, with everyone looking excited and shining, and Jesse noticed that they were carrying food. It was like a Fourth of July picnic.

"Yeah, that's where he is," said one of the men, "declare, Jesse, you going to keep us here all day long, answering your damn fool questions. Come on, we ain't got no time to waste."

"Don't bother putting up no food," cried a woman from one of the other cars, "we got enough. Just come on."

"Why, thank you," said Jesse's father, "we be right along, then."

"I better get a sweater for the boy," said his mother, "in case it turns cold."

Jesse watched his mother's thin legs cross the yard. He knew that she also wanted to comb her hair a little and maybe put on a better dress, the dress she wore to church. His father guessed this, too, for he yelled behind her, "Now don't you go trying to turn yourself into no movie star. You just come on." But he laughed as he said this, and winked at the men; his wife was younger and prettier than most of the other women. He clapped Jesse on the head and started pulling him toward the car. "You all go on," he said, "I'll be right behind you. Jesse, you go tie up that there dog while I get this car started."

The cars sputtered and coughed and shook; the caravan began to move; bright dust filled the air. As soon as he was tied up, the dog began to bark. Jesse's mother came out of the house, carrying a jacket for his father and a sweater for Jesse. She had put a ribbon in her hair and had an old shawl around her shoulders.

"Put these in the car, son," she said, and handed everything to him. She bent down and stroked the dog, looked to see if there was water in his bowl, then went back up the three porch steps and closed the door.

"Come on," said his father, "ain't nothing in there for nobody to steal." He was sitting in the car, which trembled and belched. The last car of the caravan had disappeared but the sound of singing floated behind them.

Jesse got into the car, sitting close to his father, loving the smell of the car, and the trembling, and the bright day, and the sense of going on a great and unexpected journey. His mother got in and closed the door and the car began to move. Not until then did he ask, "Where are we going? Are we going on a picnic?"

He had a feeling that he knew where they were going, but he was not sure.

"That's right," his father said, "we're going on a picnic. You won't ever forget *this* picnic—!"

"Are we," he asked, after a moment, "going to see the bad nigger—the one that knocked down old Miss Standish?"

"Well, I reckon," said his mother, "that we *might* see him."

He started to ask, *Will a lot of niggers be there? Will Otis be there?*—but he did not ask his question, to which, in a strange and uncomfortable way, he already knew the answer. Their friends, in the other cars, stretched up the road as far as he could see; other cars had joined them; there were cars behind them. They were singing. The sun seemed, suddenly very hot, and he was, at once very happy and a little afraid. He did not quite understand what was happening, and he did not know what to ask—he had no one to ask. He had grown accustomed, for the solution of such mysteries, to go to Otis. He felt that Otis knew everything. But he could not ask Otis about this. Anyway, he had not seen Otis for two days; he had not seen a black face anywhere for more than two days; and he now realized, as they began chugging up the long hill which eventually led to Harkness, that there were no black faces on the road this morning, no black people anywhere. From the houses in which they lived, all along the road, no smoke curled, no life stirred—maybe one or two chickens were to be seen, that was all. There was no one at the windows, no one in the yard, no one sitting on the porches, and the doors were closed. He had come this road many a time and seen women washing in the yard (there were no clothes on the clotheslines) men working in the fields, children playing in the dust; black men passed them on the road other mornings, other days, on foot, or in wagons, sometimes in cars, tipping their hats, smiling, joking, their teeth a solid white against their skin, their eyes as warm as the sun, the blackness of their skin like dull fire against the white of the blue or the grey of their torn clothes. They passed the nigger church—dead-white, desolate, locked up; and the graveyard, where no one knelt or walked, and he saw no flowers. He wanted to ask, *Where are they? Where are they all?* But he did not dare. As the hill grew steeper, the sun grew colder. He looked at his mother and his father. They looked straight ahead, seeming to be listening to the singing which echoed and echoed in this graveyard silence. They were strangers to him now. They were looking at something he could not see. His father's lips had a strange, cruel curve, he wet his lips from time to time, and swallowed. He was terribly aware of his father's tongue, it was as though he had never seen it before. And his father's body suddenly seemed immense, bigger than a mountain. His eyes, which were grey-green, looked yellow in the sunlight; or at least there was a light in them which he had never seen before. His mother patted her hair and adjusted the ribbon, leaning forward to look into the car mirror. "You look all right," said his father, and laughed. "When that nigger looks at you, he's going to swear he throwed his life away for nothing. Wouldn't be surprised if he don't come back to haunt you." And he laughed again.

The singing now slowly began to cease; and he realized that they were nearing their destination. They had reached a straight, narrow, pebbly road, with trees on either side. The sunlight filtered down on them from a great height, as though they were underwater; and the branches of the trees scraped against the cars with a tearing sound. To the right of them, and beneath them, invisible now, lay the town; and to the left, miles of trees which led to the high mountain range which his ancestors had crossed in order to settle in this valley. Now, all was silent, except for the bumping of the tires against the rocky road, the sputtering of motors, and the sound of a crying child. And they seemed to move more slowly. They were beginning to climb again. He watched the cars ahead as they toiled patiently upward, disappearing into the sunlight of the clearing. Presently, he felt their vehicle also rise, heard his father's changed breathing, the sunlight hit his face, the trees moved away from them, and they were there. As their car crossed the clearing, he looked around. There seemed to be millions, there were certainly hundreds of people in the clearing, staring toward something he could not see. There was a fire. He could not see the flames, but he smelled the smoke. Then they were on the other side of the clearing, among the trees again. His father drove off the road and parked the car behind a great many other cars. He looked down at Jesse.

"You all right?" he asked.

"Yes sir," he said.

"Well, come on, then," his father said. He reached over and opened the door on his mother's side. His mother stepped out first. They followed her into the clearing. At first he was aware only of confusion, of his mother and father greeting and being greeted, himself being handled, hugged, and patted, and told how much he had grown. The wind blew the smoke from the fire across the clearing into his eyes and nose. He could not see over the backs of the people in front of him. The sounds of laughing and cursing and wrath—and something else—rolled in waves from the front of the mob to the back. Those in front expressed their delight at what they saw, and this delight rolled backward, wave upon wave, across the clearing, more acrid than the smoke. His father reached down suddenly and sat Jesse on his shoulders.

Now he saw the fire—of twigs and boxes, piled high; flames made pale orange and yellow and thin as a veil under the steadier light of the sun; grey-blue smoke rolled upward and poured over their heads. Beyond the shifting curtain of fire and smoke, he made out first only a length of gleaming chain, attached to a great limb of the tree; then he saw that this chain bound two black hands together at the wrist, dirty yellow palm facing dirty yellow palm. The smoke poured up; the hands dropped out of sight; a cry went up from the crowd. Then the hands slowly came into view again, pulled upward by the chain. This time he saw the kinky, sweating, bloody head—he had never before seen a head with so much hair on it, hair so black and so tangled that it seemed like another jungle. The head was hanging. He saw the forehead, flat and high, with a kind of arrow of hair in the center, like he had, like his father had; they called it a widow's peak; and the mangled eye brows, the wide nose, the closed eyes, and the glinting eye lashes and the hanging lips, all streaming with blood and sweat. His hands were straight above his head. All his weight pulled downward from his hands; and he was a big man, a bigger man than his father, and black as an African jungle Cat, and naked. Jesse pulled upward; his father's hands held him firmly by the ankles. He wanted to say something, he did not know what, but nothing he said could have been heard, for now the crowd roared again as a man stepped forward and put more wood on the fire. The flames leapt up. He thought he heard the hanging man scream, but he was not sure. Sweat was pouring from the hair in his armpits, poured down his sides, over his chest, into his navel and his groin. He was lowered again; he was raised again. Now Jesse knew that he heard him scream. The head went back, the mouth wide open, blood bubbling from the mouth; the veins of the neck jumped out; Jesse clung to his father's neck in terror as the cry rolled over the crowd. The cry of all the people rose to answer the dying man's cry. He wanted death to come quickly. They wanted to make death wait: and it was they who held death, now, on a leash which they lengthened little by little. *What did he do?* Jesse wondered. *What did the man do? What did he do?*—but he could not ask his father. He was seated on his father's shoulders, but his father was far away. There were two older men, friends of his father's, raising and lowering the chain; everyone, indiscriminately, seemed to be responsible for the fire. There was no hair left on the nigger's privates, and the eyes, now, were wide open, as white as the eyes of a clown or a doll. The smoke now carried a terrible odor across the clearing, the odor of something burning which was both sweet and rotten.

He turned his head a little and saw the field of faces. He watched his mother's face. Her eyes were very bright, her mouth was open: she was more beautiful than he had ever seen her, and more strange. He began to feel a joy he had never felt before. He watched the hanging, gleaming body, the most beautiful and terrible object he had ever seen till then. One of his father's friends reached up and in his hands he held a knife: and Jesse wished that he had been that man. It was a long, bright knife and the sun seemed to catch it, to play with it, to caress it—it was brighter than the fire. And a wave of laughter swept the crowd. Jesse felt his father's hands on his ankles slip and tighten. The man with the knife walked toward the crowd, smiling slightly; as though this were a signal, silence fell; he heard his mother cough. Then the man with the knife walked up to the hanging body. He turned and smiled again. Now there was a silence all over the field. The hanging head looked up. It seemed fully conscious now, as though the fire had burned out terror and pain. The man with the knife took the nigger's privates in his hand, one hand, still smiling, as though he were weighing them. In the cradle of the one white hand, the nigger's privates seemed as remote as meat being weighed in the scales; but seemed heavier, too, much heavier, and Jesse felt his scrotum tighten; and huge, huge, much bigger than his father's, flaccid, hairless, the largest thing he had ever seen till then, and the blackest. The white hand stretched them, cradled them, caressed them. Then the dying man's eyes looked straight into Jesse's eyes—it could not have been as long as a second, but it seemed longer than a year. Then Jesse screamed, and the crowd screamed as the knife flashed, first up, then down, cutting the dreadful thing away, and the blood came roaring down. Then the crowd rushed forward, tearing at the body with their hands, with knives, with rocks, with stones, howling and cursing. Jesse's head, of its own weight, fell downward toward his father's head. Someone stepped forward and drenched the body with kerosene. Where the man had been, a great sheet of flame appeared. Jesse's father lowered him to the ground.

"Well, I told you," said his father, "you wasn't never going to forget *this* picnic." His father's face was full of sweat, his eyes were very peaceful. At that moment Jesse loved his father more than he had ever loved him. He felt that his father had carried him through a mighty test, had revealed to him a great secret which would be the key to his life forever.

"I reckon," he said. "I reckon."

Jesse's father took him by the hand and, with his mother a little behind them, talking and laughing with the other women, they walked through the crowd, across the clearing. The black body was on the ground, the chain which had held it was being rolled up by one of his father's friends. Whatever the fire had left undone, the hands and the knives and the stones of the people had accomplished. The head was caved in, one eye was torn out, one ear was hanging. But one had to look carefully to realize this, for it was, now, merely, a black charred object on the black, charred ground. He lay spread-eagled with what had been a wound between what had been his legs.

"They going to leave him here, then?" Jesse whispered.

"Yeah," said his father, "they'll come and get him by and by. I reckon we better get over there and get some of that food before it's all gone."

"I reckon," he muttered now to himself, "I reckon." Grace stirred and touched him on the thigh: the moonlight covered her like glory. Something bubbled up in him, his nature again returned to him. He thought of the boy in the cell; he thought of the man in the fire; he thought of the knife and grabbed himself and stroked himself and a terrible sound, something between a high laugh and a howl, came out of him and dragged his sleeping wife up on one elbow. She stared at him in a moonlight which had now grown cold as ice. He thought of the morning and grabbed her, laughing and crying, crying and laughing, and he whispered, as he stroked her, as he took her, "Come on, sugar, I'm going to do you like a nigger, just like a nigger, come on, sugar, and love me just like you'd love a nigger." He thought of the morning as he labored and she moaned, thought of morning as he labored harder than he ever had before, and before his labors had ended, he heard the first cock crow and the dogs begin to bark, and the sound of tires on the gravel road.

## WILLARD MOTLEY

*who was one of America's most successful black authors died in 1965. His best-known novels are* Knock on any Door *and* Let No Man Write My Epitaph. *For the last twelve years of his life Motley lived in Mexico City. "The Almost White Boy" was written in 1963, at the beginning stages of national black militancy in America. Its focus is not upon the broad aspects of racism as a social problem, but upon the way ingrained racism affects the relationship between two human beings. Motley leaves it to you to reflect upon the social causes of the incident his story presents.*

# THE ALMOST WHITE BOY

By birth he was half Negro and half white. Socially he was all Negro. That is when people knew that his mother was a brownskin woman with straightened hair and legs that didn't respect the color line when it came to making men turn around to look at them. His eyes were gray. His skin was as white as Slim Peterson's; his blond hair didn't have any curl to it at all. His nose was big and his lips were big—the only tip-off. Aunt Beulah-May said he looked just like "poor white trash." Other people, black and white, said all kinds of things about his parents behind their backs, even if they were married. And these people, when it came to discussing him, shook their heads, made sucking sounds with their tongues and said, "Too bad! Too bad!" And one straggly-haired Irish woman who had taken quite a liking to him had even gone so far as to tell him, blissfully unmindful of his desires in the matter, "I'd have you marry my daughter if you was white."

One thing he remembered. When he was small his dad had taken him up in his arms and carried him to the big oval mirror in the parlor. "Come here, Lucy," his father had said, calling Jimmy's mother. His mother came, smiling at the picture her two men made hugged close together; one so little and dependent, the other so tall and serious-eyed. She stood beside him, straightening Jimmy's collar and pushing his hair out of his eyes. Dad held him in between them. "Look in the mirror, son," he said. And they all looked. Their eyes were serious, not smiling, not staring, just gloom-colored with seriousness in the mirror. "Look at your mother. . . . Look at me." His dad gave the directions gravely. "Look at your mother's skin." He looked. That was the dear sweet mother he loved. "Look at the color of my skin." He looked. That was his daddy, the best daddy in the world. "We all love each other, son, all three of us," his dad said, and his mother's eyes in the mirror caught and held his father's with something shining and proud through the seriousness; and his mother's arm stole up around him and around his daddy. "People are just people. Some are good and some are bad," his father said. "People are just people. Look—and remember." He had remembered. He would never forget.

Somehow, something of that day had passed into his life. And he carried it with him back and forth across the color line. The colored fellows he palled with called him "the white nigger," and his white pals would sometimes look at him kind of funny but they never said anything. Only when they went out on dates together; then they'd tell him don't let something slip about "niggers" without meaning to. Then they'd look sheepish. Jim didn't see much difference. All the guys were swell if you liked them; all the girls flirted and necked and went on crying jags now and then. People were just people.

There were other things Jim remembered.

. . . On Fifty-eighth and Prairie. Lorenzo with white eyes in a black face. With his kinky hair screwed down tight on his bald-looking head like flies on flypaper. Ruby with her face all shiny brown and her hair in stiff-standing braids and her pipy brown legs Mom called razor-legs. Lorenzo saying, "You're black just like us." Ruby singing out, "Yeah! Yeah! You're a white nigger—white nigger!" Lorenzo taunting, "You ain't no different. My ma says so. You're just a nigger!" Lorenzo and Ruby pushing up close to him with threatening gestures, making faces at him, pulling his straight blond hair with mean fists, both yelling at the same time, "White nigger! White nigger!"

The name stuck.

. . . Women on the sidewalk in little groups. Their lips moving when he walked past with his schoolbooks under his arm. Their eyes lowered but looking at him. "Too bad! Too bad!" He could see them. He knew they were talking about him. "Too bad! Too bad!"

. . . Mom crying on the third floor of the kitchenette flat on Thirty-ninth Street. Mom saying to Dad, "We've got to move from here, Jim. We can't go on the street together without everybody staring at us. You'd think we'd killed somebody."

"What do we care how much they stare or what they say?"

"Even when I go out alone they stare. They never invite me to their houses. They say—they say that I think I'm better than they are—that I had to marry out of my race—that my own color wasn't good enough for me."

Dad saying, "Why can't people mind their own business? The

hell with them." Mom crying. No friends. No company. Just the three of them.

. . . Then moving to the slums near Halstead and Maxwell, where all nationalities lived bundled up next door to each other and even in the same buildings. Jews. Mexicans. Poles. Negroes. Italians. Greeks. It was swell there. People changed races there. They went out on the streets together. No more staring. No more name-calling.

He grew up there.

. . . Getting older. And a lot of the white fellows not inviting him to parties at their houses when there were girls from the neighborhood. But they'd still go out of the neighborhood together and pick up girls or go on blind dates or to parties somewhere else. He didn't like to think of the neighborhood parties with the girls and the music and everything, and the door closed to him.

. . . Only once he denied it. He had been going around with Tony for a couple of weeks over on Racine Avenue. They played pool together, drank beer together on West Madison Street, drove around in Tony's old rattling Chevy. One day Tony looked at him funny and said, point-blank, "Say, what are you anyway?"

Jim got red; he could feel his face burn. "I'm Polish," he said.

He was sorry afterwards. He didn't know why he said it. He felt ashamed.

. . . Then he was finished with school and he had to go to work. He got a job in a downtown hotel because nobody knew what he really was and Aunt Beulah-May said it was all right to "pass for white" when it came to making money but he'd better never get any ideas in his head about turning his back on his people. To him it was cheating. It was denying half himself. It wasn't a straight front. He knew how hard it was for colored fellows to find decent jobs. It wasn't saying I'm a Negro and taking the same chances they took when it came to getting a job. But he did it.

Jim remembered many of these things; they were tied inside of him in hard knots. But the color line didn't exist for him and he came and went pretty much as he chose. He took the girls in stride. He went to parties on the South Side, on Thirty-fifth and Michigan, on South Park. He went dancing at the Savoy Ballroom —and the Trianon. He went to Polish hops and Italian fiestas and Irish weddings. And he had a hell of a swell time. People were just people.

He had fun with the colored girls. But some of them held off from him, not knowing what he was. These were his people. No—he didn't feel natural around them. And with white people he wasn't all himself either. He didn't have any people.

Then all of a sudden he was madly in love with Cora. This had never happened before. He had sometimes wondered if, when it came, it would be a white girl or a colored girl. Now it was here. There was nothing he could do about it. And he was scared. He began to worry, and to wonder. And he began to wish, although ashamed to admit it to himself, that he didn't have any colored blood in him.

He met Cora at a dance at the Trianon. Cora's hair wasn't as blond as his but it curled all over her head. Her skin was pink and soft. Her breasts stood erect and her red lips were parted in a queer little loose way. They were always like that. And they were always moist-looking.

Leo introduced them. Then he let them alone and they danced every dance together; and when it was time to go home Leo had disappeared. Jim asked her if he could take her home.

"I think that would be awfully sweet of you," she said. Her eyes opened wide in a baby-blue smile.

She leaned back against him a little when he helped her into her coat. He flushed with the pleasure of that brief touching of their bodies. They walked through the unwinding ballroom crowd together, not having anything to say to each other, and out onto Cottage Grove, still not having anything to say. As they passed the lighted-up plate-glass window of Walgreen's drugstore Jim asked her, "Wouldn't you like a malted milk?" She didn't answer but just smiled up at him over her shoulder and he felt the softness of her arm in the doorway.

She sipped her malted milk. He sat stirring his straw around in his glass. Once in a while she'd look up over her glass and wrinkle her lips or her eyes at him, friendly-like. Neither of them said anything. Then, when Cora had finished, he held the match for her cigarette and their eyes came together and stayed that way longer than they needed to. And her lips were really parted now, with the cigarette smoke curling up into her hair.

In front of her house they stood close together, neither of them wanting to go.

"It was a nice dance," Cora said; and her fingers played in the hedge-top.

"Yes, especially after I met you."

"I'm going to see you again, aren't I?" Cora asked, looking up at him a little.

Jim looked down at the sidewalk. He hoped he could keep the red out of his cheeks. "I might as well tell you before someone else does—I'm a Negro," he said.

There was a catch in her voice, just a little noise not made of words.

"Oh, you're fooling!" she said with a small, irritated laugh.

"No, I'm not. I told you because I like you."

She had stepped back from him. Her eyes were searching for the windows of the house to see that there was no light behind the shades.

"Please, let me see you again," Jim said.

Her eyes, satisfied, came away from the windows. They looked at the sidewalk where he had looked. Her body was still withdrawn. Her lips weren't parted now. There were hard little lines at the corners of her mouth.

"Let me meet you somewhere," Jim said.

Another furtive glance at the house; then she looked at him, unbelievingly. "You didn't mean that—about being colored?"

"It doesn't matter, does it?"

"No—only—"

"Let me meet you somewhere," Jim begged.

Her lips were parted a little. She looked at him strangely, deep into him in a way that made him tremble, then down his body and back up into his eyes. She tossed her head a little. "Well—call me up tomorrow afternoon." She gave him the number.

He watched her go into the house. Then he walked to the corner to wait for his streetcar; and he kicked at the sidewalk and clenched his fists.

Jim went to meet her in Jackson Park. They walked around. She was beautiful in her pink dress. Her lips were pouted a little bit, and her eyes were averted, and she was everything he had ever wanted. They sat on a bench far away from anybody. "You know," she said, "I never liked nig—Negroes. You're not like a Negro at all." They walked to the other end of the park. "Why do you tell people?" she asked.

"People are just people," he told her, but the words didn't sound real any more.

Twice again he met her in the park. Once they just sat talking and once they went to a movie. Both times he walked her to the car line and left her there. That was the way she wanted it.

After that it was sneaking around to meet her. She didn't like to go on dates with him when he had his white friends along. She'd never tell him why. And yet she put her body up close to him when they were alone. It was all right too when she invited some of her friends who didn't know what he was.

They saw a lot of each other. And pretty soon he thought from the long, probing looks she gave him that she must like him; from the way she'd grab his hand, tight, sometimes; from the way she danced with him. She even had him take her home now and they'd stand on her porch pressed close together. "Cora, I want you to come over to my house," he told her. "My mother and father are swell. You'll like them." He could see all four of them together. "It isn't a nice neighborhood. I mean it doesn't look good, but the people are nicer than—in other places. Gee, you'll like my mother and father."

"All right, I'll go, Jimmy. I don't care. I don't care."

Dad kidded him about his new flame, saying it must be serious, that he had never brought a girl home before. Mom made fried chicken and hot biscuits. And when he went to get Cora he saw Dad and Mom both with dust rags, shining up everything in the parlor for the tenth time; he heard Dad and Mom laughing quietly together and talking about their first date.

He hadn't told them she was a white girl. But they never batted an eye.

"Mom, this is Cora."

"How do you do, dear. Jimmy has told us so much about you." Dear, sweet Mom. Always gracious and friendly.

"Dad, this is Cora." Dad grinning, looking straight at her with eyes as blue as hers, going into some crazy story about "Jimmy at the age of three." Good old Dad. "People are just people."

Dad and Mom were at ease. Only Cora seemed embarrassed. And she was nervous, not meeting Dad's eyes, not meeting Mom's eyes, looking to him for support. She sat on the edge of her chair. "Y-y-yes, sir . . . No, Mrs. Warner." She only picked at the good food Mom had spent all afternoon getting ready. And Jim, watching her, watching Dad and Mom, hoping they wouldn't notice, got ill at ease himself and he was glad when he got her outside. Then they were themselves again.

"Mom and Dad are really swell. You'll have to get to know them," he said, looking at her appealingly, asking for approval. She smiled with expressionless eyes. She said nothing.

On Fourteenth and Halstead they met Slick Harper. Slick was as black as they come. It was sometimes hard, because of his southern dialect and his Chicago black-belt expressions, to know just what he meant in English. He practiced jitterbug steps on street corners and had a whole string of girls—black, brownskin, high-yellow. Everybody called him Slick because he handed his bevy of girls a smooth line and because he wore all the latest fashions in men's clothes—high-waisted trousers, big-brimmed hats, bright sports coats, Cuban heels and coconut straws with gaudy bands. Slick hailed Jim; his eyes gave Cora the once-over.

"Whatcha say, man!" he shouted. "Ah know they all goes when the wagon comes but where you been stuck away? And no jive! Man, ah been lookin' for you. We're throwing a party next Saturday and we want you to come."

Jim stood locked to the sidewalk, working his hands in his pockets and afraid to look at Cora. He watched Slick's big purple lips move up and down as they showed the slices of white teeth. Now Slick had stopped talking and was staring at Cora with a black-faced smirk.

"Cora, this is Slick Harper."

"How do you do." Her voice came down as from the top of a building.

"Ah'm glad to meetcha," Slick said. "You sho' got good taste, Jim." His eyes took in her whole figure. "Why don't you bring her to the party?"

"Maybe I will. Well, we've got to go." He walked fast then to keep up with Cora.

Cora never came over again.

Cora had him come over to her house. But first she prepared him a lot. "Don't ever—ever—tell my folks you're colored. Please, Jimmy. Promise me. . . . Father doesn't like colored people. . . . They aren't broad-minded like me. . . . And don't mind Father, Jimmy," she warned.

He went. There was a cream-colored car outside the house. In the parlor were smoking stands, and knickknack brackets, and a grand piano nobody played. Cora's father smoked cigars, owned a few pieces of stock, went to Florida two weeks every winter, told stories about the "Florida niggers." Cora's mother had the same parted lips Cora had, but she breathed through them heavily as if she were always trying to catch up with herself. She was fat and overdressed. And admonished her husband when he told his Southern stories through the smoke of big cigars: "Now, Harry, you mustn't talk like that. What will this nice young man think of you? There are plenty of fine upright Negroes—I'm sure. Of course I don't know any personally. . . . Now, Harry, don't be so harsh. Don't forget, you took milk from a colored mammy's breast. Oh, Harry, tell them about the little darky who wanted to watch your car—'Two cents a awah, Mistah No'the'nah?'

Cora sat with her hands in her lap and her fingers laced tightly together. Jim smiled at Mr. Hartley's jokes and had a miserable time. And Jim discovered that it was best not to go to anybody's house. Just the two of them.

Jim and Cora went together for four months. And they had an awful time of it. But they were unhappy apart. Yet when they were together their eyes were always accusing each other. Sometimes they seemed to enjoy hurting each other. Jim wouldn't call her up; and he'd be miserable. She wouldn't write to him or would stand him up on a date for Chuck Nelson or Fred Schultz; then she'd be miserable. Something held them apart. And something pulled them together.

Jim did a lot of thinking. It had to go four revolutions. Four times a part-Negro had to marry a white person before legally you were white. The blood had to take four revolutions. Mulatto—that's what he was—quadroon—octoroon—then it was all gone. Then you were white. His great-grandchildren maybe. Four times the blood had to let in the other blood.

Then one night they were driving out to the forest preserves in Tony's Chevy. "What are you thinking, Jimmy?"

"Oh, nothing. Just thinking."

"Do you like my new dress? How do I look in it?"

"Isn't that a keen moon, Cora?" The car slid along the dark, deserted highway. They came to a gravel road and Jim eased the car over the crushed stone in second gear. Cora put her cheek against the sleeve of his coat. The branches of trees made scraping sounds against the sides of the car. Cora was closer to him now.

He could smell the perfume in her hair and yellow strands tickled the end of his nose. He stopped the motor and switched the lights off. Cora lifted his arm up over her head and around her, putting his hand in close to her waist with her hand over his, stroking his. "Let's sit here like this—close and warm," she whispered. Then her voice lost itself in the breast of his coat.

For a long time they sat like that. Then Jim said, "Let's take a walk." He opened the door and, half supporting her, he lifted her out. While she was still in his arms she bit his ear gently.

"Don't do that," he said, and she giggled.

Panting, they walked through the low scrub into the woods. The bushes scratched their arms. Twigs caught in Cora's hair. Their feet sank in the earth. Cora kept putting her fingers in Jim's hair and mussing it. "Don't. Don't," he said. And finally he caught her fingers and held them tight in his. They walked on like this. The moon made silhouettes of them, silhouettes climbing up the slow incline of hill.

Jim found a little rise of land, treeless, grassy. Far to the northeast, Chicago sprawled, row on row of dim lights growing more numerous but gentler.

The night was over them.

They sat on the little hillock, shoulder to shoulder; and Cora moved her body close to him. It was warm there against his shirt, open at the neck. They didn't talk. They didn't move. And when Cora breathed he could feel the movement of her body against him. It was almost as if they were one. He looked up at the splash of stars, and the moon clouding over. His arm went around her, shieldingly. He closed his eyes and put his face into her hair. "Cora! Cora!" The only answer she gave was the slight movement of her body.

"Cora, I love you."

"Do you, Jimmy?" she said, snuggling up so close to him that he could feel her heart beat against him.

He didn't move. But after a while she was slowly leaning back until the weight of her carried him back too and they lay full length. They lay like this a long time. He looked at her. Her eyes were closed. She was breathing hard. Her lips were parted and moist.

"Jimmy."

"What?"

"Nothing."

She hooked one of her feet over his. A slow quiver started in his shoulders, worked its way down the length of him. He sat up. Cora sat up.

"There's nobody here but us," she said. Her fingers unbuttoned the first button on his shirt, the second. Her fingers crept in on his chest, playing with the little hairs there.

"There's nobody here but us," she said, and she ran her fingers inside his shirt, over his shoulders and the back of his neck.

"We can't do this, Cora. We can't."

"Do you mean about you being colored? It doesn't matter to me, Jimmy. Honest it doesn't."

"No. Not that. It's because I love you. That's why I can't. That's why I want—"

He sat up straight then. His fingers pulled up some grass. He held it up to the light and looked at it. She had her head in his lap and lay there perfectly still. He could hear her breathing, and her breath was warm and moist on the back of his other hand where it lay on his leg. He threw the grass away, watched how the wind took it and lowered it down to the ground. He lifted her up by the shoulders, gently, until they were close together, looking into each other's eyes.

"I want it to be right for us, Cora," he said. "Will you marry me?"

The sting of red in her cheeks looked as if a blow had left it there; even the moonlight showed that. She sat up without the support of his hands. Her arms were straight and tense under her. Her eyes met his, burning angrily at the softness in his eyes. "You damn dirty nigger!" she said, and jumped up and walked away from him as fast as she could.

When she was gone he lay on his face where he had been sitting. He lay full length. The grass he had pulled stuck to his lips. "People are just people." He said it aloud. "People are just people." And he laughed, hoarsely, hollowly. "People are just people." Then it was only a half-laugh with a sob cutting into it. And he was crying, with his arms flung up wildly above his head, with his face pushed into the grass trying to stop the sound of his crying. Off across the far grass Cora was running away from him. The moon, bright now, lacquered the whiteness of his hands lying helplessly above his head; it touched the blondness of his hair.

## ELDRIDGE CLEAVER

*is currently in exile from American political authorities. He is best known for his book* Soul on Ice *and for his activities as Minister of Culture of the Black Panther Party, which is also undergoing political persecution. In this selection, one of Cleaver's few works of fiction, gang life among blacks and Chicanos is seen amidst the problems of surviving in the ghetto.*

# THE FLASHLIGHT

From each obstacle encountered and conquered, Stacy sapped fresh strength with which to confront the next; and from that next conquest, his depleted drive was again restored and poised to meet the latest oncoming task. Life to him was an endless series of regularly spaced hurdles he had to leap over. This was the form of his imagination—not that he was in any big hurry to reach some particular goal in life. But life was motion and motion required a direction and Stacy was young and saw the years stretched out before him as he sprinted down the track of his days. He hated dead ends and stagnation and wanted always to see ahead ample room for maneuver. He thought of himself as having no fear, as a strong, rough cat who would become even more so, because in the world he knew, strength seemed to have the edge.

He was lord of his gang and his word was law. He was light and quick on his feet, and a fierce, turbulent spirit drove him on, like a dynamo imprisoned in the blood, flesh and bone of his body. He set the pace. It was not that his gang did only the things Stacy did best but that everything they did he seemed to do better. The others deferred to him as though he were a prince among them, with mysterious powers of a higher caliber than theirs, as if somehow he was born with a built-in gun and they with built-in knives. They did not question or resent this. To them, it was life, nature. They were glad to have Stacy as one of their own and they followed his lead.

Stacy was conscious of the role he played, but he did not prance before the grandstands. It could be said that he was humble in his way and bowed low before the others even as he bullied them about, because there was always absent from this bullying that ultimate hostility of which they all knew he was so capable when up against cats from other neighborhoods. Among them, there was knowledge of each other, the thick glue of the brotherhood of youth, of their separate selves bound into one. If Stacy made a decision, it was only the summation of their interests as a whole, because as far as they wanted anything, they all wanted the same things. He was the repository of their youthful collective sovereignty. Perhaps, then, it is incorrect to say that Stacy's word was law. Their law was that of a roving band owing allegiance to itself alone. Stacy occupied his peculiar place among them precisely because he knew the restraints and sanctions implicit in the mechanics and spirit of a functioning gang. Had he been less skillful in his choices, less willing to risk all on the curve of his instincts, it would have been their loss as much as his. Together they formed a unit, clinging to one another for support. What he had he gave to them and the others did the same. There was nothing premeditated about it. It just happened that Stacy had the power of the endearing smile, the rebuking frown, the assenting nod, the admonitory shake of the head.

. . .

Of late, however, Stacy was growing friendlily disgusted with the others, primarily because they seemed content to continue in the same rut. He was beginning to feel miserably trapped and hemmed in by the thick futility of the very things he had loved and pursued with satisfaction and a sense of fulfillment. Only a few weeks ago, he could still draw delight and deep contentment from the raids they threw on El Serrano, from kicking in a window and ransacking a store, from stripping the hubcaps, wheels and accessories from cars, from stealing the clothing from clotheslines or from breaking into a restaurant or café after it had closed and eating up as much food as they could hold in their guts and taking away with them all they could carry. These things no longer filled him with a warm glow after they were all over; rather, he would feel dejected and somehow disappointed in himself and the others, as if it all had been a big waste of time. When he went on a raid now, it was only because he knew the others depended upon him and that they would be angry and confused if he refused to go with them. Besides, he did not have anything else in mind to do, and he was not the type to enjoy doing nothing.

Stacy liked the money and the extra clothes that thievery brought him, but he was burned out on the ritual of these raids. As far back as he could remember, they had been a part of his life, and he knew from neighborhood lore that the practice of the raids existed as a tradition in Crescent Heights long before he or the others came along. It seemed natural for the youth of Crescent Heights to steal whatever they could from the white people of El Serrano. At this time in Stacy's life, Crescent Heights was separated from El Serrano by two miles of unimproved vacant lots that ran up to the top of a hill, so that from Crescent Heights, El Serrano could not even be seen. The long slope of the hill was a wall between the Negro and Mexicans who lived in Crescent Heights and the whites of El Serrano.

On a clear night, the lights of El Serrano could be seen against the sky from Crescent Heights; but from El Serrano, the sky over Crescent Heights looked black and unbroken, even by the moon and stars. Stacy was fascinated by this contrast. Many times, either when setting out on a raid or on his way back, Stacy would pause at the top of the hill and brood over it. The darkness in which Crescent Heights was wrapped seemed familiar and safe to him, warm and protecting, while the lights of El Serrano held both a fascination and a terror for him. He was principally aware of the lights because they were central to the ritual of the raids. It was a maxim to his gang that "where there is light there is wealth." They often repeated this to each other when searching through El Serrano for things to steal.

Each neighborhood had its own school. The police station and fire department servicing both areas were located in El Serrano. El Serrano was a thriving community with a frisky business section, while Crescent Heights was a residential slum devoid of any business except for a few corner grocery stores, liquor stores, gas stations and beer joints.

The only swimming pool and motion-picture theater in the region were in El Serrano, and during the summer, the kids from Crescent Heights hiked over the steep hill, paid their money and went in for a swim. On Saturday and Sunday, they'd go to the movies and, on their way home, fan out through El Serrano, looking for loot. By bedtime, the wealth of Crescent Heights was certain to have increased in proportion to a corresponding decrease in that of El Serrano's. Stacy's gang not only picked up things on the way back from the swimming pool or movies but two or three times each week, they'd wait for nightfall and then trek over the hill to throw a raid.

All this seemed so futile to Stacy now. He could feel that a change had to be made—just what, he could not tell. But he knew that something would happen and a way would open up for him. In the meantime, he continued to lead the raids and, although he would be just as systematic and cautious as ever, it was no longer a pleasure. It was a task.

. . .

Stacy loved Crescent Heights. He did not feel comfortable or secure anywhere else. When he ventured out of the neighborhood, on infrequent trips downtown or to the East Side or to Watts, he was always relieved when the trip was over and he was back among the familiar sights and sounds of Crescent Heights. Even school was still far enough away from his part of Crescent Heights that he felt alien and uncomfortable until he was away from the school and back on his own stamping grounds. He hated the teachers at Crescent Heights School for their way of talking down to the Negro and Mexican students and the superior attitude he saw reflected in them. He hated most of all the discipline they imposed upon him, the authority they tried to assert over him, to which they wanted him willingly to submit but which he resisted and rebelled against. The school seemed to him more like a prison than a school, the teachers seemed more like custodial guards than instructors and the atmosphere seemed more like that of a battlefield than of a place of learning. Stacy never got into fights with the teachers, as some of the others did, but he let it be known that if any of the teachers ever hit him—if the boys' vice-principal, for example, ever took him into his office and tried to force him to bend over and look at the rainbow colors drawn on the lower part of the wall, while the v.p. swatted him on his ass with his huge perforated paddle, as he did some of the others —there would be blood. Understanding this, the teachers would turn their heads from certain infractions when committed by Stacy, while they would pounce on other students for precisely the same transgressions. Sometimes, in the dreams of his heart, Stacy longed for one of the teachers to lay a hand on him, so he could work him over. In his mind, he saw himself grabbing a teacher and beating him down to a bloody pulp. The teachers, sensing something of this desire in him, left him alone.

Stacy loved the freedom he found in Crescent Heights. He felt he was losing it each time he set foot on the school grounds. It was not that he found the schoolwork difficult—he found it easy and was quick to catch on—but the whole situation repelled him. He felt that books and the knowledge in them were part of a world that was against him, a world to which he did not belong and which he did not want to enter, the world of which the hateful teachers were representatives and symbols. After school each day, it took several blocks of walking before he was free of its field of force. Then he blossomed, felt himself. His pace quickened and became his own again.

Stacy's loyalty went to Crescent Heights. To him, his neighborhood was the center of the world. Isolated somewhat from the rest of Los Angeles, in the way that each part of that scattered metropolis is isolated from every other, Crescent Heights was a refuge. If Stacy had been captured by beings from another planet, who cast him into a prison filled with inhabitants from all the planets, and if he were asked by the others where he lived, he would have said:

"I'm Stacy Mims from Crescent Heights."

"Crescent Heights?" they would ask, puzzled.

"Oh," Stacy would remember, "Crescent Heights is the name of my neighborhood. I'm from Planet Earth. Crescent Heights is on Earth. It's in the United States of America, in the state of California."

. . .

The nucleus of the neighborhood was the Crescent Heights housing project, a low-rent complex of 100 units, laid out in long rows. They looked like two-story elongated boxcars painted a pale yellow or a weak pink, the colors alternating row by row. At the center of the project was the administration building and in back of it was a large playground. Behind the playground was a huge incinerator with a chimney that towered high above the buildings of Crescent Heights. Tenants from all over the project brought their trash to the incinerator to burn. The project sat down in sort of a valley formed by hills on three sides, with the fourth side wide open and leading down to Los Angeles. All traffic entered Crescent Heights through this side. As one traveled farther up into the valley, the streets ran out of pavement and asphalt and became dirt roads. The dirt roads turned into well-worn foot-paths; the paths tapered into intermittent trails; the trails evaporated into the rolling hills, which the people of

Crescent Heights regarded with a peculiar love. And while the county of Los Angeles had built the housing project with its drawn-to-scale playground laid out scientifically—basketball court here, volleyball court there, horseshoe pits here, swings there, slide over there, monkey bars and ladder here, tetherball there, hopscotch here—Stacy's playground and that of the members of his gang had always been the hills of Crescent Heights.

Scattered throughout the hills surrounding the project were the ramshackle houses of the old families, the houses Stacy and his gang grew up in. There was a subtle distinction between the old families, who lived in the hills, and the inhabitants of the project. It was not that the houses in the hills had been there long years before the project; there had been similar houses on the site where the project now stood. The owners of those houses had been evicted by the county and state authorities after a bitter fight, which was lost by the homeowners before it ever began. The memory of it was still fresh, and there was a lingering undercurrent of resentment at this encroachment. The project itself was a symbol of the forces that had gutted the old neighborhood against the will and desire of the people, breaking up lifelong friendships and alliances, demolishing the familiar environment and substituting a new one. Although this prejudice was not as strong as in former times, it lingered on in the lore of the people.

The major point of difference was that most of the inhabitants of the project were women with small children, women who had not grown up in Crescent Heights but who had come there from other areas of Los Angeles, whose ties were with friends and relations who were strangers to the people who had lived in Crescent Heights all their lives. The names of these women had popped up on the Housing Authority's long waiting list downtown and, eager to get the apartment for which they might have been waiting for a year or more, they accepted a vacancy in Crescent Heights, sight unseen. These were unwed mothers on state aid, divorcees, women who had been abandoned by their men and the waiting wives, living on allotment checks, of Servicemen stationed always somewhere far away. The turnover was rapid among residents of the project; someone always seemed to be moving in or out. But no one ever moved out of the surrounding hills. There, whole families lived. Most of them, like Stacy's family, owned the little plots of ground on which they lived.

. . .

After school each day, and after they had eaten their evening meals and performed whatever chores they had to do, Stacy's gang used to meet at the playground in the project, pouring down from the hills, drawn there like moths to a light. On weekends and holidays, they usually hiked deep into the hills. They would take along their slingshots to shoot at the doves, pigeons and quail, which were plentiful in those hills. Sometimes they would return home in the evening with fowl for their mothers to cook. Or they would give the birds to women in the project, who always received them gladly, sometimes giving the boys some small change in return. In season, they would collect wild walnuts from the trees, and there were wild peaches, apricots, pears, figs, loquats and quince. Wild berries grew in patches here and there. Old Mexican men plowed sections of the hills and sowed them with corn, squash and sugar cane. There was always plenty for all who took the trouble to help themselves. Stacy and the others would sometimes harvest large quantities of the corn and sell it to the women of the project.

Those hills were the soul of Crescent Heights. Old-timers spun out legends concerning them. They told how somewhere in those hills was hidden an ancient Indian burial ground and that the graves were filled with priceless treasures. There was gold, intricately worked by artisans and set with splendid jewels, goblets encrusted with precious stones. The old-timers would talk and the youngsters would listen. A curse would fall on anyone who went looking for the treasures to reach them, one had to disturb the sleep of the dead. It was said that many people had gone into those hills and were never seen or heard from again. Under this ominous cloud, Stacy and the others would test their courage by roaming deep into the hills, their eyes peeled for signs of an Indian grave, half expecting to be pounced upon by supernatural guardians of the dead, deliciously savoring the sweet taste of fear defied. With a gentle breeze waving the tall grass, they walked barefooted under the sun, drawing strength from each kiss of the soil on the soles of their feet.

Once in a while, shepherds from out of nowhere would appear, bringing huge herds of sheep to pasture and graze there for a few months. From his house, Stacy sometimes looked out to see the dark, undulating mass of shaggy creatures sweeping in a rolling wave across the hills, the bells tinkling around the necks of the leaders and the sheep dogs running back and forth, keeping the strays in line. The shepherds would be seen with long sticks, trudging along with their flocks. It always reminded Stacy of scenes from the Bible. Only the style of clothes had changed.

During summer, when the grass on the hills dried out, sometimes it would catch on fire, by the working of the sun through the prism of a broken wine bottle. Sometimes Stacy and the others grew impatient with the sun and would, out of sight of everyone, toss a match or two and wait for the fire trucks to come racing over from El Serrano. They would hear the sirens screaming in the distance, listening tensely as they came closer and closer, until finally the huge red engines would swing into sight and the firemen would go into action. With guilty knowledge or not, Stacy and the others would watch the firemen and sometimes would even help them. Sometimes, to avoid inconvenient surprises and possible disasters, the county would send out crews and deliberately set a fire and control it, burning all the grass near the houses and back for about a mile into the hills as a safety measure. The whole neighborhood would turn out to watch a fire, to see the flames walk across those hills, leaving a black sheet of ash in its wake. It was always something of a shock to Stacy to see those hills transformed in an instant from tall grass to burned-out cinders. Black and barren, the hills were no good for walking barefooted, and there was no hope of finding any fowl concealed in a clump of grass. The youngsters of Crescent Heights did not enjoy the hills when the grass had burned. Fortunately for them, the fires never succeeded in burning all the grass, and they could always go deep into the hills until they found a point to which the flames had not penetrated.

One time the hills were so burned out that the gang had to hike a long way before reaching the green grass. Mitch, characteristically, set the grass on fire to spoil their day. Helplessly, Stacy and the others watched as the fowl took to the air. Turning on Mitch, they punched and kicked him until he cried. Stacy did not tell them to stop. Mitch was mean as a dog. From him, the others learned early that a human being is full of surprises and capable of evil improvisations.

Mitch was full of peevish taciturnity. He was sullen and vicious. The others watched him, waiting for each new manifestation of his scurviness. Many times Stacy had sat mystified in

Mitch's back yard and listened with astonishment as he cursed out his mother. He would hurl at her the most vile names, in English and Spanish and combinations of both languages, and his mother, who seemed not at all surprised or shocked, would never raise her voice. She would ask him, in very gentle tones, how he could talk to his own mother that way, inspiring an infuriated Mitch to a new torrent of epithets. She would stand there, at the top of the stairs, gently, calmly drying her hands on her apron, waiting for him to finish, never interrupting him. If she had started to speak and he cut her off, she would stop in mid-sentence, half apologetically, and let him finish; then she would start again, very slowly, cautiously, kindly.

"I'm your own mother," she would say to him in Spanish, or: "Come inside and talk to me, son; you can bring Stacy with you, too, if you like."

Mitch would only curse her more.

After a while, Stacy, unable to stand it longer, would make Mitch come away with him. Stacy liked Mitch's mother. He saw her as a sweet old woman who always gave the neighborhood kids little Mexican goodies to eat, which she made up and kept on hand for when they came around. Big and fat, she went to Mass every Sunday morning, rain or shine, with a black shawl over her head and shoulders, her small children trailing behind her. These small children were one of the mysteries of Crescent Heights and the subject of endless rumors. Mrs. Chapultapec had children who were over 40 years old, while Mitch was 14. There were always new children being added to the household. Around the yard, they followed her like tiny shadows. Nobody seemed to know just which of the children were her own or, in fact, if any of them were actually hers. If asked, she would only smile and say that all the children in the world were her own, and refuse to discuss it further. The older people understood that she had had, all her life, a great love and tenderness for children, and she would take in anybody's unwanted child and raise him as her own. Nobody knew how many children she had actually raised. Some she would keep for a few years, then their parents would come and take them back. At the bottom of Mitch's rage lay the fact that he did not know who his parents were, because he did not believe anything Mrs. Chapultapec told him.

Once, a new little face showed up in the house, and it so

happened that Mitch knew that the little boy belonged to one of the women who lived in the project. Overhearing Mrs. Chapultapec telling someone, in her way, that the little boy was her own, Mitch was suddenly blasted by a vision that Mrs. Chapultapec was not really his own mother and that he did not know who his real mother was. When he asked Mrs. Chapultapec about it, she just told him that he was her very own. He accused her of being a notorious liar.

Mitch used to threaten to kill his father, or, rather, Mr. Chapultapec, whom Mitch always had believed to be his father but whom he later "disowned." A small, stooped, white-haired old man with quick, bird-like movements, he would never scold or correct the children. He was terrified of them. He would go straight to work and come straight home in the evening, except on Friday evening, when he would stop off at the Cozy Corner Café, down a few beers with the old-timers and listen to a few Spanish records on the jukebox. Tipsy from the beers, his spirits charged from the music and the few moments spent in the company of the gents he had known all his life, he would walk crisply home, speaking to all he met.

"*Buenas noches, Señor Chapultapec,*" Stacy and the others would say to him on Friday evenings.

"*Salud, muchachos,*" he'd answer with extreme good feeling.

If Mitch was there he would hurl a curse at the old man, who would cast a frightened look Mitch's way and continue on without a pause.

On Sunday evenings, Mr. Chapultapec could be found down at the Catholic church across the street from the project, sitting in the little area set aside for *fiestas,* sanctioned by the Church, which were held several times each year. There were booths set up where bingo was played; where darts three for a dime were tossed at balloons to win a Kewpie doll or a piggy bank; where washing machines and sets of silverware were raffled off; where kids, their eyes blindfolded, took turns trying to burst the *piñata* with a stick, then scrambled over the ground to retrieve the prizes that had been inside. At *fiesta* time, the whole neighborhood would turn out, drop by the church to look, to be seen, to participate. And although the church belonged more to the people of the hills than to those of the project—most of whom seemed to be Protestants or atheists or people who did not belong to anything—they, too, came round.

But on these Sunday evenings, the churchyard would be quiet; and while Mr. Chapultapec sat outside with one or two old men, watching the cars going up and down Mercury Avenue, watching the people passing by, Mrs. Chapultapec would be in the little kitchen in the back of the church with four or five other old women. They would make *tacos, tamales, burritos* and chili with fried beans, which were sold over a counter through a slitted window, like tellers in banks. The customers would mostly take their purchases with them to eat from paper napkins like hot dogs; but if they chose, as often happened if a fellow had a girl with him, they spread their orders on a table in the yard and enjoyed the serene atmosphere. Stacy could recall that when he was very little, he and the others would go to the window and the old women would give them a *taco* or a *tamale* free, with a kind word and a smile. After he was older and had the money, Stacy would still drop by Sunday evenings to purchase these warm goodies. He loved these old women and their quiet Mexican dignity. They asked no questions and condemned no one and seemed always to have their inner eyes fixed on a distant star.

It was from these old ladies that Stacy first heard of the legend of *Llorona*. He had been younger and the story fascinated him. In the long, long ago, the old women had said, in a small village deep in old Mexico, a wicked woman murdered her three children in a jealous rage, to get revenge on her unfaithful husband, who had run off with a beautiful *señorita*. She hid their tiny bodies so well that even she could not find where she had hidden them. Sometime later, an angel from God vested her to deliver a divine sentence. Until she found the bodies of her children and took them to the priest for a proper burial, she would know no peace. The wicked woman searched all over but could never find her little ones. Her doom was to wander the world over—in vain!—searching for her lost *niños*. When the wind, blowing down from the hills, whistled through the trees, or when a coyote or a dog howled mournfully, or when there was any other strange noise in the night, it was said to be the *Llorona* crying for her lost *niños* and for mercy from God. The mothers of Crescent Heights kept their kids in line by saying that if they were bad, the *Llorona* would come carry them away. That was why, when Mitch cursed Mrs. Chapultapec, sometimes he would put in, "Fuck the *Llorona* up her ass!" At this, Stacy would feel a chill down his back. One day, Mitch screamed at Mrs. Chapultapec:

"You're the *Llorona*!"

. . .

Stacy's would be the last generation to grow up in the old Crescent Heights, the Crescent Heights of the hills. They sort of felt that. They felt themselves to be part of something that was passing away. The world of the housing project would conquer in the end. Along with the houses, which were succumbing to decay, Crescent Heights was dying. An image of its death was reflected in the decaying bodies of the old men and women. The younger people were moving deeper into the central city, drawn from the outskirts of town to the inner core by the same forces that attracted other generations of Americans into the new cities from off the farms and out of the countryside. Like all those other great neighborhoods of Los Angeles of the first half of the 20th Century, Crescent Heights had commanded a fierce tribal loyalty from its inhabitants and, along with Maravilla, Flats, Temple, Clanton, The Avenues, Hazard, Happy Valley, Alpine and Rose Hill, it had achieved a greatness and a notoriety in the folklore of Los Angeles. But the glory of these neighborhoods was of a genre alien to that inscribed in the official histories of the city. These were outlaw neighborhoods inhabited by Negroes and Mexicans, viewed by the whites in the core of the city as a ring of barbarians around their Rome, a plague of sunburned devils raging against the city gates. But the people of these neighborhoods had their lives to live. They were born and they died, they loved and they hated, they danced and mated with each other and fought against each other and won their reputations by day and by night.

A clue to the unimportance with which the city fathers regarded Crescent Heights is the fact that during election campaigns, the candidates never bothered to visit there in search of votes. They neither needed nor wanted those tainted votes. In turn, the people of areas such as this viewed the metropolis with distrust and hostility, if not hatred and scorn. Their sons were inducted into its Army and were locked into its jails and were channeled, along with their daughters, into its factories. But it could not claim, nor did it seem to want, their loyalty and respect. The metropolis asked no such tender sentiments of the peripheral neighborhoods: It asked only for their sons and daughters.

After the heart had been cut out of Crescent Heights and the housing project built in its place, the inhabitants of the old neighborhood, or what was left of it, lived on in an uncertain wind, under the threat that at any moment, county and state authorities would take over their land, invoking eminent domain. There were all kinds of rumors, inspired by uncertainty and the memory of how suddenly and without warning the other homes had been condemned. One would hear of secret plans to build a country club and golf course in the hills, that the hills would be the site of a huge new campus of the University of California, that the Brooklyn Dodgers were coming to L.A. to build a stadium in the hills or that the Housing Authority would extend the project, covering vast areas of the hills with concrete, with the pink and yellow rows of apartments designed to official specifications. The only sure thing about these rumors was their effect on the people. No one bothered to lay plans, because they might be forced to move at any moment. No one bothered to improve or repair their houses and land, because they did not want to go to the trouble and expense, only to see their work rolled down the hills by bulldozers—just as they had seen the other houses and dreams demolished to make way for the project. All that was left of the old Crescent Heights were the old people and the last of their children. And in the new, the Crescent Heights of the project, there were only the women with their fatherless children—and the Marijuanos.

. . .

In that underground world, psychologically as far beneath the consciousness of a city's solid citizens as a city's sewerage system is beneath its streets, in the subterranean realm of narcotics peddlers and users, marijuana peddlers, gamblers, pimps, prostitutes, the thugs and the cutthroats, the burglars and the robbers, and the police—Crescent Heights had long been known as the marijuana capital of Los Angeles. If the old Crescent Heights was dying, the marijuana traffic did not feel the sting of its death, and it was not the odor of decay that the marijuana pushers smelled but the aroma of folding greenbacks. Even before the project, there was marijuana in Crescent Heights, grown in the hills in modest quantities. But the demand so vastly exceeded the supply that could be cultivated with safety in the hills that of the tons of marijuana flowing into Los Angeles from Mexico, hundreds of pounds of the weed found their way to Crescent Heights. The project became the base of operation, and the weed was controlled by the outlaws of old Crescent Heights, known by the local people as the Marijuanos. They were the alienated sons, in their 20s, of the people of the hills, those sons whom the metropolis had found indigestible. They had criminal records or had dropped out of school without acquiring any skills to fit into the economy. And they were either unfit or disinclined to enter the Armed Forces. They had fallen back on the skill of the hills, the knack of eluding the police while trafficking in contraband.

While he was very young, Stacy had the exciting experience of knowing a neighborhood hero who happened also to be one of Mitch's older "brothers." Known as Flamingo, his heroism consisted of the fact that he was the first guy from Crescent Heights to go to San Quentin. Surprised in the act of robbing a liquor store in El Serrano, he was wounded in a blazing gun fight with police. His crime partner was shot dead. When, years later, he got out of prison, Flamingo joined the Marijuanos and started dealing in weed. Soon, however, he disappeared from the scene. No one seemed to know where he had gone, but it was said, with knowing winks, that he had gone to Mexico and bought a fabulous hacienda from which he directed the flow of marijuana into Crescent Heights.

In Stacy and his gang, the Marijuanos inspired a romantic apprehension just short of fear. Not that they had anything to fear from the Marijuanos, whom they had known all their lives and to whom they were connected by memories and, in some cases, by blood. But the presence of the Marijuanos infused Crescent Heights with an aura of danger and mystery. At night, while Stacy and the others would be down at the playground, loafing, they would see the strangers who came to Crescent Heights furtively, after dark, and who would sometimes ask them:

"Are any of the guys around?"

Stacy had directed many an inquirer to the spot where the Marijuanos might be. But if, when out at night, Stacy's gang was always aware of the whereabouts of the Marijuanos, it was more for the purpose of keeping out of their way than anything else. If the Marijuanos came too near, Stacy and his gang, with the excited feeling of being brushed by danger, would run away to another part of the project. But the Marijuanos kept generally to the darker sections of the project and Stacy and the others had the playground and other lighted areas to themselves. It was commonly known that the Marijuanos sometimes knocked out street lights to make it darker in certain favored spots; it would be a couple of months before the county sent someone around to fix them.

If Stacy or the others ever saw a policeman, they'd run tell the Marijuanos. "The narcs are over there," they'd say, and the Marijuanos would melt away into the shadows. But every so often, Stacy would hear that one of them had gotten caught by the narcs and was put in jail.

. . .

Stacy wanted something to happen. The gang was beginning to seem like a prison and, although he continued to play his role, he went through the steps mechanically, his mind drifting, looking for somewhere to lodge. He had toyed with the idea of quitting school to look for a job somewhere, but it did not occur to him that he would really do this; it was more or less his way of threatening himself. He did want profoundly for his life to change. He felt that he could no longer endure school, the gang and the endless round of throwing raids on El Serrano. Now, when he burglarized a building, he would come away feeling disappointed, no matter what the haul. He no longer had the patience to search out all the hiding places, and so if things were not left out in plain sight, he would miss them. And this had been Stacy's main function in the gang. He was known to have a nose for sniffing out the valuables hidden by the owners in some secret cranny. Now he could feel a growing dissatisfaction among the others and, although no one criticized him, he knew they were watching him, wondering. How could he explain to them what was going on inside himself, when he himself didn't know? How could he explain that his pride was offended by what they were doing? How could he make them understand that if they carried off everything in El Serrano, it would not be enough to satisfy what he was beginning to feel inside?

He did not voice these questions; they were the ghosts behind his changed attitude toward the others. It began to bother him that when they burglarized a place, he was always the first one to go in, to look around and make sure it was safe before the others entered. If he didn't go in first, they'd just stand there and scare each other, and the fear would travel round the circle until panic set in. But even after he had crawled through the window, searched the whole place for hidden danger—a night watchman, a dog—

they were still afraid, it seemed to him, of the dark, of what they could not see in the dark if something were there. It was easy for them to imagine anything being there: a squad of policemen crouching in the corner, waiting until they were all inside, before switching on the lights to mow them down with shotguns or to capture them and take them to Juvenile Hall; or a pack of menacing Doberman pinschers or German shepherds too cool to bark that would leap on them from behind and rip their flesh to shreds. This fear had always been with them and, in the past, they all used to laugh at it. But now it seemed totally unacceptable to Stacy.

Mitch, though, was never afraid. The danger with him was that, spurred on by his total contempt for everything, he would crawl through a window as if he owned the place and, once inside, while shaking it down to see if it was safe, would growl viciously to attract any dogs, kick over packing crates, upset tables and chairs, in an effort to smoke out something. He'd open closets and storerooms. Unable to see in the dark, he would not hesitate to yell into the void:

"Hey, you in there, I see you! Get the fuck out of there!"

The first time he did that, pandemonium broke loose among the others and they took off, running. Stacy had to run after them, overtake them, shake some sense into them before they could understand that it was only Mitch who had shouted. It had been a hard job persuading them to go back with him and impossible to get them to crawl through the window into the dark room, because Mitch, when Stacy called to him to prove to the others that it was safe, refused to answer. Stacy pictured him, leering at them through the dark, that sullen, scornful scowl on his face. In that moment, Stacy wanted to kick that face. He knew that Mitch was probably looking right at them, at the window that was a patch of light silhouetted against the night sky, but would not answer.

"You lousy bastard, Mitch!" Stacy said into the dark window. But in another sense, Stacy thought it was beautiful of Mitch not to answer, especially at a time like this, when he himself was absolutely serious and the others were afraid and they all were a long way from home and in danger of being shot or taken to jail. It took real dedication for Mitch to remain perverse in such circumstances. The others refused to precede Stacy through the window.

"Well, fuck all of you, then," he said, exasperated, and went swiftly through the window.

The others hesitated at first, decided all at the same time that they'd rather be inside than out, and they all tried to squeeze through the window at once, making a ton of racket, cursing and scratching each other as they fought to get through.

Then Mitch, somewhere in the darkness, hissed at them, "Shut the fuck up!"

Guided by his voice, Stacy caught Mitch in the dark and, bringing up his knee with just slightly less than hostile force, he shook Mitch up and shoved him to the floor. "Next time, you better answer me, you stupid shit!" he said. And, extending his foot in the dark, he made contact with Mitch, jarring him with a stiff thrust. It felt like he got him in the side.

Now that they were inside, Stacy could hear the others as they scuffled about in the dark, searching for objects of value with which to fill their gunny sacks. Stacy did not even unroll his sack. He leaned against the wall and let his mind drift as he waited for the others to finish. He was thinking of what had happened the previous week, when he had first made up his mind that this could not go on, that something had to change, that he had to find himself a new life.

. . .

The thought had come to him during a raid on a school cafeteria a week before. After eating all they could hold and filling their sacks, they had thrown all the other food on the floor, gutted the refrigerator, smashed all the cups, salt and pepper shakers and glasses, scattered the silverware, bent the trays out of shape and overturned the tables.

"Stacy, make Mitch stop!" Turtle said.

Mitch had turned all the jets of the gas range up full blast. Flames leaped at the ceiling. Shoving Mitch aside, Stacy began spinning the knobs to shut off the flow of gas. Screaming, Mitch came at him with a fork. Stacy feinted at him and, when Mitch slashed at him with the fork, Stacy stepped back and caught his arm, twisting it behind his back.

"Drop it!" Stacy demanded, applying pressure.

"You cocksucker!" hissed Mitch, defeated, holding the fork just long enough to register his defiance.

Stacy turned all the burners down.

"Let's burn this motherfucker down!" Mitch pleaded. "Then the *gavachos* won't have a school to go to!"

"That's going too far," the others protested in a chorus.

That did it. That nauseated Stacy. *That's going too far.* The words burned into his mind. What did they mean by that? That's when Stacy really knew that he was finished, that he had to cut all this loose. Like a sailor locking the hatches on a submarine, he twirled the knobs, opening all the jets all the way, and the range burst into flames again.

"Let's go!" he shouted. He helped the others out the window. Looking around, he saw Mitch in front of the range, jumping up and down, laughing hysterically and cursing the flames in Spanish. Stacy rushed back and dragged him away by his belt.

"Leave go! Leave go!" Mitch yelled, as he struggled to free himself, straining toward the flames.

The building was mostly of wood and in a minute it would be one raging inferno. Stacy, seeing that Mitch would not relent in his efforts to return to the fire, hit him in his gut and shoved him up and out through the window. As Stacy came through the window, just as he expected, Mitch tried to kick him in the face to knock him back into the burning room. Catching Mitch's foot in the air, Stacy hurled him backward into the dark night air, landing him on his ass; and as Stacy ran past Mitch, he was very careful not to miss stepping on him. He heard curses behind him in the night as he ran to catch up with the others.

The idea, voiced by the others, that Mitch had been "going too far," bothered Stacy. It sounded like the belief that if one sailed far enough over the open seas, one would eventually sail off the edge of the world. He found solace in repeating to himself: The world is round; you can sail on and on and end up where you started. It was as if the others were saying to him that the world is flat. His mind seized upon this incident to justify breaking with his gang. He was only waiting for the right moment.

. . .

The next time the others asked him to go on a raid, Stacy said no. After the others resigned themselves to inactivity for the night, Mitch and he stole away from them, leaving them sitting around the playground looking dejected, and the two of them headed for El Serrano by themselves. They prowled around for hours, without spotting anything worth while. It was Saturday night and every house seemed occupied; every business establishment, though they saw some that were obviously deserted and closed down for the weekend, seemed strangely forbidding and whispering of threat, crawling with hidden danger. They both felt this, without speaking about it, tacitly deciding there was no chance for action that night. Walking through alleys, down dark streets, always in the shadows, cutting back, zigzagging, to avoid the glow of street lights, they trekked to the heart of El Serrano. They knew they could not afford to be seen by anyone, because only whites lived there and one look at them and it would be all over. If a car headed their way, they scrambled for cover, crouching behind parked cars, lying flat behind trees, kneeling down in the shrubbery near houses. The police would know, upon seeing them, that their only business there was to steal. El Serrano was their happy hunting ground. They had been hunting there for years, and for as long as he had been doing it, not one of his gang had got caught. The cops would lie in wait for them, leaving a bait of valuables out in clear sight, but they always passed it up. "That's a fishhook," they'd whisper to each other in the dark, gliding through the shadows. Sometimes they'd sneak noiselessly right past the cops sitting in their patrol car parked in the shadows. Once, Mitch had crawled up to their car on his belly, like a commando, and removed the valve from a rear tire. By the time the cops detected the flat, Mitch was well away.

"Let's hit a few cars, if nothing else," Stacy said to Mitch, as they crept silently down an alley.

"OK," Mitch said.

With their screwdrivers, they jimmied the vent windows on the passenger side of a few cars, sticking in an arm to roll down the window, then shoving their heads through the window to look around inside the car. It was their habit to take anything of value. They'd take coats, binoculars, guns, tools, radios, groceries, anything they could use or sell. Most of their loot they sold to the people of the project at cheap prices. They didn't care; all they wanted was a little something to keep them going from day to day. Goods in hand, they'd go from door to door and show what they had. The people would jokingly call them bad boys, but they were always glad to see them. They'd let them in, pull the curtains and examine the display. Clothes for their children, for themselves, cooking utensils, lamps, clocks, radios—everything went. If they could not sell something, the gang would give it away. If nobody wanted it, they'd throw it away. But most of the time, if they had something that wouldn't sell, they'd let Mitch keep it. His cellar contained a wealth of worthless loot.

Their pockets and sacks filled, Stacy and Mitch had almost called it quits when Stacy saw another car that seemed to beckon to him. That car, he was to think later, communicated with him. He had already got himself a nice leather jacket that, because he was big for his age, was not a bad fit. He got to the car and opened the window. On the front seat was the long, snaky body of a five-battery flashlight with a fifth of whiskey in a bag. Good for a few bucks, Stacy thought. He fell in with Mitch and they headed for home.

As soon as they were a safe distance away, Stacy tested the flashlight, playing it down a pitch-black alley, fascinated by its powerful beam.

"Put out that fucking light, man!" Mitch growled curtly. "You trying to signal to the cops where we are, or something?"

Stacy shined the light in Mitch's face. Mitch tried to stare the beam down, but it wounded his eyes, forcing him to turn his head.

"You crazy fucker," he said in disgust.

Stacy felt giddy about the flashlight, his new possession. Its properties he seemed to appropriate and incorporate into his own being. The light, he felt, was a powerful extension of himself.

. . .

The next night, when they all met at the playground, Stacy took his flashlight with him. It was an instrument that had to be used, a charge that by its potency refused to lie idle. As he left his room, it all but leaped into his hand, guiding itself into his palm. He had taken it completely apart several times, feeling a flush of triumph each time he reassembled it, flicked the button and saw the bulb glow. It seemed to him that when he assembled the parts, he was creating the light. And he had the strange feeling that this light would be the instrument by which great change would come into his life.

He loved his light. When he broke it down, he would caress the five batteries with his fingers, and the bulb, the gaskets, the spring in the cap. So closely did he examine each part that he had no doubt that out of a mountain of similar parts, he could easily select his own.

He would use the power of the batteries sparingly. As they all lay on the grass of the playground, the others kept urging him to turn it on, to show them how powerful was its beam. Stacy stood up and cast the beam into the hills, and a patch of light could be seen dimly sweeping the surface of the hills at a great distance. The others were impressed. Stacy lay on the lawn, fondling the metallic tube that held the mysteries of his future.

"Where did you score it?" asked one of the others.

"El Serrano," Stacy answered.

"When?"

"Last night."

"Last night?" Turtle perked up. "I thought you said last night you weren't going?"

Stacy made no reply. A heavy silence ensued. The others, not looking directly at Stacy, were nevertheless watching him closely, waiting for an answer to clarify what looked now like a betrayal.

Stacy said nothing.

A few minutes passed in this silence.

Then Mitch said, "Don't you punks know when you're not wanted along? Can't you take a hint?" Mitch spoke in a harsh, contemptuous tone, which was not directed to Turtle alone but to all the others. "Me and Stacy ducked you suckers last night and we scored heavy by ourselves. I got myself a flashlight, too, just like that one." After a significant pause, he added, "Who needs you guys with them? All you ever do is make noise."

Stacy was embarrassed, for he could feel himself how Mitch's words were hurting the others. He smothered an impulse to smash Mitch's face, to make him shut up, to make him retract that lie about his own flashlight—but he held back. Inside, he was glad that Mitch had spoken these things, for now something was done that could never be undone, and he had the intimation that Mitch was setting him free. Then he said, "You've got a big, dumb mouth, Mitch."

"It's my mouth," Mitch snapped back, "big or not."

Suddenly, Stacy felt a deep loathing for the position he was in. He hated the necessity of giving them an explanation. If he acknowledged that he owed them an explanation, he would be sucked back in and lose this chance. Jumping up, he kicked Mitch in his side, and as he ran off into the night, he could hear Mitch's laughter following him.

He ran until he was exhausted, then walked until he found himself at the other end of the project. Around him, it was quiet and dark. The apartment windows were yellow squares where the shades stopped the light. He sat down on the lawn, propped himself up against a tree and closed his eyes. His heart still raced in his chest from running. He clung to his flashlight, glad to be alone.

Sometime later, he became aware of the sound of movement near him; he heard the muffled rustling of paper. Opening his eyes, at first he could make out nothing, then just below him, where the lawn on which he sat sloped down to meet the sidewalk, he saw a shadowy form kneeling and reaching into the hedge next to Mrs. Chapman's front door. Stacy realized it was a Marijuano, but he couldn't make out which one. As he sat there, watching, it seemed to him that he was becoming aware of the Marijuanos for the first time. Then he wondered, what would the Marijuano do if he shined the flashlight on him? This thought, this possibility of making something happen, already had fastened upon his imagination; and even as he hesitated, he knew that he would end by doing it. He perceived, in a flash, that such a step would set in motion forces of which he was not even aware. What will happen? he wondered. Am I afraid to do it? By putting the question to himself in terms of his courage, he knew that he had to do it.

Silently, he got to his feet and squatted on his haunches. Aiming his flashlight at the phantom, he savored the keen edge of the moment before the action, anticipating it with sharp exhilaration. Then he pressed the button. It was Chango! Chango froze, all lit up, his face contorted, eyes wide with panic. For the briefest moment, Chango remained motionless, his arm buried in the hedge up to his shoulder. Then he exploded, scooting backward on his knees, stumbling to his feet, tripping, falling down, crawling, looking over his shoulder to see if he was being chased, his face hysterical. Stacy kept the light on him till he turned the corner on the hump, then he flicked off the light and ran toward the playground. When he came to another dark spot, he fell onto the lawn and laughed till he could hardly breathe, rolling on the ground. The way Chango had looked when the beam first split his face, how he had flown! For long after, just the thought of it would send him chuckling.

That night, he dreamed that the world was inside a box with steep sides and no top, like the walls of a frontier fort, and the sun was a huge flashlight of a billion batteries with a tube so long it never ended; and some kid in the sky watching the people groping in darkness below pressed the button and the people said "Day" and he released the button and the people said "Night." Stacy woke up in a sweat, clutching his flashlight, keenly appreciative of the powers of light.

. . .

The next day, time seemed to slow down on purpose to torture him. It was with a keen foretaste of pleasure that he awaited the setting of the sun. All during school, he could think of nothing but his flashlight, the Marijuanos and how he would terrorize them again tonight. He saw himself chasing them all over the project. They would be there tonight, he had not the slightest doubt. They were always there. When it rained, they donned heavy coats and plastic slickers and did business as usual. The only time the Marijuanos would leave was when the cops came; and when the cops went away, the Marijuanos reappeared, like air drawn into a vacuum. That evening, Stacy hid in the bushes around the square at the end of the row of apartments in which Mrs. Chapman lived, not far from the spot where he had surprised Chango. The square was one of several located at strategic intervals throughout the project, placed there by the architects to add beauty to public housing. It was a concrete-covered clearing 30 feet by 40 feet, surrounded with hedges and flowers and shaded by a tall tree. The tree's rich foliage hung over the square like a giant umbrella. It could actually stop rain. On each side of the square were four cement benches of the type often seen in public parks: a flat slab resting on two upright stays. During the daylight hours, the little kids scampered and romped in the square, riding in their wagons and on tricycles, catching and bouncing big rubber balls, jumping rope, playing jacks and hopscotch. At night, the Marijuanos took it over, using it to contact customers who came to Crescent Heights from all over Los Angeles to score their weed.

Stacy waited for the right moment. Hidden in the shadows of the square, the Marijuanos were smoking weed and making transactions. The acrid aroma tantalized Stacy's nostrils. He had smelled burning marijuana before, but never from so close. He knew that what he was doing was very dangerous and this knowledge, coupled with the intrigue of the night, the smell of the burning marijuana and the sight of men moving back and forth, talking in low voices and laughing now and then, gave it all a touch of adventure. Stacy felt keenly alive. He was doing something not often done, something he had never done before, something none of the others had ever dreamed of doing. He knew also that if a bush moved, the Marijuanos noticed it. Like him, they were all neighborhood boys who had spent their entire lives in the immediate area. They knew every tree, every hole in the ground, every rock, every bush and everybody. They could feel a cop coming. No cop could have snuck up on them as Stacy had done. It would not have been natural. But Stacy, who knew and loved every inch of the earth of Crescent Heights, had crept right up on the Marijuanos. With a little effort, he could have reached out and touched them. When he could bear it no longer, Stacy aimed his flashlight into the square. Before pressing the button, he gave the bushes a violent shake, drawing the Marijuanos' attention to him, then let go with the light. The Marijuanos gave up the square in a mad stampede, crashing through the bushes and running over each other. Stacy then dashed off in the direction the Marijuanos were least likely to take: He sprinted to the well-lit playground.

Three days later, at school, Mitch said, "The Marijuanos are after you."

"After me for what?" Stacy asked, a look of surprise on his face.

"You know for what," Mitch said curtly. "You and that flashlight, that's what."

"What about my flashlight?" Stacy asked, hungrily wanting to hear any details.

"You won't be playing dumb when they catch you," said Mitch. "Cutie, Chico and Chango said they're going to catch you and fuck you up. You know better than to fool around with those guys."

Stacy had not expected the Marijuanos to send him congratulations, but he did not really feel in danger; just as when he went on raids to El Serrano, he had not regarded the dangers as real.

They were part of a game, like a penalty in football. If one made no mistakes, it was as if the penalties did not even exist.

"Fuck the Marijuanos," Stacy said.

"That's easy to say," said Mitch, "but wait till they get their hands on you. The Marijuanos don't play around when they mean business."

Stacy had assumed that each time he turned on his light, the Marijuanos would automatically react the same way—run. But now that they knew it was he and not the cops, he knew their reaction would change. Whereas their main purpose had been to flee from a cop, it was now an angry desire to extinguish Stacy's light.

"The Marijuanos said you're putting the heat on them," Mitch had said.

"Later for them," Stacy said. But he was jolted by that charge. In Crescent Heights, only a rat would knowingly put the heat on someone. And a known rat couldn't last five minutes in Crescent Heights. It was unheard of. Stacy had not expected such a charge. He threw it from his mind as too absurd and unpleasant to think about. He continued to creep up on the Marijuanos and flash his light on them. And when he did, it was he who had to take off, running, because the Marijuanos would be right on his heels. It was easy for Stacy to outdistance them. They laid traps for him. Some of them hid in the bushes while the others tried to sucker him in. They laid up a store of bricks, bottles and beer cans. Once, they hid near Stacy's home to ambush him on his way home. Stacy laughed at them and outflanked their every maneuver. Their battle, the Marijuanos' efforts to catch Stacy and his efforts to escape, became notorious in Crescent Heights. Everybody knew they were after him. Everyone waited for news that Stacy had at last been caught. Eluding the Marijuanos became his full-time occupation. He defied them with pride.

But underneath it all, Stacy had some regrets that the feud had ever gotten started. He would have liked nothing better than to be out of the spot he was in, which was becoming more difficult to occupy. He wished that he could just leave them alone and drop the whole thing, to be done with the whole affair, to be free from worrying about how to get away from the Marijuanos in a given situation. But he continued to force the issue, convinced that he would somehow come through it all unscathed.

The Marijuanos became marksmen with bricks and bottles and it took some prize footwork by Stacy to keep from getting his brains knocked out. Even so, they hit him in the side once with a heavy rock that took the wind out of him, and the only thing that kept him from collapsing on the spot was the sure knowledge of what they would do to him if they caught him.

The Marijuanos sent people to talk to Stacy, but he refused to listen. They repeated that he was ruining their business.

Stacy's mother said to him: "Son, you better mind your Ps and Qs. I know what you been doing and you'd better stop it."

"I know what I'm doing," Stacy said.

Now the other members of the gang shied away from Stacy. They said he had gone crazy and they saw nothing positive in his keen thrill of excitement in outwitting the Marijuanos. They didn't know how it felt to be hunted by them, to elude their traps, to spring out of the bushes unannounced with a blazing torch and scare the pants off of the Marijuanos. The Marijuanos were all in their 20s and Stacy, who felt neither old nor young, enjoyed this relationship with individuals already grown. He was a factor in their existence, whether they liked it or not. He had chosen them, like some gadfly in a dangerous game. They were stuck with Stacy and it was up to them to solve the problem. For his part, Stacy's course was clear. He would continue to bug them with his light.

One night, he climbed up a tree and from his perch saw Polio, a fat, phlegmatic Mexican, hide a little bag behind a bush. Several times, Polio returned to the bush, extracted from the bag, replaced it and went away. Stacy shinnied down the tree and chose a spot ten feet away from Polio's stash. The next time Polio came back, Stacy waited until he had gotten the bag and stuck his hand into it, then he hit him in the face with the blinding beam of the light. Dropping the bag, Polio uttered a cry and was in full flight before he realized it was Stacy, himself already running through the night in the opposite direction. He had scored again. It was coups like that that egged him on.

The Marijuanos tried a new trick. As Stacy walked home from school with the others one evening, two cars, one in front of him and one behind, pulled sharply into the curb and out poured the Marijuanos. They had not, however, counted on the speed of Stacy's legs. Stacy leaped over a fence into someone's yard and, before the startled dog in the yard realized what was happening, ran out the back way, was over the back fence and cutting out up the hill. Looking back, he saw the Marijuanos pile into their cars, burning rubber getting out of there. The stakes were going up. Such desperation!

When Stacy was in his classrooms, he was careful to sit near a window, in case the Marijuanos burst in to trap him. He suffered through his third-period class, because it was on the second floor and there was no ledge outside the windows. He felt trapped in that room. He fully expected the Marijuanos to know all about this particular room, and he would not have been surprised to look up one day and find them there. He watched for them in the halls, on the stairways, in the schoolyard, behind lockers in the gymnasium. During lunch hour, he often saw the Marijuanos drive by the school, their faces sweeping the crowd with Stacy-seeking eyes.

. . .

One day, the Marijuanos stopped chasing him and they stopped throwing things at him. When he crept up on them and flashed his light, they'd just look at him, in his direction. Stacy couldn't figure it out, but he didn't hang around waiting for answers. He ran away, as usual. One evening, Stacy was down at the playground, loafing, with his flashlight stuck in his belt like a knife or a gun. Turtle walked up to him.

"Chico wants to talk to you," Turtle said, pointing to another part of the playground, where, dressed in blue denims and wearing dark glasses, Chico stood waiting on the other side of the Cyclone fence. Warily, Stacy walked over, staying on his side of the fence, continually looking over his shoulder to see if the other Marijuanos were sneaking up on him while Chico held his attention.

"What do you want?" Stacy asked, mistrustfully.

"Say, Stacy," Chico began, "this shit has got to stop, man."

Stacy could see that Chico was burning with anger but trying also to conceal it. It shone like flaming coals in his black eyes. His mouth was set in a fixed, down-thrusting scowl. Through the fence, Stacy got the same feeling he had had when, at the Griffith Park Zoo, he had stood outside the cage of a lion and stared into its huge cat eyes. He was thankful for the fence between them. He said nothing, only stared into Chico's dark glasses, at the fire in those eyes, and he saw something there besides anger and hatred, something that surprised him: He saw the embryo of a smile.

"I want to make a deal with you," Chico said.

"What kind of a deal?" Stacy asked, regarding Chico narrowly. His anxiety was that the other Marijuanos were sure to try something.

"Here," Chico said, and he shoved a ten-dollar bill into a square of the fence. Stacy let it lie there, wedged in the wire.

"What's that for?" asked Stacy.

"For your flashlight," Chico said.

"For ten dollars, you can buy three or four like this one," Stacy said, patting his flashlight on his side.

"I want yours," said Chico.

The flashlight weighed heavily on Stacy's side. The full realization of what a burden it had become flowed in upon him. He wanted with all his heart to be rid of it.

"Listen to me, Stacy," Chico said. "You're a young cat and you don't realize what's going on. But you'd better think fast, because you don't have much time left. You know what the other guys want to do? Look." He lifted the corner of his shirt and showed Stacy the handle of a pistol stuck in his belt. "They want to just kill you. Because you're ranking our play. You're messing with our bread and butter, man."

Strangely, Stacy was not afraid. But he felt a knot in his chest, to think that the Marijuanos had been discussing his death.

"Listen, man," Chico went on. "We could kill you and bury you up on Walnut Hill and nobody would ever find your body. It would be no trouble at all. The cops wouldn't even look for you. You're just another nigger to them and they don't give a fuck about you. You know why we haven't done you up?"

Stacy stared at him impassively, not trusting himself to ask why, for not wanting to sound too urgent.

"Because you're one of us. You're from Crescent Heights." Chico paused. "So we decided to give you the respect of letting you make a choice. But maybe you're too fucking wild to see what's happening. We never like to fight with each other in Crescent Heights, Stacy, you know that. Because by sticking together, we can all make it, maybe. At least better than by fighting ourselves. At least we'll have a better chance. I'm a married man and I have my family to look out for. I don't have time to fuck around with you or anybody else. This is strictly business with me. If I get caught, I'm going to the can, and I don't look forward to that. I'm going to do everything in my power to see to it that I never get caught. Right now"—Chico paused, then went on—"right now, you are more of a problem than the narcs. So we've got to settle this right now. Right now. You know what, Stacy?" Chico looked at him and seemed to be measuring him. "You're getting to be about that age. . . . Do you get high? Do you blow weed?"

"No," Stacy said.

"Well, pretty soon. . . ." he paused. "It won't be long before you're going to get tired of running around in a pair of dirty Levis, fucking off your time with those other young cats. I've dug you and I know that you've got something on the ball. Pretty soon, you're going to want some nice clothes and some money in your pocket, some of that folding money, and you're going to want a little car of your own to ride around in with the bitches. But then you're going to find out the world is not a"—he broke off, looking around him, and swept the area with his arm—"a playground. You're going to find out the world is not a merry-go-round. It's hard, hard, Stacy. But we've got a good thing going for us here in Crescent Heights, and we intend to keep it working for us. You guys call us Marijuanos. . . . Yeah, we're Marijuanos, all right. But there are lots more Marijuanos in L.A., and lots of them come to us to score their jive. And you, with your flashlight, are fucking with all of that. I used to think like you and act like you. You know my brother Black Jack, don't you?"

"Yeah," Stacy said. "Everybody knows Black Jack."

"He used to control the action in Crescent Heights," Chico went on. "And he used to try getting me interested, but my mind was locked somewhere else. I was about your age and I used to call him Marijuano. Now I've got the bag and you're calling me Marijuano. It goes around and comes around; you take it a little way and then pass it on. Pretty soon, the little kids will be calling you Marijuano and, someday, kids that are not even born yet will be calling them Marijuanos. It will never end. But it's going to end for you unless you straighten up your hand.

"Take the money," Chico said, "and we'll forget the whole thing. We'll forget it all happened."

Stacy hesitated for a long moment, then said, "What about the others?"

"Same with them," Chico said. "Nobody will bother you. I give you my word. But you have to give me your word that you won't fool around anymore. I'm not giving you the money to buy you off. I'm giving it to you to wake you up."

"What good is your word?" Stacy asked. "How do I know you're not just setting me up?"

Chico looked at Stacy fiercely. "I never break my word when I give it like this. If I say I won't bother you, I won't. If I say I'm going to kill you, you're as good as dead."

Stacy walked down to the end of the fence, where it was lower. As he jumped over, he saw Mitch and the others watching. He walked up to Chico and handed him the flashlight. Chico pulled the ten-dollar bill from the fence and placed it in Stacy's hand.

"Play it cool," Chico said and walked away.

Stacy did not turn around to look after Chico. It felt good. It was a relief not to have to look over his shoulder anymore. The others walked over to Stacy. They all understood what had happened. They were all glad it was over. They all laughed and punched each other lightly to the body.

"You punks are crazy," said Mitch, off to the side.

"Let's throw a raid on El Serrano tonight," Turtle suggested.

"Count me out," Stacy said with mock astonishment, "I might find another flashlight!"

. . .

That night, Stacy walked into the square. When they saw who it was, the Marijuanos quickly surrounded him. There was murder in the intense way they crowded him.

"What the fuck you want?" Cutie snapped, fuming, his voice menacing, with overtones of blood.

"Nothing," Stacy said. He felt crushed, confused.

"Leave him alone," Chico spoke up. "Forget about it. I gave him my word that it was all over."

"You gave him your word," said Cutie, "but I didn't give him mine."

Stacy heard the click of Cutie's knife as it sprang open, although he couldn't see it in the darkness. He was afraid. Cutie was breathing in his face. The others stepped back. Stacy calculated his chances of running. All Cutie had to do was thrust upward with the blade to do damage.

"When I gave him my word, I gave him yours," Chico said. "And nobody's going to make me out a liar. Leave him alone, Cutie." Chico spoke with force and authority and he added, lowering his voice ominously: "Or are you going to make me out a liar?"

Cutie stepped back from Stacy and put his knife up. Tension evaporated from the square. The Marijuanos lit up joints of the weed.

Chico offered Stacy a joint.

"Never mind," Stacy said halfheartedly.

Chico fumbled with the joint and then lit it from the one being smoked by Gato. After he had taken a couple of drags, he passed it to Stacy.

"Here," he said.

Stacy took the joint between his fingers and raised it to his mouth, puffing in and immediately coughing out the acrid smoke. It felt like breathing over a burning rag. He was amazed at how the others could be smoking it if it tasted so bad.

"Do it like this," Chico said, taking the joint from Stacy. Chico took a long, powerful drag. Stacy watched the coal of fire travel up the joint as Chico consumed about half of it in that one drag. "Take it down into your lungs and hold it," he said. "You'll get used to it. The main thing is to hold it in your lungs as long as you can."

Stacy struggled over the remainder of the joint, coughing and choking occasionally, his throat getting raw, his eyes running, his heart racing. He was confused and a little apprehensive but continued to inhale the weed and hold in the smoke until his lungs expelled it. Then it was as if he ceased to exist. He was confronting a stranger in a body he recognized as his own but with which he was out of touch. His former state was now a memory; his new state was a soft, jet-smooth present fact. He had the sensation of being two disembodied beings fighting to inhabit one yielding body. His body, offering no resistance, became a battlefield on which two rival armies contended. The pitch of the war escalated as he took in more marijuana from the joints being passed around the circle of Marijuanos. Stacy accepted every one offered to him, and once he ended up with a lit reefer in each hand, puffing first one and then the other. He no longer cared or tried to keep track of how the war inside him was progressing. No matter which way it went, he thought, he'd still be the winner. He lost track of time. Everything seemed to occur without sequence, as if it was all happening simultaneously and spontaneously, separated rather by space than by time. He was dimly aware of people entering the square, engaging one or another of the Marijuanos in short, snappy conversation. He watched as the Marijuanos collected money and disappeared from the square for a few moments, to return and hand something to the customer. These furtive shadows would brace up and, in a moment, fade from the square into the vast Los Angeles night.

Stacy was so high off the weed that the center of his vision was blotted out, although he could see perfectly well around the edges; and through these clear edges, he was trying to see into the center, around the dark spot. He had the impression that someone had taken a bottle of liquid shoe polish and, using the dauber, painted his eyeballs down the center. He did not notice that everyone was leaving, had drifted out of the square and gone for the night—except Chico, who was talking. At first, Stacy could make no sense of what he was saying.

"What? What?" Stacy kept asking him, over and over again.

"Go home, Stacy."

"What?"

"Go to your pad, man. I'm going to split."

"What?"

"It's one o'clock, man. You got too high."

Chico was laughing in Stacy's face. He was really having a big laugh. Stacy laughed, too. His face felt like rubber and he couldn't control his expression, though it was very dark in the square and Chico could not tell. Stacy's face seemed to be sagging and he was flexing his facial muscles to hold it in place, but it kept sliding down again. "I'm not high," he said.

"No, you're not high," Chico said, laughing. "You're wasted!"

Stacy was laughing, too.

"Do you think you can find your way to your pad?" Chico asked.

"Sure," Stacy said. "Who could forget that?" Even as he spoke, he experienced the panic of having no idea where he lived. "Where are we right now?" he asked Chico.

Chico knew that, although it was funny, it was also a serious phase Stacy was going through; and if he had not been there, Stacy might have wandered around Crescent Heights all night, looking for his house.

"We're in the square by Mrs. Chapman's house," Chico said.

"Where is Mrs. Chapman's house?" Stacy asked.

Chico turned Stacy to his right and he recognized Mrs. Chapman's apartment at the end of the row. From there, traveling like a beam of light, his mind raced off into infinity, reconstructing that portion of the universe of which he was aware. . . . There is Mrs. Chapman's pad, this is the square, the playground is down there, that's Boundary Avenue up there, Florizel Street over there, Mercury Avenue over there, downtown L.A. is that way, Pasadena is that way, Lincoln Heights is over there, El Serrano and Alhambra are over there—I live down that way. Stacy felt serene, lucid, triumphant, peculiarly masterful and at peace.

"I'm going home," he said to Chico.

"Think you can make it?"

"Sure," he said. "Ain't nothing to it."

"I'll see you around," Chico said.

Stacy had started to walk in the direction of home when he missed something. He stopped, wondering what it was he was forgetting. Then he remembered the flashlight and laughed to himself. He did not know yet whether a Marijuano had any use for a flashlight. As he walked dreamily home, he had no doubt that he would soon find out.

## AL YOUNG

*is a black writer who teaches at Stanford University. He contributed this poem to* Green Flag, *a journal published in support of the Berkeley People's Park movement. He has published a volume of poetry,* Dancing. *This poem shows the possibilities for joy and love in the experience of fighting repression.*

## THE DANCER

When white people speak of being uptight
theyre talking about dissolution & deflection
but when black people say uptight
they mean everything's all right.
I'm all right.
The poem brushes gayly past me
on its way toward completion,
things exploding in the background
a new sun
in a new sky
canteloupes & watermelon for breakfast
in the Flamingo Motel
with cousin Inez
her brown face stretching & tightening
to keep control of the situation,
pretty Indian cheeks
cold black wavelets of hair,
her boyfriend
smiling from his suit.
We discuss concentration camps
& the end of time.
My mustache
wet with canteloupe juice
would probably singe
faster than the rest of me
like a thin bird over flame
in final solution of
the Amurkan problem.
Ah, Allah,
that thou hast not forsaken me
is proven by the light

playing around the plastic slats
of half-shut venetian blinds
rattling in this room on time
in this hemisphere on fire.
The descendants of slaves
brush their teeth
adorn themselves before mirrors
speak of peace & of living kindness &
touch one another
intuitively & in open understanding.
"It could be the end of the world,"
she says, "they use to didnt be afraid
of us but now that they are
what choice do they have
but to try & kill us?"
but she laughs and & I laugh & he laughs
& the calmness in their eyes
reaches me finally
as I dig my spoon into the belly of a melon

## LEROI JONES

*is one of the leading black playwrights and poets on the contemporary American scene. His plays, short stories, and poems describe and attack the Black man's plight in white America. He has also been known for his active participation in the black liberation movement. Among his better known works are* The Slave, The Toilet, *and* Dutchman, *the latter two deal with the harsh realities of being black in American society. These two poems address the desperation of response to untenable social conditions.*

# A CONTRACT.
# (for the destruction and rebuilding of Paterson)

Flesh, and cars, tar, dug holes beneath stone
a rude hierarchy of money, band saws cross out
music, feeling. Even speech, corrodes.
I came here
from where I sat boiling in my veins, cold fear
at the death of men, the death of learning, in
cold fear, at my own. Romantic vests of same death
blank at the corner, blank when they raise their fingers
Criss the hearts, in dark flesh staggered so marvelous
are their lies. So complete, their mastery, of these
stupid niggers. Loud spics kill each other, and will not
make the simple trip to Tiffany's. Will not smash their stainless
heads, against the simpler effrontery of so callous a code as gain.
You are no brothers, dirty woogies, dying under dried rinds, in massa's
droopy tuxedos. Cab Calloways of the soul, at the soul's juncture, a
music, they think will save them from our eyes. (In back of the terminal
where the cricus will not go. At the backs of crowds, stooped and vulgar
breathing hate syllables, unintelligible rapes of all that linger in
our new world. Killed in white fedora hats, they stand so mute at what
whiter slaves did to my fathers. They muster silence. They pray at the

steps of abstract prisons, to be kings, when all is silence, when all is stone. When even the stupid fruit of their loins is gold, or
do something
else they cannot eat.

# BLACK DADA NIHILISMUS

Against what light

is false what breath
sucked, for deadness.
Murder, the cleansed

purpose, frail, against
God, if they bring him
bleeding, I would not

forgive, or even call him
black dada nihilismus.

The protestant love, wide windows,
color blocked to Mondrian, and the
ugly silent deaths of jews under
the surgeon's knife. (To awake on
69th street with money and a hip
nose. Black dada nihilismus, for

the umbrella'd jesus. Trilby intrigue
movie house presidents sticky the floor.
B.D.N., for the secret men, Hermes, the

blacker art. Thievery (ahh, they return
those secret gold killers. Inquisitors
of the cocktail hour. Trismegistus, have

them, in their transmutation, from stone
to bleeding pearl, from lead to burning

looting, dead Moctezuma, find the West
a grey hideous space.

2.

From Sartre, a white man, it gave
the last breath. And we beg him die,
before he is killed. Plastique, we

do not have, only thin heroic blades.
The razor. Our flail against them, why
you carry knives? Or brutaled lumps of

heart? Why you stay, where they can
reach? Why you sit, or stand, or walk
in this place, a window on a dark

warehouse. Where the minds packed in
straw. New homes, these towers, for those
lacking money or art. A cult of death,

need of the simple striking arm under
the streetlamp. The cutters, from under
their rented earth. Come up, black dada

nihilismus. Rape the white girls. Rape
their fathers. Cut the mothers' throats.
Black dada nihilismus, choke my friends

in their bedrooms with their drinks spilling
and restless for tilting hips or dark liver
lips sucking splinters from the master's thigh.

Black scream
and chant, scream,
and dull, un
earthly
hollering. Dada, bilious
what ugliness, learned
in the dome, colored holy
shit (i call them sinned

or lost
burned masters
of the lost
nihil German killers
all our learned

art, 'member
what you said
money, God, power,
a moral code, so cruel
it destroyed Byzantium, Tenochtitlan, Commanch
(got it, *Baby!*

For tambo, willie best, dubois, patrice, mantan, the
bronze buckaroos.

For Jack Johnson, asbestos, tonto, buckwheat,
billie holiday.

For tom russ, l'overture, vesey, beau jack,

(may a lost god damballah, rest or save us
against the murders we intend
against his lost white children
black dada nihilismus

## CLARENCE MAJOR

*is a black writer who was born in Atlanta and grew up in Chicago. He has written short fiction and art criticism in addition to poetry. "Vietnam #4" is self-explanatory.*

## VIETNAM #4

a cat said
on the corner

the other day
dig man

how come so many
of us
niggers

are dying over there
in that white
man's war

they say more of us
are dying

than them peckerwoods
& it just
                don't make sense
unless it's true
that the honkeys

are trying to kill us out
with the same stone

they killing them other cats
with
you know, he said
two birds with one stone

## OUOLOGUEM YAMBO

*was born in Mali in 1940. A student of the* Ecole Normale Supérieure, *he is a* Licencié en Lettres, Licencié en Philosophie *and has a diploma in English. His first novel,* Le devoir de violence, *won the Prix Renaudot (Paris) in 1968. "When Negro Teeth Speak" shows a Black African using visionary and mystical language to come to terms with the white stereotypes projected upon his race. The focus of this reader is on American society, but clearly the question of white exploitation and black liberation in the United States has a vital relationship to the same issue throughout the world, particularly in Africa.*

## WHEN NEGRO TEETH SPEAK

Everyone thinks me a cannibal
But you know how people talk

Everyone sees my red gums but who
Has white ones
Up with tomatoes

Everyone says fewer tourists will come
Now
But you know
We aren't in America and anyway everyone
Is broke

Everyone says it's my fault and is afraid
But look
My teeth are white not red
I haven't eaten anyone

People are wicked and say I gobble
the tourists roasted
Or perhaps grilled
Roasted or grilled I asked them
They fell silent and looked fearfully at my gums
Up with tomatoes

Everyone knows an arable country has agriculture
Up with vegetables

Everyone maintains that vegetables
Don't nourish the grower well

"When Negro Teeth Speak" (*Quand parlent les dents nègres*) was first published in N° 57 of the review *Presence Africaine* (Paris), 1st Quarterly 1966.

And that I am well-grown for an undeveloped man
Miserable vermin living on tourists
Down with my teeth

Everyone suddenly surrounded me
Fettered
Thrown down prostrated
At the feet of justice

Cannibal or not cannibal
Speak up
Ah you think yourself clever
And try to look proud

Now we'll see you get what's coming to you
What is your last word
Poor condemned man

I shouted up with tomatoes

The men were cruel and the women curious you see
There was one in the peering circle
Who with her voice rattling like the lid of a casserole
Screamed
Yelped
Open him up
I'm sure papa is still inside

The knives being blunt
Which is understandable among vegetarians
Like the Westerners
They grabbed a Gillette blade
And patiently
Crisss
Crasss
Floccc
They opened my belly

A plantation of tomatoes was growing there
Irrigated by streams of palm wine
Up with tomatoes

## HUBERT SELBY, Jr.

*has worked in the Merchant Marine and at various other jobs, and has published fiction in numerous magazines. The selection reprinted below is from a group of interconnected stories published as* Last Exit to Brooklyn. *"Tralala" reveals a society and subculture developed by a minority group in America—the "white trash" of our urban slums—as a reaction to white, middle-class society.*

# TRALALA

Tralala was 15 the first time time she was laid. There was no real passion. Just diversion. She hungout in the Greeks with the other neighborhood kids. Nothin to do. Sit and talk. Listen to the jukebox. Drink coffee. Bum cigarettes. Everything a drag. She said yes. In the park. 3 or 4 couples finding their own tree and grass. Actually she didnt say yes. She said nothing. Tony or Vinnie or whoever it was just continued. They all met later at the exit. They grinned at each other. The guys felt real sharp. The girls walked in front and talked about it. They giggled and alluded. Tralala shrugged her shoulders. Getting laid was getting laid. Why all the bullshit? She went to the park often. She always had her pick. The other girls were as willing, but played games. They liked to tease. And giggle. Tralala didn't fuckaround. Nobody likes a cock-teaser. Either you put out or you dont. Thats all. And she had big tits. She was built like a woman. Not like some kid. They preferred her. And even before the first summer was over she played games. Different ones though. She didnt tease the guys. No sense in that. No money either. Some of the girls bugged her and she broke their balls. If a girl liked one of the guys or tried to get him for any reason Tralala cut in. For kicks. The girls hated her. So what. Who needs them. The guys had what she wanted. Especially when they lushed a drunk. Or pulled a job. She always got something out of it. Theyd take her to the movies. Buy cigarettes. Go to a PIZZERIA for a pie. There was no end of drunks. Everybody had money during the war. The waterfront was filled with drunken seamen. And of course the base was filled with doggies. And they were always good for a few bucks at least. Sometimes more. And Tralala always got her share. No tricks. All very simple. The guys had a ball and she got a few bucks. If there was no room to go to there was always the Wolffe Building cellar. Miles and miles of cellar. One screwed and the others played chick. Sometimes for hours. But she got what she wanted. All she had to do was putout. It was kicks too. Sometimes. If not, so what? It made no difference. Lay on your back. Or bend over a garbage can. Better than working. And its kicks. For a while anyway. But time always passes. They grew older. Werent satisfied with the few bucks they got from drunks. Why wait for a drunk to passout. After theyve spent most of their loot. Drop them on their way back to the Army-base. Every night dozens left Willies, a bar across the street from the Greeks. Theyd get them on their way back to the base or the docks. They usually let the doggies go. They didn't have too much. But the seamen were usually loaded. If they were too big or too sober theyd hit them over the head with a brick. If they looked easy one would hold him and the other(s) would lump him. A few times they got one in the lot on 57th street. That was a ball. It was real dark back by the fence. Theyd hit him until their arms were tired. Good kicks. Then a pie and beer. And Tralala. She was always there. As more time passed they acquired valuable experience. They were more selective. And stronger. They didn't need bricks anymore. Theyd make the rounds of the bars and spot some guy with a roll. When he left theyd lush him. Sometimes Tralala would set him up. Walk him to a doorway. Sometimes through the lot. It worked beautifully. They all had new clothes. Tralala dressed well. She wore a clean sweater every few days. They had no trouble. Just stick to the seamen. They come and go and who knows the difference. Who gives a shit. They have more than they need anyway. And whats a few lumps. They might get killed so whats the difference. They stayed away from doggies. Usually. They played it smart and nobody bothered them. But Tralala wanted more than the small share she was getting. It was about time she got something on her own. If she was going to get laid by a couple of guys for a few bucks she figured it would be smarter to get laid by one guy and get it all. All the drunks gave her the eye. And stared at her tits. It would be a slopeout. Just be sure to pick a liveone. Not some bum with a few lousy bucks. None of that shit. She waited, alone, in the Greeks. A doggie came in and ordered coffee and a hamburger. He asked her if she wanted something. Why not. He smiled. He pulled a bill from a thick roll and dropped it on the counter. She pushed her chest out. He told her about his ribbons. And medals. Bronze Star. And a

Purpleheart with 2 Oakleaf Clusters. Been overseas 2 years. Going home. He talked and slobbered and she smiled. She hoped he didnt have all ones. She wanted to get him out before anybody else came. They got in a cab and drove to a downtown hotel. He bought a bottle of whiskey and they sat and drank and he talked. She kept filling his glass. He kept talking. About the war. How he was shot up. About home. What he was going to do. About the months in the hospital and all the operations. She kept pouring but he wouldnt pass out. The bastard. He said he just wanted to be near her for a while. Talk to her and have a few drinks. She waited. Cursed him and his goddamn mother. And who gives a shit about your leg gettin all shotup. She had been there over an hour. If hed fucker maybe she could get the money out of his pocket. But he just talked. The hell with it. She hit him over the head with the bottle. She emptied his pockets and left. She took the money out of his wallet and threw the wallet away. She counted it on the subway. 50 bucks. Not bad. Never had this much at once before. Shouldve gotten more though. Listenin to all that bullshit. Yeah. That sonofabitch. I shoulda hitim again. A lousy 50 bucks and hes talkin like a wheel or somethin. She kept 10 and stashed the rest and hurried back to the Greeks. Tony and Al were there and asked her where she was. Alex says ya cutout with a drunken doggie a couple a hours ago. Yeah. Some creep. I thought he was loaded. Didja score? Yeah. How much? 10 bucks. He kept bullshittin how much he had and alls he had was a lousy 10. Yeah? Lets see. She showed them the money. Yasure thats all yagot? Ya wanna search me? Yathink I got somethin stashed up my ass or somethin? We/ll take a look later. Yeah. How about you? Score? We got a few. But you dont have ta worry aboutit. You got enough. She said nothing and shrugged her shoulders. She smiled and offered to buy them coffee. And? Krist. What a bunch of bloodsuckers. OK Hey Alex . . . They were still sitting at the counter when the doggie came in. He was holding a bloodied handkerchief to his head and blood had caked on his wrist and cheek. He grabbed Tralala by the arm and pulled her from the stool. Give me my wallet you goddamn whore. She spit in his face and told him ta go fuck himself. Al and Tony pushed him against the wall and asked him who he thought he was. Look, I dont know you and you dont know me. I got no call to fight with you boys. All I want is my wallet. I need my ID Card or I cant get back in the Base. You can keep the goddamn money. I dont care. Tralala screamed in his face that he was a no good mothafuckin sonofabitch and then started kicking him, afraid he might say how much she had taken. Ya lousy fuckin hero. Go peddle a couple of medals if yaneed money so fuckin bad. She spit in his face again, no longer afraid he might say something, but mad. Goddamn mad. A lousy 50 bucks and he was cryin. And anyway, he shouldve had more. Ya lousy fuckin creep. She kicked him in the balls. He grabbed her again. He was crying and bent over struggling to breathe from the pain of the kick. If I don't have the pass I can't get in the Base. I have to get back. Theyre going to fly me home tomorrow. I havent been home for almost 3 years. I've been all shot up. Please, PLEASE. Just the wallet. Thats all I want. Just the ID Card. PLEASE PLEASE!!! The tears streaked the caked blood and he hung on Tonys and Als grip and Tralala swung at his face, spitting, cursing and kicking. Alex yelled to stop and get out. I dont want trouble in here. Tony grabbed the doggie around the neck and Al shoved the bloodied handkerchief in his mouth and they dragged him outside and into a darkened doorway. He was still crying and begging for his ID Card and trying to tell them he wanted to go home when Tony pulled his head up by his hair and Al punched him a few times in the stomach and then in the face, then held him up while Tony hit him a few times; but they soon stopped, not afraid that the cops might come, but they knew he didn't have any money and they were tired from hitting the seaman they had lushed earlier, so they dropped him and he fell to the ground on his back. Before they left Tralala stomped on his face until both eyes were bleeding and his nose was split and broken then kicked him a few times in the balls. Ya rotten scumbag, then they left and walked slowly to 4th avenue and took a subway to manhattan. Just in case somebody might put up a stink. In a day or two he/ll be shipped out and nobodyll know the difference. Just another fuckin doggie. And anyway he deserved it. They ate in a cafeteria and went to an allnight movie. They next day they got a couple of rooms in a hotel on the east side and stayed in manhattan until the following night. When they went back to the Greeks Alex told them some MPs and a detective were in asking about the guys who beat up a soldier the other night. They said he was in bad shape. Had to operate on him and he may go blind in one eye. Aint that just too bad. The MPs said if they get ahold of the guys who did it theyd killem. Those fuckin punks. Whatd the law say. Nottin. You know. Yeah. Killus! The creeps. We oughtta dumpem on general principles. Tralala laughed. I shoulda pressed charges fa rape. I wont be 18 for a week. He raped me the dirty freaky sonofabitch. They laughed and ordered coffeeand. When they finished Al and Tony figured theyd better make the rounds of a few of the bars and see what was doin. In one of the bars they noticed the bartender slip an envelope in a tin box behind the bar. It looked like a pile of bills on the bottom of the box. They checked the window in the MENS ROOM and the alley behind it then left the bar and went back to the Greeks. They told Tralala what they were going to do and went to a furnished room they had rented over one of the bars on 1st avenue. When the bars closed they took a heavy duty screwdriver and walked to the bar. Tralala stood outside and watched the street while they broke in. It only took a few minutes to force open the window, drop inside, crawl to the bar, pickup the box and climb out the window and drop to the alley. They pried open the box in the alley and started to count. They almost panicked when they finished counting. They had almost 2 thousand dollars. They stared at it for a moment then jammed it into their pockets. Then Tony took a few hundred and put it into another pocket and told Al theyd tell Tralala that that was all they got. They smiled and almost laughed then calmed themselves before leaving the alley and meeting Tralala. They took the box with them and dropped it into a sewer then walked back to the room. When they stepped from the alley Tralala ran over to them asking them how they made out and how much they got and Tony told her to keep quiet that they got a couple a hundred and to play it cool until they got back to the room. When they got back to the room Al started telling her what a snap it was and how they just climbed in and took the box but Tralala ignored him and kept asking how much they got. Tony took the lump of money from his pocket and they counted it. Not bad eh Tral? 250 clams. Yeah. How about giving my 50 now. What for? You aint going no where now. She shrugged and they went to bed. The next afternoon they went to the Greeks for coffee and two detectives came in and told them to come outside. They searched them, took the money from their pockets and pushed them into their car. The detectives waved the money in front of their faces and shook their heads. Dont you know better than to knock over a bookie drop? Huh? Huh, Huh! Real clever arent you. The detectives laughed and actually felt a professional amazement as they looked at their dumb expressions and realized that they really didnt know who they had robbed. Tony slowly started to come out of the coma and started to protest that they didnt do nothin. One of the detectives slapped his face and told him to shutup. For Christs sake dont give us any of that horseshit. I suppose you just found a couple of grand lying in an empty lot? Tralala screeched, a what? The detectives looked at her briefly then turned back to Tony and Al. You can lush a few drunken seamen now and then and get away with it, but when you start taking money from my pocket youre going too far sonny. What a pair of stupid punks . . . OK sister, beat it. Unless you want to come along for the ride? She automatically backed away from the car, still staring at Tony and Al. The doors slammed shut and they drove away. Tralala went back to the Greeks and sat at the counter cursing Tony and Al and then the bulls for pickinem up before she could get hers. Didn't even spend a penny of it. The goddamn bastards. The rotten stinkin sonsofbitches. Those thievin flat-footed bastards. She sat drinking coffee all afternoon then left and went across the street to Willies. She walked to the end of the bar and started talking with Ruthy, the barmaid, telling her what happened, stopping every few minutes to curse Tony, Al, the bulls and lousy luck. The bar was slowly filling and Ruthy left her every few minutes to pour a drink and when she came back Tralala would repeat the story from the beginning, yelling about the 2 grand and they never even got a chance to spend a penny. With the repeating of the story she forget about Tony and Al and just cursed the bulls and her luck and an occasional seaman or doggie who passed by and asked her if she wanted a drink or just looked at her. Ruthy kept filling Tralalas glass as soon as she emptied it and told her to forget about it. Thats the breaks. No sense in beatin yahead against the wall about it. Theres plenty more. Maybe not that much, but enough. Tralala snarled, finished her drink and told Ruthy to fill it up. Eventually she absorbed her anger and quieted down and when a young seaman staggered over to her she glanced at him and said yes. Ruthy brought them two drinks and smiled. Tralala watched him take the money out of his pocket and figured it might be worthwhile. She told him there were better places to drink than this crummy dump. Well, lez go baby. He gulped his drink and Tralala left hers on the bar and they left. They got into a cab and the seaman asked her whereto and she said she didnt care, anywhere. OK. Takeus to Times Square. He offered her a cigarette and started telling her about everything. His name was Harry. He came from Idaho. He just got back from Italy. He was going to— she didnt bother smiling but watched him, trying to figure out how soon he would pass out. Sometimes they last allnight. Cant really tell. She relaxed and gave it thought. Cant konkim here. Just have ta wait until he passes out or maybe just ask for some money. The way they throw it around. Just gotta getim in a room alone. If he dont pass out I/ll just rapim with somethin—and you should see what we did to that little ol . . . He talked on and Tralala smoked and the lampposts flicked by and the meter ticked. He stopped talking when the cab stopped in front of the Crossroads. They got out and tried to get in the Crossroads but the bartender looked at the drunken seaman and shook his head no. So they crossed the street and went to another bar. The bar was jammed, but they found a small table in the rear and sat down. They ordered drinks and Tralala sipped hers then pushed her unfinished drink across the table to him when he finished his. He started talking again but the lights and the music slowly affected him and the subject matter was changed and he started telling Tralala what a good lookin girl she was and what a good time he was going to show her; and she told him that she would show him the time of his life and didnt bother to hide a yawn. He beamed and drank faster and Tralala asked him if he would give her some money. She was broke and had to have some money or she/d be locked out of her room. He told her not to worry that hed find a place for her to stay tonight and he winked and Tralala wanted to shove her cigarette in his face, the cheap sonofabitch, but figured she/d better wait and get his money before she did anything. He toyed with her hand and she looked around the bar and noticed an Army Officer staring at her. He had a lot of ribbons just like the one she had rolled and she figured hed have more money than Harry. Officers are usually loaded. She got up from the table telling Harry she was going to the ladies room. The Officer swayed slightly as she walked up to him and smiled. He took her arm and asked her where she was going. Nowhere. O, we cant have a pretty girl like you going nowhere. I have a place thats all empty and a sack of whiskey. Well . . . She told him to wait and went back to the table. Harry was almost asleep and she tried to get the money from his pocket and he started to stir. When his eyes opened she started shaking him, taking her hand out of his pocket, and telling him to wakeup. I thought yawere goin to show me a good time. You bet. He nodded his head and it slowly descended toward the table. Hey Harry, wakeup. The waiter wants to know if yahave any money. Showem ya money so I wont have to pay. He slowly took the crumpled mess of bills from his pocket and Tralala grabbed it from his hand and said I toldya he had money. She picked up the cigarettes from the table, put the money in her pocketbook and walked back to the bar. My friend is sleeping so I dont think he/ll mind, but I think we/d better leave. They left the bar and walked to his hotel. Tralala hoped she didnt make a mistake. Harry mightta had more money stashed somewhere. The Officer should have more though and anyway she probably got everything Harry had and she could get more from this jerk if he has any. She looked at him trying to determine how much he could have, but all Officers look the same. Thats the trouble with a goddamn uniform. And then she wondered how much she had gotten from Harry and how long she would have to wait to count it. When they got to his room she went right into the bathroom, smoothed out the bills a little and counted them. 45. Shit. Fuckit. She folded the money, left the bathroom and stuffed the money in a coat pocket. He poured two small drinks and they sat and talked for a few minutes then put the light out. Tralala figured there was no sense in trying anything now, so she relaxed and enjoyed herself. They were having a smoke and another drink when he turned and kissed her and told her she had the most beautiful pair of tits he had ever seen. He continued talking for a few minutes, but she didnt pay any attention. She thought about her tits and what he had said and how she could get anybody with her tits and the hell with Willies and those slobs, she/d hang around here for a while and do alright. They put out their cigarettes and for the rest of the night she didn't wonder how much money he had. At breakfast the next morning he tried to remember everything that had happened in the bar, but Harry was only vaguely remembered and he didn't want to ask her. A few times he tried speaking, but when he looked at her he started feeling vaguely guilty. When they had finished eating he lit her cigarette, smiled, and asked her if he could buy her something. A dress or something like that. I mean, well you know . . . Id like to buy you a little present. He tried not to sound maudlin or look sheepish, but he found it hard to say what he felt, now, in the morning, with a slight hangover, and she looked to him pretty and even a little innocent. Primarily he didnt want her to think he was offering to pay her or think he was insulting her by insinuating that she was just another prostitute; but much of his loneliness was gone and he wanted to thank her. You see, I only have a few days leave left before I go back and I thought perhaps we could—that is I thought we could spend some more time together . . . he stammered on apologetically hoping she understood what he was trying to say but the words bounced off her and when she noticed that he had finished talking she said sure. What thefuck. This is much better than wresslin with a drunk and she felt good this morning, much better than yesterday (briefly remembering the bulls and the money they took from her) and he might even give her his money before he went back overseas (what could he do with it) and with her tits she could always makeout and whatthehell, it was the best screwin she ever had . . . They went shopping and she bought a dress, a couple of sweaters (2 sizes too small), shoes, stockings, a pocketbook and an overnight bag to put her clothes in. She protested slightly when he told her to buy a cosmetic case (not knowing what it was when he handed it to her and she saw no sense in spending money on that when he could as well give her cash), and he enjoyed her modesty in not wanting to spend too much of his money; and he chuckled at her childlike excitement at being in the stores, looking and buying. They took all the packages back to the hotel and Tralala put on her new dress and shoes and they went out to eat and then to a movie. For the next few days they went to movies, restaurants (Tralala trying to make a mental note of the ones where the Officers hung-out), a few more stores and back to the hotel. When they woke on the 4th day he told her he had to leave and asked her if she would come with him to the station. She went thinking he might give her his money and she stood awkwardly on the station with him, their bags around them, waiting for him to go on the train and leave. Finally the time came for him to leave and he handed her an envelope as she lifted her face slightly so he could kiss her. It was thin and she figured it might be a check. She put it in her pocketbook, picked up her bag and went to the waiting room and sat on a bench and opened the envelope. She opened the paper and started reading: Dear Tral: There are many things I would like to say and should have said, but—A letter. A goddamn LETTER. She ripped the envelope apart and turned the letter over a few times. Not a cent. I hope you understand what I mean and am unable to say—she looked at the words—if you do feel as I hope you do Im writing my address at the bottom. I dont know if I/ll live through this war, but—Shit. Not vehemently but factually. She dropped the letter and rode the subway to Brooklyn. She went to Willies to display her finery. Ruthy was behind the bar and Waterman Annie was sitting in a booth with a seaman. She stood at the bar talking with Ruthy for a few minutes answering her questions about the clothes and telling her about the rich john she was living with and how much money he gave her and where they went. Ruthy left occasionally to pour a drink and when she came back Tralala continued her story, but soon Ruthy tired of listening to her bullshit as Tralalas short imagination bogged down. Tralala turned and looked at Annie and asked her when they leter out. Annie told her ta go screw herself. Youre the only one who would. Annie laughed and Tralala told her ta keep her shiteatin mouth shut. The seaman got up from the booth and staggered toward Tralala. You shouldnt talk to my girl friend like that. That douchebag? You should be able ta do betteran that. She smiled and pushed her chest out. The seaman laughed and leaned on the bar and asked her if she would like a drink. Sure. But not in this crummy place. Lets go ta some place thats not crawlin with stinkin whores. The seaman roared, walked back to the table, finished his drink and left with Tralala. Annie screamed at them and tried to throw a glass at Tralala but someone grabbed her arm. Tralala and Jack (he was an oiler and he . . .) got into a cab and drove downtown. Tralala thought of ditching him rightaway (she only wanted to break Annies balls), but figured she ought to wait and see. She stayed with him and they went to a hotel and when he passedout she took what he had and went back uptown. She went to a bar in Times Square and sat at the bar. It was filled with servicemen and a few drunken sailors smiled at her as she looked around, but she ignored them and the others in the bar ignored her. She wanted to be sure she picked up a liveone. No drunken twobit sailor or doggie for her. O no. Ya bet ya sweetass no. With her clothes and tits? Who inthehell do those punks think they are. I oughtta go spit in their stinkin faces. Shit! They couldnt kiss my ass. She jammed her cigarette out and took a short sip of her drink. She waited. She smiled at a few Officers she thought might have loot, but they were with women. She cursed the dames under her breath, pulled the top of her dress down, looked around and sipped her drink. Even with sipping the drink was soon gone and she had to order another. The bartender refilled her glass and marked her for an amateur. He smiled and was almost tempted to tell her that she was trying the wrong place, but didnt. He just refilled her glass thinking she would be better off in one of the 8th avenue bars. She sipped the new drink and lit another cigarette. Why was she still alone? What was with this joint? Everybody with a few bucks had a dame. Goddamn pigs. Not one ofem had a pair half as big as hers. She could have any sonofabitch in Willies or any bum stumbling into the Greeks. Whats with the creeps in here. They should be all around her. She shouldnt be sitting alone. She/d been there 2 hours already. She felt like standing up and yelling fuck you to everybody in the joint. Youre all a bunch of goddamn creeps. She snarled at the women who passed. She pulled her dress tight and forced her shoulders back. Time still passed. She still ignored the drunks figuring somebody with gelt would popup. She didn't touch her third drink, but sat looking around, cursing every sonofabitch in the joint and growing more defiant and desperate. Soon she was screaming in her mind and wishing takrist she had a blade, she/d cut their goddamn balls off. A CPO came up to her and asked her if she wanted a drink and she damn near spit in his face, but just mumbled as she looked at the clock and said shit. Yeah, yeah, lets go. She gulped down her drink and they left. Her mind was still such a fury of screechings (and that sonofabitch gives me nothin but a fuckin letter) that she just lay in bed staring at the ceiling and ignored the sailor as he screwed her and when he finally rolled off for the last time and fell asleep she continued staring and cursing for hours before falling asleep. The next afternoon she demanded that he giver some money and he laughed. She tried to hit him but he grabbed her arm, slapped her across the face and told her she was out of her mind. He laughed and told her to take it easy. He had a few days leave and he had enough money for both of them. They could have a good time. She cursed him and spit and he told her to grab her gear and shove off. She stopped in a cafeteria and went to the ladies room and threw some water on her face and bought a cup of coffee and a bun. She left and went back to the same bar. It was not very crowded being filled mostly with servicemen trying to drink away hangovers, and she sat and sipped a few drinks until the bar started filling. She tried looking for a liveone, but after an hour or so, and a few drinks, she ignored everyone and waited. A couple of sailors asked her if she wanted a drink and she said whatthefuck and left with them. They roamed around for hours drinking and then she went to a room with two of them and they gave her a few bucks in the morning so she stayed with them for a few days, 2 or 3, staying drunk most of the time and going back to the room now and then with them and their friends. And then they left or went somewhere and she went back to the bar to look for another one or a whole damn ship. Whats the difference. She pulled her dress tight but didnt think of washing. She hadnt reached the bar when someone grabbed her arm, walked her to the side door and told her to leave. She stood on the corner of 42nd & Broadway cursing them and wanting to know why they let those scabby whores in but kick a nice young girl out, ya lousy bunch apricks. She turned and crossed the street, still mumbling to herself, and went in another bar. It was jammed and she worked her way to the back near the jukebox and looked. When someone came back to play a number she smiled, threw her shoulder back and pushed the hair from her face. She stood there drinking and smiling and eventually left with a drunken soldier. They screwed most of the night, slept for a short time then awoke and started drinking and screwing again. She stayed with him for a day or two, perhaps longer, she wasnt sure and it didnt make any difference anyway, then he was gone and she was back in a bar looking. She bounced from one bar to another still pulling her dress tight and occasionally throwing some water on her face before leaving a hotel room, slobbering drinks and soon not looking but just saying yeah, yeah, whatthefuck and pushing an empty glass toward the bartender and sometimes never seeing the face of the drunk buying her drinks and rolling on and off her belly and slobbering over her tits; just drinking then pulling off her clothes and spreading her legs and drifting off to sleep or a drunken stupor with the first lunge. Time passed—months, maybe years, who knows, and the dress was gone and just a beatup skirt and sweater and the Broadway bars were 8th avenue bars, but soon even these joints with their hustlers, pushers, pimps, queens and wouldbe thugs kicked her out and the inlaid linoleum turned to wood and then was covered with sawdust and she hung over a beer in a dump on the waterfront, snarling and cursing every sonofabitch who fucked herup and left with anyone who looked at her or had a place to flop. The honeymoon was over and still she pulled the sweater tight but there was no one there to look. When she crawled out of a flophouse she fell in the nearest bar and stayed until another offer of a flop was made. But each night she would shove her tits out and look around for a liveone, not wanting any goddamn wino but the bums only looked at their beers and she waited for the liveone who had an extra 50¢ he didnt mind spending on beer for a piece of ass and she flopped from one joint to another growing dirtier and scabbier. She was in a South street bar and a seaman bought her a beer and his friends who depended on him for their drinks got panicky fearing he would leave them and spend their beer money on her so when he went to the head they took the beer from her and threw her out into the street. She sat on the curb yelling until a cop came along and kicked her and told her to move. She sprawled to her feet cursing every sonofabitch and his brother and told them they could stick their fuckin beer up their ass. She didnt need any goddamn skell to buy her a drink. She could get anything she wanted in Willies. She had her kicks. She/d go back to Willies where what she said goes. That was the joint. There was always somebody in there with money. No bums like these cruds. Did they think she/d let any goddamn bum in her pants and play with her tits just for a few bucks. Shit! She could get a seamans whole payoff just sittin in Willies. People knew who she was in Willies. You bet yasweet ass they did. She stumbled down the subway and rode to Brooklyn, muttering and cursing, sweat streaking the dirt on her face. She walked up the 3 steps to the door and was briefly disappointed that the door wasnt closed so she could throw it open. She stood for just a second in the doorway looking around then walked to the rear where Waterman Annie, Ruthy and a seaman were sitting. She stood beside the seaman, leaned in front of him and smiled at Annie and Ruthy then ordered a drink. The bartender looked at her and asked her if she had any money. She told him it was none of his goddamn business. My friend here is going to pay for it. Wontya honey. The seaman laughed and pushed a bill forward and she got her drink and sneered at the ignorant sonofabitchin bartender. The rotten scumbag. Annie pulled her aside and told her if she tried cuttin her throat she/d dump her guts on the floor. Mean Ruthys gonna leave as soon as Jacks friend comes and if ya screw it up youll be a sorry sonofabitch. Tralala yanked her arm away and went back to the bar and leaned against the seaman and rubbed her tits against his arm. He laughed and told her to drinkup. Ruthy told Annie not to botha witha, Fredll be here soon and we/ll go, and they talked with Jack and Tralala leaned over and interrupted their conversation and snarled at Annie hoping she burns like hell when Jack left with *her* and Jack laughed at everything and pounded the bar and bought drinks and Tralala smiled and drank and the jukebox blared hillbilly songs and an occasional blues song, and the red and blue neon lights around the mirror behind the bar sputtered and winked and the soldiers seamen and whores in the booths and hanging on the bar yelled and laughed and Tralala lifted her drink and said chugalug and banged her glass on the bar and she rubbed her tits against Jacks arm and he looked at her wondering how many blackheads she had on her face and if that large pimple on her cheek would burst and ooze and he said something to Annie then roared and slapped her leg and Annie smiled and wrote Tralala off and the cash register kachanged and the smoke just hung and Fred came and joined the party and Tralala yelled for another drink and asked Fred how he liked her tits and he poked them with a finger and said I guess theyre real and Jack pounded the bar and laughed and Annie cursed Tralala and tried to get them to leave and they said lets stay for a while, we/re having fun and Fred winked and someone rapped a table and roared and a glass fell to the floor and the smoke fell when it reached the door and Tralala opened Jacks fly and smiled and he closed it 5 6 7 times laughing and stared at the pimple and the lights blinked and the cashregister crooned kachang kachang and Tralala told Jack she had big tits and he pounded the bar and laughed and Fred winked and laughed and Ruthy and Annie wanted to leave before something screwed up their deal and wondered how much money they had and hating to see them spend it on Tralala and Tralala gulped her drinks and yelled for more and Fred and Jack laughed and winked and pounded the bar and another glass fell to the floor and someone bemoaned the loss of a beer and two hands fought their way up a skirt under a table and she blew smoke in their faces and and someone passedout and his head fell on the table and a beer was grabbed before it fell and Tralala glowed she had it made and she/d shove it up Annies ass or anybody elses and she gulped another drink and it spilled down her chin and she hung on Jacks neck and rubbed her chest against his cheek and he reached up and turned them like knobs and roared and Tralala smiled and O she had it made now and piss on all those mothafuckas and someone walked a mile for a smile and someone pulled the drunk out of the booth and dropped him out the back door and Tralala pulled her sweater up and bounced her tits on the palms of her hands and grinned and grinned and grinned and Jack and Fred whooped and roared and the bartender told her to put those goddamn things away and get thehelloutahere and Ruthy and Annie winked and Tralala slowly turned around bouncing them hard on her hands exhibiting her pride to the bar and she smiled and bounced the biggest most beautiful pair of tits in the world on her hands and someone yelled is that for real and Tralala shoved them in his face and everyone laughed and another glass fell from a table and guys stood and looked and the hands came out from under the skirt and beer was poured on Tralalas tits and someone yelled that she had been christened and the beer ran down her stomach and dripped from her nipples and she slapped his face with her tits and someone yelled youl smotherim ta death—what a way to die—hey, whats for desert—I said taput those goddamn things away ya fuckin hippopotamus and Tralala told him she had the prettiest tits in the world and she fell against the jukebox and the needle scraped along the record sounding like a long belch and someone yelled all tits and no cunt and Tralala told him to comeon and find out and a drunken soldier banged out of a booth and said comeon and glasses fell and

Jack knocked over his stool and fell on Fred and they hung over the bar nearing hysteria and Ruthy hoped she wouldnt get fired because this was a good deal and Annie closed her eyes and laughed relieved that they wouldn't have to worry about Tralala and they didnt spend too much money and Tralala still bounced her tits on the palms of her hands turning to everyone as she was dragged out the door by the arm by 2 or 3 and she yelled to Jack to comeon and she/d fuckim blind not like that fuckin douchebag he was with and someone yelled we/re coming and she was dragged down the steps tripping over someones feet and scraping her ankles on the stone steps and yelling but the mob not slowing their pace dragged her by an arm and Jack and Fred still hung on the bar roaring and Ruthy took off her apron getting ready to leave before something happened to louse up their deal and the 10 or 15 drunks dragged Tralala to a wrecked car in the lot on the corner of 57th street and yanked her clothes off and pushed her inside and a few guys fought to see who would be first and finally a sort of line was formed everyone yelling and laughing and someone yelled to the guys on the end to go get some beer and they left and came back with cans of beer which were passed around the daisychain and the guys from the Greeks cameover and some of the other kids from the neighborhood stood around watching and waiting and Tralala yelled and shoved her tits into the faces as they occurred before her and beers were passed around and the empties dropped or thrown and guys left the car and went back on line and had a few beers and waited their turn again and more guys came from Willies and a phone call to the Armybase brought more seamen and doggies and more beer was brought from Willies and Tralala drank beer while being laid and someone asked if anyone was keeping score and someone yelled who can count that far and Tralalas back was streaked with dirt and sweat and her ankles stung from the sweat and dirt in the scrapes from the steps and sweat and beer dripped from the faces onto hers but she kept yelling she had the biggest goddamn pair of tits in the world and someone answered ya bet ya sweet ass yado and more came 40 maybe 50 and they screwed her and went back on line and had a beer and yelled and laughed and someone yelled that the car stunk of cunt so Tralala and the seat were taken out of the car and laid in the lot and she lay there naked on the seat and their shadows hid her pimples and scabs and she drank flipping her tits with the other hand and somebody shoved the beer can against her mouth and they all laughed and Tralala cursed and spit out a piece of tooth and someone shoved it again and they laughed and yelled and the next one mounted her and her lips were split this time and the blood trickled to her chin and someone mopped her brow with a beer soaked handkerchief and another can of beer was handed to her and she drank and yelled about her tits and another tooth was chipped and the split in her lips was widened and everyone laughed and she laughed and she drank more and more and soon she passedout and they slapped her a few times and she mumbled and turned her head but they couldnt revive her so they continued to fuck her as she lay unconscious on the seat in the lot and soon they tired of the dead piece and the daisychain brokeup and they went back to Willies the Greeks and the base and the kids who were watching and waiting to take a turn took out their disappointment on Tralala and tore her clothes to small scraps put out a few cigarettes on her nipples pissed on her jerkedoff on her jammed a broomstick up her snatch then bored they left her lying amongst the broken bottles rusty cans and rubble of the lot and Jack and Fred and Ruthy and Annie stumbled into a cab still laughing and they leaned toward the window as they passed the lot and got a good look at Tralala lying naked covered with blood urine and semen and a small blot forming on the seat between her legs as blood seeped from her crotch and Ruthy and Annie happy and completely relaxed now that they were on their way downtown and their deal wasnt lousedup and they would have plenty of money and Fred looking through the rear window and Jack pounding his leg and roaring with laughter . . .

# Masters of War: America against the World

War and revolution are as old as history. In recent times, most such conflicts have revolved around the issues of colonialism, nationalism, and starvation. Revolutions have increasingly been launched against Western powers bent on maintaining their colonial territories. At the same time, problems of overpopulation and hunger have intensified revolutionary demands within so-called underdeveloped societies.

This section provides no solutions. Rather, it poses a multitude of questions. We chose the works below arranged in historical order—from World War II to Vietnam—to illustrate war and revolution, violence and nonviolence, and individual commitment or withdrawal in relation to America's participation in international social conflict. War is not a game—many men suffer and die at the hands of other men. These selections enable you to feel the anguish of their suffering and death, and to face the questions such suffering raises.

Is war an absolute evil in itself, or is it evil only when waged by the haves against the have-nots? Does the use of violence necessarily corrupt the person who uses it, no matter how pure his intentions? The philosophy of the peace movement is decentralist and antiauthoritarian. Do violent revolutionary tactics inherently contradict these basic principles? Is it possible to effect real social change without violence? Do Martin Luther King's life and death prove the ultimate futility of nonviolent resistance?

Is it possible for the revolutionary youth movement in America to make meaningful contact with the guerrilla movements among oppressed peoples over the world? Can Marxist or Maoist ideology be meaningful to American radicals, or are these value systems just as repressive, dehumanizing, and authoritarian as the systems that gave birth to the Movement in the first place?

On the international scale, is the Movement a romantic, fuzzy daydream or a potentially effective political force?

Is politics worth the trouble?

## DALTON TRUMBO

*was blacklisted as a Hollywood screenwriter for many years due to the paranoia of the McCarthy era, but has recently been readmitted to the fold; one of his recent screenplays was* Spartacus. *The selection which appears below is from* Johnny Got His Gun, *a powerful critique of what war does to man. The novel was written about World War II, but this is incidental to the novel's message. As the excerpt shows, Americans are not immune to the tragic effects of participation in this method of "resolving" human conflict.*

*From*

# JOHNNY GOT HIS GUN

He drifted again. He was hurt. He was bad hurt. The bell was fading. He was dreaming. He wasn't dreaming. He was awake even though he couldn't see. He was awake even though he couldn't hear a thing except a telephone that really wasn't ringing. He was mighty scared.

He remembered how when he was a kid he read *The Last Days of Pompeii* and awakened in the middle of a dark night crying in terror with his face suffocating in the pillow and thinking that the top of one of his Colorado mountains had blown off and that the covers were lava and that he was entombed while yet alive and that he would lie there dying forever. He had that same gasping feeling now. He had that same cowardly griping in his bowels. He was unchristly scared so he gathered his strength and made like a man buried in loose earth clawing out with his hands toward air.

Then he sickened and choked and fainted half away and was dragged back by pain. It was all over his body like electricity. It seemed to shake him hard and then throw him back against the bed exhausted and completely quiet. He lay there feeling the sweat pour out of his skin. Then he felt something else. He felt hot damp skin all over him and the dampness enabled him to feel his bandages. He was wrapped in them from top to bottom. Even his head.

He really was hurt then.

The shock caused his heart to smash against his ribs. He grew prickly all over. His heart was pounding away in his chest but he couldn't hear the pulse in his ear.

Oh god then he was deaf. Where did they get that stuff about bombproof dugouts when a man in one of them could be hit so hard that the whole complicated business of his ears could be blown away leaving him deaf so deaf he couldn't hear his own heart beat? He had been hit and he had been hit bad and now he was deaf. Not just a little deaf. Not just halfway deaf. He was stone deaf.

He lay there for a while with the pain ebbing and thinking this will give me something to chew on all right all right. What about the rest of the guys? Maybe they didn't come out so lucky. There were some good boys down in that hole. How'll it seem being deaf and shouting at people? You write things on paper. No that's wrong they write things on paper to you. It isn't anything to kick up your heels and dance about but it might be worse. Only when you're deaf you're lonesome. You're god-forsaken.

So he'd never hear again. Well there were a hell of a lot of things he didn't want to hear again. He never wanted to hear the biting little castanet sound of a machine gun or the high whistle of a .75 coming down fast or the slow thunder as it hit or the whine of an airplane overhead or the yells of a guy trying to explain to somebody that he's got a bullet in his belly and that his breakfast is coming out through the front of him and why won't somebody stop going forward and give him a hand only nobody can hear him they're so scared themselves. The hell with it.

Things were going in and out of focus. It was like looking into one of those magnified shaving mirrors and then moving it toward you and away from you. He was sick and probably out of his head and he was badly hurt and he was lonesome deaf but he was also alive and he could still hear far away and sharp the sound of a telephone bell. . . .

He shot up through cool waters wondering whether he'd ever make the surface or not. That was a lot of guff about people sinking three times and then drowning. He'd been rising and sinking for days weeks months who could tell? But he hadn't drowned. As he came to the surface each time he fainted into reality and as he went down again he fainted into nothingness. Long slow faints all of them while he struggled for air and life. He was fighting too hard and he knew it. A man can't fight always. If he's drowning or suffocating he's got to be smart and hold back some of his strength for the last the final the death struggle.

He lay back quietly because he was no fool. If you lie back

you can float. He used to float a lot when he was a kid. He knew how to do it. His last strength going into that fight when all he had to do was float. What a fool.

They were working on him. It took him a little while to understand this because he couldn't hear them. Then he remembered that he was deaf. It was funny to lie there and have people in the room who were touching you watching you doctoring you and yet not within hearing distance. The bandages were still all over his head so he couldn't see them either. He only knew that way out there in the darkness beyond the reach of his ears people were working over him and trying to help him.

They were taking part of his bandages off. He could feel the coolness the sudden drying of sweat on his left side. They were working on his arm. He felt the pinch of a sharp little instrument grabbing something and getting a bit of his skin with each grab. He didn't jump. He simply lay there because he had to save his strength. He tried to figure out why they were pinching him. After each pinch there was a little pull in the flesh of his upper arm and an unpleasant point of heat like friction. The pulling kept on in short little jerks with his skin getting hot each time. It hurt. He wished they'd stop. It itched. He wished they'd scratch him.

He froze all over stiff and rigid like a dead cat. There was something wrong about this pricking and pulling and friction heat. He could feel the things they were doing to his arm and yet he couldn't rightly feel his arm at all. It was like he felt inside his arm. It was like he felt through the end of his arm. The nearest thing he could think of to the end of his arm was the heel of his hand. But the heel of his hand the end of his arm was high high high as his shoulder.

Oh Jesus Christ they'd cut his left arm off.

They'd cut it right off at the shoulder he could feel it plain now.

Oh my god why did they do a thing like that to him?

They couldn't do it the dirty bastards they couldn't do it. They had to have a paper signed or something. It was the law. You can't just go out and cut a man's arm off without asking him without getting permission because a man's arm is his own and he needs it. Oh Jesus I have to work with that arm why did you cut it off? Why did you cut my arm off answer me why did you cut my arm off? Why did you why did you why did you?

He went down into the water again and fought and fought and then came up with his belly jumping and his throat aching. And all the time that he was under the water fighting with only one arm to get back he was having conversation with himself about how this thing couldn't possibly happen to him only it had.

So they cut my arm off. How am I going to work now? They don't think of that. They don't think of anything but doing it their own way. Just another guy with a hole in his arm let's cut it off what do you say boys? Sure cut the guy's arm off. It takes a lot of work and a lot of money to fix up a guy's arm. This is a war and war is hell and what the hell and so to hell with it. Come on boys watch this. Pretty slick hey? He's down in bed and can't say anything and it's his tough luck and we're tired and this is a stinking war anyhow so let's cut the damn thing off and be done with it.

My arm. My arm they've cut my arm off. See that stump there? That used to be my arm. Oh sure I had an arm I was born with one I was normal just like you and I could hear and I had a left arm like anybody. But what do you think of those lazy bastards cutting it off?

How's that?

I can't hear either. I can't hear. Write it down. Put it on a piece of paper. I can read all right. But I can't hear. Put it down on a piece of paper and hand the paper to my right arm because I have no left arm.

My left arm. I wonder what they've done with it. When you cut a man's arm off you have to do something with it. You can't just leave it lying around. Do you send it to hospitals so guys can pick it to pieces and see how an arm works? Do you wrap it up in an old newspaper and throw it onto the junk heap? Do you bury it? After all it's part of a man a very important part of a man and it should be treated respectfully. Do you take it out and bury it and say a little prayer? You should because it's human flesh and it died young and it deserves a good sendoff.

My ring.

There was a ring on my hand. What have you done with it? Kareen gave it to me and I want it back. I can wear it on the other hand. I've got to have it because it means something it's important. If you've stolen it I'll turn you in as soon as I get these bandages off you thieving bastards you. If you've stolen it you're grave robbers because my arm that is gone is dead and you've taken the ring from it and you've robbed the dead that's what you've done. Where is my ring Kareen's ring before I go under again? I want the ring. You've got the arm isn't that enough where's my ring Kareen's ring our ring please where is it? The hand it was on is dead and it wasn't meant to be on rotten flesh. It was meant always to be on my living finger on my living hand because it meant life. . . .

It was hot. So hot that he seemed to be burning up inside and out. It was so hot he couldn't breathe. He could only gasp. Far off against the sky there was a foggy line of mountains and moving straight across the desert was the railroad track dancing and leaping in the heat. It seemed that he and Howie were working on the railroad. That was funny. Oh hell things were getting mixed up again. He'd seen all this before. It was like going into a new drug store for the first time and sitting down and suddenly feeling that you've been there many times before and that you've already heard what the clerk is going to say as soon as he comes up to serve you. He and Howie working on the railroad in the heat? Sure. Sure. It was all right. Things were under control. . . .

He couldn't get used to the way things were melting into each other. Sometimes he was drifting on top of white clouds frightened at his smallness in the midst of a thing so big as the sky. Sometimes he was cushioned in soft pillows that had a way of sliding him feet first over rough and uneven ground. But mostly he was floating in some backwash of the Colorado River where it wandered through Shale City. He was lying in the water of a river that ran through home long before he came to Los Angeles long before he met Kareen long long before he went away on a bunting-covered train with the mayor making speeches.

He was floating on his back. There were willows near the edge of the water and sweet clover. There was hot sunshine on his face but his stomach and back were cool from water that had been snow in the mountains not long ago. He was floating there and thinking about Kareen.

It's fine Kareen floating here. Lie back more like this like that. Isn't it nice Kareen I love it I love you. Float Kareen keep your head out of the water so you can breathe. Keep real close to me Kareen isn't it swell floating here not going anywhere and not even caring to go anywhere? Just letting the river take care of things. Nothing to do and nowhere to go. Being on top of the river cool and hot and thoughtful yet not thinking a thing.

Stay closer Kareen. Don't go away. Closer closer Kareen and watch out for the water coming over your face. I can't turn over on my stomach to swim Kareen I can only float so please don't go so far away. Kareen where are you I can't find you and the water was coming over your face. Don't sink Kareen don't let the water come over your face. Come back Kareen you'll choke you'll fill up like I'm filling up. You'll go down Kareen watch out please watch out. Come back Kareen. You're gone. You weren't even there. Just me alone in the river with water coming over my nose and mouth and eyes.

The water was washing over his face and he couldn't stop it. It was like his head was too heavy for his body and he couldn't let it lie back without sinking. Or maybe his body was too light for his head so that there wasn't enough weight to balance his head and keep it high. The water was lapping over his eyes and nose and mouth and he was sputtering from it. It seemed like he was going feet first on his back against the stream only he was going like a sled with his feet and legs entirely out of the water and his head below the surface. He was going faster and faster and if he didn't stop why he'd drown from so much water rushing over his face.

He was beginning to drown already. He strained the muscles of his neck trying to raise his nose out of the water but it wouldn't come up. He tried to swim but how can a man swim if he hasn't got any arms? He sank down and down and down and finally he drowned. It seemed like he drowned without even a struggle way down in the dark bottom of the river while above him maybe only six or eight feet there was sunlight and willows and sweet clover and air. He drowned without a struggle because he couldn't struggle. He didn't seem to have anything to struggle with. It was like a bad dream where someone is chasing you and you're scared to death only there's nothing to do about it because you can't run. Your legs are stuck in concrete and you can't move a muscle. That was why he drowned.

He lay there under the water and thought what a shame it is to drown when you're maybe only six or eight feet from air and sunlight. What a goddam shame it is to drown when if you could only stand up and stretch your hand above your head you might touch a willow branch trailing in the water like the hair of a girl like Kareen's hair. But when you're drowned you can't stand up. When you're dead and drowned there's nothing left except time going on and on like water over your body.

Things began to shoot back and forth in front of his eyes. Rockets and bombs and pinwheels and curves of fire and great white flares whirled through his head and sank into the soft wet part of his brain with a hissing sound. He could hear the hissing very plainly. It was like the escape of steam from a locomotive. He could hear explosions and howls and whines and words that didn't mean anything and whistles so high and shrill that they cut through his ears like knives. Everything was dazzling and deafening. It hurt so much that he thought all the pain in the world was trapped somewhere between his forehead and the back of his skull and trying to hammer its way out. The pain was so bad that all he could think of was please please please I'd rather die.

Then things quieted down all of a sudden. Everything went still inside his head. The lights before his eyes snapped out as quickly as if somebody had shut them off with a switch. The pain went away too. The only feeling he had was the strong throb of blood in his brain swelling and contracting his head. But it was peaceful. It was painless. It was such a relief that he came out of his drowning. He could think.

He thought well kid you're deaf as a post but there isn't the pain. You've got no arms but you don't hurt. You'll never burn your hand or cut your finger or smash a nail you lucky stiff. You're alive and you don't hurt and that's much better than being alive and hurting. There are lots of things a deaf guy without arms can do if he doesn't hurt so much he goes crazy from pain. He can get hooks or something for arms and he can learn to read lips and while that doesn't exactly put him on top of the world still he's not drowned in the bottom of a river with pain tearing his brain to pieces. He's still got air and he's not struggling and he's got willow trees and he can think and he's not in pain.

He couldn't understand why the nurses or whoever had charge of him wouldn't lay him out level. The lower half of him was light as a feather while his head and chest were dead weights. That was why he had thought he was drowning. His head was too low. If he could move whatever was under his legs and bring his body to an even level he'd feel better. He wouldn't have that drowning dream any more.

He started to kick out with his feet to move what was under his legs. He only started because he didn't have any legs to kick with. Somewhere just below his hip joints they had cut both of his legs off.

No legs.

No more running walking crawling if you have no legs. No more working.

No legs you see.

Never again to wiggle your toes. What a hell of a thing what a wonderful beautiful thing to wiggle your toes.

No no.

If he could only think of real things he would destroy this dream of having no legs. Steamships loaves of bread girls Kareen machine guns books chewing gum pieces of wood Kareen but thinking of real things didn't help because it wasn't a dream.

It was the truth.

That was why his head had seemed lower than his legs. Because he had no legs. Naturally they seemed light. Air is light too. Even a toenail is heavy compared to air.

He had no arms and no legs.

He threw back his head and started to yell from fright. But he only started because he had no mouth to yell with. He was so surprised at not yelling when he tried that he began to work his jaws like a man who has found something interesting and wants to test it. He was so sure the idea of no mouth was a dream that he could investigate it calmly. He tried to work his jaws and he had no jaws. He tried to run his tongue around the inside of his teeth and over the roof of his mouth as if he were chasing a raspberry seed. But he didn't have any tongue and he hadn't any teeth. There was no roof to his mouth and there was no mouth. He tried to swallow but he couldn't because he had no palate and there weren't any muscles left to swallow with.

He began to smother and pant. It was as if someone had pushed a mattress over his face and was holding it there. He was breathing hard and fast now but he wasn't really breathing because there wasn't any air passing through his nose. He didn't have a nose. He could feel his chest rise and fall and quiver but not a breath of air was passing through the place where his nose used to be.

He got a wild panicky eagerness to die to kill himself. He tried to calm his breathing to stop breathing entirely so he would suffocate. He could feel the muscles at the bottom of his throat close tight against the air but the breathing in his chest kept right on. There wasn't any air in his throat to be stopped. His lungs were sucking it in somewhere below his throat.

He knew now that he was surely dying but he was curious. He didn't want to die until he had found out everything. If a man has no nose and no mouth and no palate and no tongue why it stands to reason he might be shy a few other parts as well. But that was nonsense because a man in that shape would be dead. You couldn't lose that much of yourself and still keep on living. Yet if you knew you had lost them and were thinking about it why then you must be alive because dead men don't think. Dead men aren't curious and he was sick with curiosity so he must not be dead yet.

He began to reach out with the nerves of his face. He began to strain to feel the nothingness that was there. Where his mouth and nose had been there must now be nothing but a hole covered with bandages. He was trying to find out how far up that hole went. He was trying to feel the edges of the hole. He was grasping with the nerves and pores of his face to follow the borders of that hole and see how far up they extended.

It was like staring into complete darkness with your eyes popping out of your head. It was a process of feeling with his skin of exploring with something that couldn't move where his mind told it to. The nerves and muscles of his face were crawling like snakes toward his forehead.

The hole began at the base of his throat just below where his jaw should be and went upward in a widening circle. He could feel his skin creeping around the rim of the circle. The hole was getting bigger and bigger. It widened out almost to the base of his ears if he had any and then narrowed again. It ended somewhere above the top of what used to be his nose.

The hole went too high to have any eyes in it.

He was blind.

It was funny how calm he was. He was quiet just like a storekeeper taking spring inventory and saying to himself I see I have no eyes better put that down in the order book. He had no legs and no arms and no eyes and no ears and no nose and no mouth and no tongue. What a hell of a dream. It must be a dream. Of course sweet god it's a dream. He'd have to wake up or he'd go nuts. Nobody could live like that. A person in that condition would be dead and he wasn't dead so he wasn't in that condition. Just dreaming.

But it wasn't a dream.

He could want it to be a dream forever and that wouldn't change things. Because he was alive alive. He was nothing but a piece of meat like the chunks of cartilage old Prof Vogel used to have in biology. Chunks of cartilage that didn't have anything except life so they grew on chemicals. But he was one up on the cartilage. He had a mind and it was thinking. That's more than Prof Vogel could ever say of his cartilages. He was thinking and he was just a thing.

Oh no. No no no.

He couldn't live like this because he would go crazy. But he couldn't die because he couldn't kill himself. If he could only breathe he could die. That was funny but it was true. He could hold his breath and kill himself. That was the only way left. Except that he wasn't breathing. His lungs were pumping air but he couldn't stop them from doing it. He couldn't live and he couldn't die.

No no no that can't be right.

No no. . . .

I can't. I can't stand it. Scream. Move. Shake something. Make a noise any noise. I can't stand it. Oh no no no.

Please I can't. Please no. Somebody come. Help me. I can't lie here forever like this until maybe years from now I die. I can't. Nobody can. It isn't possible. . . .

I can't breathe but I'm breathing. I'm so scared I can't think but I'm thinking. Oh please please no. No no. It isn't me. Help me. It can't be me. Not me. No no no.

Oh please oh oh please. No no no please no. Please.

Not me.

. . .

During the second year of his new time world nothing happened except that once a night nurse stumbled and fell to the floor setting up a fine vibration in his bedsprings. During the third year he was moved to a new room. The heat of the sun in the new room came in over the foot of his bed and by checking against the bath hour he figured that his head was to the east and his other end to the west. His new bed had a softer mattress and its springs were stiffer. They carried vibrations longer and that helped him a great deal. It took him months to locate the door and the dresser but they were months filled with calculation and excitement and finally with triumph. They were the shortest months he could remember in his whole life. All of this made the third year whisk by like a dream.

The fourth year started very slowly. He spent a lot of time trying to remember the books of the bible in their order but the only ones he could be sure of were Matthew Mark Luke and John and First and Second Samuel and First and Second Kings. He tried to put words to the story of David and Goliath and Nebuchadnezzar and Shadrack Meshack and Abednego. He remembered how his father used to yawn loudly around ten o'clock at night and stretch his arms and get up out of his chair and say Shadrack Meshack and to bed we go. But he couldn't remember the stories that went with the characters very clearly so they were poor time fillers. That was bad because when he couldn't fill in the time he got to worrying. He got to thinking I wonder if I haven't made a mistake in figuring the days the weeks the months? He got to thinking it wouldn't be impossible to drop even a whole year if a person were careless. Then he would get excited and frantic. He would check back and back to make sure he hadn't made a mistake so far back that he would get more confused than before. Every time he fell asleep he tried to have the day and month and year numbers firmly planted in his mind lest he forget them while he dreamed and every time he awakened his first panicky thought leaped at the terrible possibility he might not have remembered correctly the numbers he had in his mind when he fell asleep.

And then an astonishing thing happened. One day toward the middle of the year the nurse gave him a completely fresh change of bed linen when he had received a change only the day before. This had never happened before. Every third day he was changed no sooner no later. Yet here everything was upset and for two days in a row he was getting the change. He felt all in a hub-bub. He felt like bustling around from room to room and chattering about how busy he was and what great things were going to happen. He felt all bright with expectation and excitement. He wondered if he would get a fresh change of linen every day from now on or whether they would return again to the old schedule. This was as important as if an ordinary man with legs and arms and other parts were suddenly confronted with the possibility of living in a new house every day. It would be something to look forward to from day to day throughout the years. It would be something to break up time to make it something a guy could stand without mulling over Matthew Mark Luke and John.

Then he noticed something else. In addition to giving him an unexpected bath the nurse was spraying him with something. He could feel the spray cool and misty against his skin. Then she put a clean nightshirt on him and folded the covers back at his throat. This was different too. He could feel her hand through the covers as it passed over the fold smoothing smoothing smoothing. He was given a fresh mask which the nurse arranged very fussily so that it fell to his throat and there was carefully tucked under the fold of the bedcovers. After that she combed his hair carefully and left. He could feel the vibrations of her footsteps as she went away and the little jar of the door closing behind her. Then he was alone.

He lay perfectly still because it was a very luxurious feeling to be so completely redone. His body glowed and his sheets were cool and crisp and even his scalp felt good. He was afraid to move for fear he would spoil the good feeling. There was only a moment of this and then he felt the vibrations of four maybe five people coming into his room. He lay tense trying to catch their vibrations and wondering why they were there. The vibrations got heavier and then they stopped and he knew that people were gathered around his bed more people than ever before had been in his room at the same time. It was like the first time he went to school and was embarrassed and bewildered with so many people around. Little tremors of expectation ran through his stomach. He was stiff with excitement. He had visitors.

The first thought that passed through his mind was that they might be his mother and sisters and Kareen. There was just a chance that Kareen forever lovely and young was standing by him was looking down at him was even this minute putting out her hand her soft and tiny hand her beautiful beautiful hand to touch his forehead.

And then just as he could almost feel the touch of her hand

his delight turned suddenly to shame. He hoped more than anything else in the world that it was not his mother and sisters and Kareen who had come to visit him. He didn't want them to see him. He didn't want anybody he had ever known to see him. He knew now how foolish it had been to wish for them as sometimes in his loneliness he had. It was all right to think about having them near it was comforting it was warm and pleasant. But the idea that they might be beside his bed right now was too terrible to cope with. He jerked his head convulsively away from his visitors. He knew this dislodged his mask but he was beyond thinking of masks. He only wanted to hide his face to turn his blind sockets away from them to keep them from seeing the chewed up hole that used to be a nose and mouth that used to be a living human face. He got so frantic that he began to thrash from side to side like someone very sick with a high fever who can only monotonously repeat a motion or a word. He fell into his old rocking motion throwing his weight from one shoulder to the other back and forth back and forth back and forth.

A hand came to rest on his forehead. He quieted because it was the hand of a man heavy and warm. Part of it lay on the skin of his forehead and part of it he felt through the mask which cut across his forehead. He lay still again. Then another hand began to fold the covers back from his throat. One fold. One and a half folds. He grew very quiet very alert very curious. He thought very hard about who they might be.

Then he had it. They were doctors come to examine him. They were visiting firemen. He was probably a very famous guy by this time and the doctors were beginning to make pilgrimages. One doctor was probably saying to the others you see how we were able to do it? You see what a clever job we did? You see where the arm came off and you see the hole in his face and you see he still lives? Listen to his heart it's beating just like your heart or mine. Oh we did a fine job when we got him. It was a great piece of luck and we're all very proud. Stop by in my office on your way out and I'll give you one of his teeth for a souvenir. They take a wonderful polish he was young you see and his teeth were in good condition. Would you like a front one or would you prefer a good thick tusker from farther back? The thick ones look best on a watch chain.

Somebody was plucking at his nightshirt over his left breast.

It was as if a forefinger and thumb were pinching up a portion of it. He lay very quiet now deathly quiet his mind jumping in a hundred different directions at once. He could sense that something important was about to happen. There was a little more fumbling with the pinch of nightshirt and then the cloth fell back against his chest once more. It was heavy now weighted down by something. He felt the sudden coolness of metal through his nightshirt against his chest over his heart. They had pinned something on him.

Suddenly he did a curious thing a thing he hadn't done for months. He started to reach with his right hand for the heavy thing they had pinned on him and it seemed that he almost clutched it in his fingers before he realized that he had no arm to reach with and no fingers for clutching.

Someone was kissing his temple. There was a slight tickling of hair as the kiss was given. He was being kissed by a man with a moustache. First his left temple and then his right one. Then he knew what they had done to him. They had come into his room and they had decorated him with a medal. . . .

**LAWRENCE FERLINGHETTI**

*as poet and proprietor of City Lights Books in San Francisco was closely identified with the beat writers of the 1950s who prefigured today's new generation of poetic revolutionaries. His books include* A Coney Island of the Mind *and* Unfair Arguments with Existence.

*"Where Is Vietnam?" is set in the Johnson Era, showing American foreign policy as directed by a cowboy-conquistador who views the world as his personal province.*

# WHERE IS VIETNAM?

Meanwhile back at the Ranch the then President also known as Colonel Cornpone got out a blank Army draft and began to fill in the spaces with men and Colonel Cornpone got down to the bottom of the order where there is a space to indicate just where the troops are to be sent and Colonel Cornpone got a faraway look in his eye and reached out and started spinning a globe of the world and his eye wandered over the spinning surface of the world and after a long time he said I See No Relief so they brought him a relief map of the world and he looked at it a long time and said Thank You Gentlemen I see it all very clearly now yes indeed everything stands out very clearly now and I can see the oceans themselves rolling back and Western Civilization still marching Westward around the world and the New Frontier now truly knows no boundaries and those there Vietnamese don't stand a Chinaman's chance in Hell but still there's all these Chinamen who think they do and also think they can actually reverse the Westward march of civilization and actually reverse the natural Westward spin of our globe but Gentlemen these are not War Games this is not Space Angels this is the real thing Gentlemen and I know right exactly where this here Vietnam is Gentlemen and I want to make doubly sure that all our own people know right exactly where this here Vietnam is Gentlemen in case any of you should happen to get cornered by some eggheads or someone And just then Ladybird came running and Colonel Cornpone stepped into the cloakroom and whispered to her The world really does rotate Westward don't it? and she being smarter than he as is usually the case whispered back that this here Vietnam was not a place but a state of mind and Colonel Cornpone got that old faraway look again and stepped back onto the front porch and sat there rocking for a long time and then said Gentlemen I am a family man and this is for real and I am hereby ordering the complete and final liberation of Vietmind I mean Vietnam for the roots of the trouble are found wherever the landless and oppressed the poor and despised stand before the gates of opportunity and are not allowed across the Frontier into the Great Society which seems to lie out before me like a land of dreams and so Gentlemen here we go fasten your seatbelts we are powerful and free and united there ain't much we can't do and so Gentlemen let me point out to you exactly where it is we all are going on this here globe because Gentlemen even though I am reputed never to have been out of the United States I do know right where we are going on the brink of Vietmind I mean Vietnam and even though we don't want to stop the world spinning in the right direction even for an instant I do want to slow it down just long enough for me to put my finger for you right on this here sore spot which is Vietmine I mean Vietnam and Colonel Cornpone put out his hand to slow down the world just a bit but this world would not be slowed down a bit this world would not stop spinning at all and Texas and Vietnam spun on together faster and faster slipping away under Colonel Cornpone's hand because the surface of this world had suddenly become very very slippery with a strange kind of red liquid that ran on it across all the obscene boundaries and this world went on spinning faster and faster in the same so predestined direction and kept on spinning and spinning and spinning and spinning!

## DAVID IGNATOW

*was born in Brooklyn in 1914. He has published poems in* The Nation, Saturday Review, *and many other periodicals, and has produced several books of verse. "All Quiet" invites speculation on who the narrator is. Is this the voice of the "Silent Majority?" Who supports America's wars?*

# ALL QUIET

How come nobody is being bombed today?
I want to know, being a citizen
of this country and a family man.
You can't take my fate in your hands,
without informing me.
I can blow up a bomb or crush a skull—
whoever started this peace bit
without advising me
through a news leak
at which I could have voiced a protest,
running my whole family off a cliff.

## DENISE LEVERTOV

*is the author of several distinguished books of poetry. She was born in England, came to the United States in 1948 and now lives in New York.*

*In question-and-answer format reminiscent of a college quiz, "What Were They Like?" expresses the death of a delicate and sophisticated culture under the wheels of the indomitable American machine.*

## WHAT WERE THEY LIKE?

1) Did the people of Viet Nam
use lanterns of stone?
2) Did they hold ceremonies
to reverence the opening of buds?
3) Were they inclined to rippling laughter?
4) Did they use bone and ivory,
jade and silver, for ornament?
5) Had they an epic poem?
6) Did they distinguish between speech and singing?

1) Sir, their light hearts turned to stone.
It is not remembered whether in gardens
stone lanterns illumined pleasant ways.
2) Perhaps they gathered once to delight in blossom,
but after the children were killed
there were no more buds.
3) Sir, laughter is bitter to the burned mouth.
4) A dream ago, perhaps. Ornament is for joy.
All the bones were charred.
5) It is not remembered. Remember,
most were peasants; their life
was in rice and bamboo.
When peaceful clouds were reflected in the paddies
and the water buffalo stepped surely along terraces,
maybe fathers told their sons old tales.
When bombs smashed the mirrors
there was time only to scream.
6) There is an echo yet, it is said,

of their speech which was like a song.
It is reported their singing resembled
the flight of moths in moonlight.
Who can say? It is silent now.

# Nineteenth Nervous Breakdown: Jobs

Americans, feeling it their sacred duty and obligation to work, have often found themselves in a contradictory position. For while work has been deemed necessary, it has not always proved worthwhile or challenging. With the advent of automation and large scale bureaucratic corporate business organizations, the individual has increasingly had less and less control over any specific part of the production process. Yet society at large has not developed an ethic which justifies not working, which alleviates the guilt one feels from not participating in the production of consumer goods.

Much of our work orientation has at the same time been shifted toward the *use* of leisure time, for, seemingly, such leisure time must be justified in much the same way as work is justified. You must *do* something—paint the house, mow the lawn—you cannot simply sit and stare absentmindedly at the sea. Those who do are "lazy and shiftless." Yet, after spending forty to sixty hours at such a task, how is one to become creative and innovative in his leisure-time pursuits; if the mind is deadened at work, can it suddenly be revived when transposed to the suburb? The selections in this section offer a brief glimpse into the occupational boredom that awaits most of today's college graduates.

## HAROLD PINTER

*was born in London in 1930 and was an actor for several years before writing his first play,* The Room, *in 1957. Since then he has become one of England's foremost playwrights. His plays suggest that under the veneer of routine and convention is a terrible abyss of meaninglessness; many of his works are frightening, but* Trouble in the Works *suggests the same things in the comic mode. This sketch was written for a music hall revue entitled* One to Another, *produced in 1959. Pinter's best-known works are* The Caretaker, The Birthday Party, *and* Homecoming. *He also wrote the screenplays for* The Servant *and* Accident.

Trouble in the Works *is set in a British factory, but it just as well might be an American one, in which scores of people busily dedicate the greater parts of their lives to the duplication of meaningless objects.*

# TROUBLE IN THE WORKS

*An office in a factory.* MR. FIBBS *at the desk. A knock at the door. Enter* MR. WILLS.

FIBBS: Ah, Wills. Good. Come in. Sit down, will you?

WILLS: Thanks, Mr. Fibbs.

FIBBS: You got my message?

WILLS: I just got it.

FIBBS: Good. Good.
*Pause.*
Good. Well now . . . Have a cigar?

WILLS: No, thanks, not for me, Mr. Fibbs.

FIBBS: Well, now, Wills, I hear there's been a little trouble in the factory.

WILLS: Yes, I . . . I suppose you could call it that, Mr. Fibbs.

FIBBS: Well, what in heaven's name is it all about?

WILLS: Well, I don't exactly know how to put it, Mr. Fibbs.

FIBBS: Now come on, Wills, I've got to know what it is, before I can do anything about it.

WILLS: Well, Mr. Fibbs, it's simply a matter that the men have . . . well, they seem to have taken a turn against some of the products.

FIBBS: Taken a turn?

WILLS: They just don't seem to like them much any more.

FIBBS: Don't like them? But we've got the reputation of having the finest machine part turnover in the country. They're the best paid men in the industry. We've got the cheapest canteen in Yorkshire. No two menus are alike. We've got a billiard hall, haven't we, on the premises, we've got a swimming pool for use of staff. And what about the long-playing record room? And you tell me they're dissatisfied?

WILLS: Oh, the men are very grateful for all the amenities, sir. They just don't like the products.

FIBBS: But they're beautiful products. I've been in the business a lifetime. I've never seen such beautiful products.

WILLS: There it is, sir.

FIBBS: Which ones don't they like?

WILLS: Well, there's the brass pet cock, for instance.

FIBBS: The brass pet cock? What's the matter with the brass pet cock?

WILLS: They just don't seem to like it any more.

FIBBS: But what exactly don't they like about it?

WILLS: Perhaps it's just the look of it.

FIBBS: That brass pet cock? But I tell you it's perfection. Nothing short of perfection.

WILLS: They've just gone right off it.

FIBBS: Well, I'm flabbergasted.

WILLS: It's not only the brass pet cock, Mr. Fibbs.

FIBBS: What else?

WILLS: There's the hemi unibal spherical rod end.

FIBBS: The hemi unibal spherical rod end? Where could you find a finer rod end?

WILLS: There are rod ends and rod ends, Mr. Fibbs.

FIBBS: I know there are rod ends and rod ends. But where could you find a finer hemi unibal spherical rod end?

WILLS: They just don't want to have anything more to do with it.

FIBBS: This is shattering. Shattering. What else? Come on, Wills. There's no point in hiding anything from me.

WILLS: Well, I hate to say it, but they've gone very vicious about the high speed taper shank spiral flute reamers.

FIBBS: The high speed taper shank spiral flute reamers! But that's absolutely ridiculous! What could they possibly have against the high speed taper shank spiral flute reamers?

WILLS: All I can say is they're in a state of very bad agitation about them. And then there's the gunmetal side outlet relief with handwheel.

FIBBS: What!

WILLS: There's the nippled connector and the nippled adaptor and the vertical mechanical comparator.

FIBBS: No!

WILLS: And the one they can't speak about without trembling is the jaw for Jacob's chuck for use on portable drill.

FIBBS: My own Jacob's chuck? Not my very own Jacob's chuck?

WILLS: They've just taken a turn against the whole lot of them, I tell you. Male elbow adaptors, tubing nuts, grub screws, internal fan washers, dog points, half dog points, white metal bushes—

FIBBS: But not, surely not, my lovely parallel male stud couplings.

WILLS: They hate and detest your lovely parallel male stud couplings, and the straight flange pump connectors, and back nuts, and front nuts, *and* the bronzedraw off cock with handwheel and the bronzedraw off cock without handwheel!

FIBBS: Not the bronzedraw off cock with handwheel?

WILLS: And without handwheel.

FIBBS: Without handwheel?

WILLS: And with handwheel.

FIBBS: Not with handwheel?

WILLS: And without handwheel.

FIBBS: Without handwheel?

WILLS: With handwheel *and* without handwheel.

FIBBS: With handwheel *and* without handwheel?

WILLS: With or without!
*Pause.*

FIBBS [*broken*]: Tell me. What do they want to make in its place?

WILLS: Brandy balls.

MARGE PIERCY*

# The morning half-life blues

Girls buck the wind in the grooves toward work
in fuzzy coats promised to be warm as fur.
The shop windows snicker
flashing them hurrying over dresses they cannot afford:
you are not pretty enough, not pretty enough.

Blown with yesterday's papers through the boiled coffee morning
they dream of the stop on the subway without a name,
the door in the heart of the grove of skyscrapers,
that garden where we nestle to the teats of a furry world,
lie in mounds of peony eating grapes,
and need barter ourselves for nothing,
not by the hour, not by the pound, not by the skinful,
that party to which no one will give or sell them the key
though we have all thought briefly we had found it
drunk or in bed.

Black girls with thin legs and high necks stalking like herons,
plump girls with blue legs and green eyelids and strawberry
    breasts,
swept off to be frozen in fluorescent cubes,
the vacuum of your jobs sucks your brains dry
and fills you with the ooze of melted comics.
Living is later. This is your rented death.
You grasp at specific commodities and vague lusts
to make up, to pay for each day
which opens like a can and is empty, and then another,
afternoons like dinosaur eggs stuffed with glue.

* See page 142.

Girls of the dirty morning, ticketed and spent,
you will be less at forty than at twenty.
Your living is a waste product of somebody's mill.
I would fix you like buds to a city where people work
to make and do things necessary and good,
where work is real as bread and babies and trees in parks
and you would blossom slowly and ripen to sound fruit.

## JEAN-CLAUDE VAN ITALLIE

*graduated from Harvard University in 1958. "Interview" is from* America Hurrah, *a show consisting of three interrelated plays of which the critic* Robert *Brustein has written: "He has . . . discovered the deepest poetic function of the theatre which is not, like most American dramatists, to absorb the audience into the author's own personal problems under the pretext that they are universal, but rather to invent metaphors which can poignantly suggest a nation's nightmares and afflictions."* [1]

*Like Pinter's* Trouble in the Works, *Van Itallie's play shows the mechanical drabness of the occupational maze our society offers to those who seek work. "Interview" presents people desperately searching for jobs—income sources—to which they can bring their whole selves, and finding only routines with strictly codified rules. Van Itallie's people lack the ability to break the routines, and thus their frustrations lead sometimes to numbness, sometimes to madness. The malaise of meaningless occupations seeps over into all areas of their lives.*

[1] From "Introduction" to *America Hurrah* (New York, 1967), p. 9.

# INTERVIEW
# A Fugue for Eight Actors

First Interviewer
First Applicant
Second Applicant
Third Applicant
Fourth Applicant
Second Interviewer
Third Interviewer
Fourth Interviewer

The set is white and impersonal.

Two subway stairs are at the back of the stage. On the sides there is one entrance for Applicants and another entrance for Interviewers.

The only furniture or props needed are eight grey blocks.

The actors, four men and four women, are dressed in black-and-white street clothes. During the employment agency section only, Interviewers wear translucent plastic masks.

There is an intermittent harpsichord accompaniment: dance variations (minuet, Virginia reel, twist) on a familiar American tune. But much of the music (singing, whistling, humming) is provided by the actors on stage. It is suggested, moreover, that as a company of actors and a director approach the play they find their own variations in rhythmic expression. The successful transition from one setting to the next depends on the actors' ability to play together as a company and to drop character instantaneously and completely in order to assume another character, or for a group effect.

(*The First Interviewer for an employment agency, a young woman, sits on stage as the First Applicant, a Housepainter, enters.*)

FIRST INTERVIEWER (*standing*) How do you do?

FIRST APPLICANT (*sitting*) Thank you, I said, not knowing where to sit.

(*The characters will often include the audience in what they say, as if they were being interviewed by the audience.*)

FIRST INTERVIEWER (*pointedly*) Won't you sit down?

FIRST APPLICANT (*standing again quickly, afraid to displease*) I'm sorry.

FIRST INTERVIEWER (*busy with imaginary papers, pointing to a particular seat*) There. Name, please?

FIRST APPLICANT Jack Smith.

FIRST INTERVIEWER Jack what Smith?

FIRST APPLICANT Beg pardon?

FIRST INTERVIEWER Fill in the blank space, please. Jack blank space Smith.

FIRST APPLICANT I don't have any.

FIRST INTERVIEWER I asked you to sit down.
(*pointing*)
There.

FIRST APPLICANT (*sitting*) I'm sorry.

FIRST INTERVIEWER Name, please?

FIRST APPLICANT Jack Smith.

FIRST INTERVIEWER You haven't told me your MIDDLE name.

FIRST APPLICANT I haven't got one.

FIRST INTERVIEWER (*suspicious but writing it down*) No middle name.

(*Second Applicant, a woman, a Floorwasher, enters.*)

FIRST INTERVIEWER How do you do?

SECOND APPLICANT (*sitting*) Thank you, I said, not knowing what.

FIRST INTERVIEWER Won't you sit down?

SECOND APPLICANT (*standing*) I'm sorry.

FIRST APPLICANT I am sitting.

FIRST INTERVIEWER (*pointing*) There. Name, please?

SECOND APPLICANT (*sitting*) Jane Smith.

FIRST APPLICANT Jack Smith.

FIRST INTERVIEWER What blank space Smith?

SECOND APPLICANT Ellen.

FIRST APPLICANT Haven't got one.

FIRST INTERVIEWER What job are you applying for?

FIRST APPLICANT Housepainter.

SECOND APPLICANT Floorwasher.

FIRST INTERVIEWER We haven't many vacancies in that. What experience have you had?

FIRST APPLICANT A lot.

SECOND APPLICANT Who needs experience for floorwashing?

FIRST INTERVIEWER You will help me by making your answers clear.

FIRST APPLICANT Eight years.

SECOND APPLICANT Twenty years.

(*Third Applicant, a Banker, enters.*)

FIRST INTERVIEWER How do you do?

SECOND APPLICANT I'm good at it.

FIRST APPLICANT Very well.

THIRD APPLICANT (*sitting*) Thank you, I said, as casually as I could.

FIRST INTERVIEWER Won't you sit down?

THIRD APPLICANT (*standing again*) I'm sorry.

SECOND APPLICANT I am sitting.

FIRST APPLICANT (*standing again*) I'm sorry.

FIRST INTERVIEWER (*pointing to a particular seat*) There. Name, please?

FIRST APPLICANT Jack Smith.

SECOND APPLICANT Jane Smith.

THIRD APPLICANT Richard Smith.

FIRST INTERVIEWER What EXACTLY Smith, please?

THIRD APPLICANT Richard F.

SECOND APPLICANT Jane Ellen.

FIRST APPLICANT Jack None.

FIRST INTERVIEWER What are you applying for?

FIRST APPLICANT Housepainter.

SECOND APPLICANT I need money.

THIRD APPLICANT Bank president.

FIRST INTERVIEWER How many years have you been in your present job?

THIRD APPLICANT Three.

SECOND APPLICANT Twenty.

FIRST APPLICANT Eight.

(*Fourth Applicant, a Lady's Maid, enters.*)

FIRST INTERVIEWER How do you do?

FOURTH APPLICANT I said thank you, not knowing where to sit.

THIRD APPLICANT I'm fine.

SECOND APPLICANT Do I have to tell you?

FIRST APPLICANT Very well.

FIRST INTERVIEWER Won't you sit down?

FOURTH APPLICANT I'm sorry.

THIRD APPLICANT (*sitting again*) Thank you.

SECOND APPLICANT (*standing again*) I'm sorry.

FIRST APPLICANT (*sitting*) Thanks.

FIRST INTERVIEWER (*pointing to a particular seat*) There. Name, please?

(*Fourth Applicant sits.*)

ALL APPLICANTS Smith.

FIRST INTERVIEWER What Smith?

FOURTH APPLICANT Mary Victoria.

THIRD APPLICANT Richard F.

SECOND APPLICANT Jane Ellen.

FIRST APPLICANT Jack None.

FIRST INTERVIEWER How many years' experience have you had?

FOURTH APPLICANT Eight years.

SECOND APPLICANT Twenty years.

FIRST APPLICANT Eight years.

THIRD APPLICANT Three years four months and nine days not counting vacations and sick leave and the time both my daughters and my wife had the whooping cough.

FIRST INTERVIEWER Just answer the questions, please.

FOURTH APPLICANT Yes, sir.

THIRD APPLICANT Sure.

SECOND APPLICANT I'm sorry.

FIRST APPLICANT That's what I'm doing.

*(Second Interviewer, a young man, enters and goes to inspect Applicants. With the entrance of each Interviewer, the speed of the action accelerates.)*

SECOND INTERVIEWER How do you do?

FIRST APPLICANT *(standing)* I'm sorry.

SECOND APPLICANT *(sitting)* Thank you.

THIRD APPLICANT *(standing)* I'm sorry.

FOURTH APPLICANT *(sitting)* Thank you.

SECOND INTERVIEWER What's your name?

FIRST INTERVIEWER Your middle name, please.

FIRST APPLICANT Smith.

SECOND APPLICANT Ellen.

THIRD APPLICANT Smith, Richard F.

FOURTH APPLICANT Mary Victoria Smith.

FIRST INTERVIEWER What is your exact age?

SECOND INTERVIEWER Have you any children?

FIRST APPLICANT I'm thirty-two years old.

SECOND APPLICANT One son.

THIRD APPLICANT I have two daughters.

FOURTH APPLICANT Do I have to tell you that?

FIRST INTERVIEWER Are you married, single, or other?

SECOND INTERVIEWER Have you ever earned more than that?

FIRST APPLICANT No.

SECOND APPLICANT Never.

THIRD APPLICANT Married.

FOURTH APPLICANT Single, now.

*(Third Interviewer, a woman, enters.)*

THIRD INTERVIEWER How do you do?

FIRST APPLICANT (*sitting*) Thank you.

SECOND APPLICANT (*standing*) I'm sorry.

THIRD APPLICANT (*sitting*) Thank you.

FOURTH APPLICANT (*standing*) I'm sorry.

(*Fourth Interviewer, a man, appears on the heels of Third Interviewer.*)

FOURTH INTERVIEWER How do you do?

FIRST APPLICANT (*standing*) I'm sorry.

SECOND APPLICANT (*sitting*) Thank you.

THIRD APPLICANT (*standing*) I'm sorry.

FOURTH APPLICANT (*sitting*) Thank you.

ALL INTERVIEWERS What is your Social Security Number, please?

(*Applicants do the next four speeches simultaneously.*)

FIRST APPLICANT 333 dash 6598 dash 5590765439 dash 003.

SECOND APPLICANT 999 dash 5733 dash 699075432 dash 11.

THIRD APPLICANT (*sitting*) I'm sorry. I left it home. I can call if you let me use the phone.

FOURTH APPLICANT I always get it confused with my Checking Account Number.

(*Interviewers do the next four speeches in a round.*)

FIRST INTERVIEWER Will you be so kind as to tell me a little about yourself?

SECOND INTERVIEWER Can you fill me in on something about your background please?

THIRD INTERVIEWER It'd be a help to our employers if you'd give me a little for our files.

FOURTH INTERVIEWER Now what would you say, say, to a prospective employer about yourself?

(*Applicants address parts of the following four speeches, in particular, directly to the audience.*)

FIRST APPLICANT I've been a Union member twenty years, I said to them, if that's the kind of thing you want to know.

Good health, I said. Veteran of two wars. Three kids. Wife's dead. Wife's sister, she takes care of them. I don't know why I'm telling you this, I said smiling.

(*sits*)

SECOND APPLICANT (*standing*) So what do you want to know, I told the guy. I've been washin' floors for twenty years. Nobody's ever complained. I don't loiter after hours, I said to him. Just because my boy's been in trouble is no reason, I said, no reason—I go right home, I said to him. Right home.

(*sits*)

THIRD APPLICANT (*standing*) I said that I was a Republican and we could start right there. And then I said that I spend most of my free time watching television or playing in the garden of my four-bedroom house with our two lovely daughters, aged nine and eleven. I mentioned that my wife plays with us too, and that her name is Katherine, although, I said casually, her good friends call her Kitty. I wasn't at all nervous.

(*sits*)

FOURTH APPLICANT (*standing*) Just because I'm here, sir, I told him, is no reason for you to patronize me. I've been a lady's maid, I said, in houses you would not be allowed into. My father was a gentleman of leisure, AND what's more, I said, my references are unimpeachable.

FIRST INTERVIEWER I see.

SECOND INTERVIEWER All right.

THIRD INTERVIEWER That's fine.

FOURTH INTERVIEWER Of course.

(*Applicants do the following four speeches simultaneously.*)

FIRST APPLICANT Just you call anybody at the Union and ask them. They'll hand me a clean bill of health.

SECOND APPLICANT I haven't been to jail if that's what you mean. Not me. I'm clean.

THIRD APPLICANT My record is impeccable. There's not a stain on it.

FOURTH APPLICANT My references would permit me to be a governess, that's what.

FIRST INTERVIEWER (*going to First Applicant and inspecting under his arms*) When did you last have a job housepainting?

SECOND INTERVIEWER (*going to Second Applicant and inspecting her teeth*) Where was the last place you worked?

THIRD INTERVIEWER (*going to Third Applicant and inspecting him*) What was your last position in a bank?

FOURTH INTERVIEWER (*going to Fourth Applicant and inspecting her*) Have you got your references with you?

(*Applicants do the following four speeches simultaneously, with music under.*)

FIRST APPLICANT I've already told you I worked right along till I quit.

SECOND APPLICANT Howard Johnson's on Fifty-first Street all last month.

THIRD APPLICANT First Greenfield International and Franklin Banking Corporation Banking and Stone Incorporated.

FOURTH APPLICANT I've got a letter right here in my bag. Mrs. Muggintwat only let me go because she died.

(*Interviewers do the next four speeches in a round.*)

FIRST INTERVIEWER (*stepping around and speaking to Second Applicant*) Nothing terminated your job at Howard Johnson's? No thanks, say, missing at the end of the day, I suppose?

SECOND INTERVIEWER (*stepping around and speaking to Third Applicant*) It goes without saying, I suppose, that you could stand an FBI Security Test?

THIRD INTERVIEWER (*stepping around and speaking to Fourth

*Applicant*) I suppose there are no records of minor thefts or, shall we say, borrowings from your late employer?

FOURTH INTERVIEWER (*stepping around and speaking to First Applicant*) Nothing political in your Union dealings? Nothing Leftist, I suppose? Nothing Rightist either, I hope.

(*Applicants and Interviewers line up for a square dance. Music under the following.*)

FIRST APPLICANT (*bowing to First Interviewer*) What's it to you, buddy?

SECOND APPLICANT (*bowing to Second Interviewer*) Eleanor Roosevelt wasn't more honest.

THIRD APPLICANT (*bowing to Third Interviewer*) My record is lily-white, sir!

FOURTH APPLICANT (*bowing to Fourth Interviewer*) Mrs. Thumbletwat used to take me to the bank and I'd watch her open her box!

(*Each Interviewer, during his next speech, goes upstage to form another line.*)

FIRST INTERVIEWER Good!

SECOND INTERVIEWER Fine!

THIRD INTERVIEWER Swell!

FOURTH INTERVIEWER Fine!

(*Applicants come downstage together; they do the next four speeches simultaneously and directly to the audience.*)

FIRST APPLICANT I know my rights. As a veteran. AND a citizen. I know my rights. AND my cousin is very well-known in certain circles, if you get what I mean. In the back room of a certain candy store in the Italian district of this city my cousin is VERY well known, if you get what I mean. I know my rights. And I know my cousin.

SECOND APPLICANT (*putting on a pious act, looking up to heaven*) Holy Mary Mother of God, must I endure all the sinners of this earth? Must I go on a poor washerwoman in this City of Sin? Help me, oh my God, to leave this earthly crust, and damn your silly impudence, young man, if you think you can treat an old woman like this. You've got another thought coming, you have.

THIRD APPLICANT I have an excellent notion to report you to the Junior Chamber of Commerce of this city of which I am the Secretary and was in line to be elected Vice President and still will be if you are able to find me gainful and respectable employ!

FOURTH APPLICANT Miss Thumblebottom married into the Twiths and if you start insulting me, young man, you'll have to start in insulting the Twiths as well. A Twith isn't a nobody, you know, as good as a Thumbletwat, AND they all call me their loving Mary, you know.

ALL INTERVIEWERS (*in a loud raucous voice*) Do you smoke?

(*Each Applicant, during his next speech, turns upstage.*)

FIRST APPLICANT No thanks.

SECOND APPLICANT Not now.

THIRD APPLICANT No thanks.

FOURTH APPLICANT Not now.

ALL INTERVIEWERS (*again in a harsh voice and bowing or curtsying*) Do you mind if I do?

FIRST APPLICANT I don't care.

SECOND APPLICANT Who cares?

THIRD APPLICANT Course not.

FOURTH APPLICANT Go ahead.

(*Interviewers form a little group off to themselves.*)

FIRST INTERVIEWER I tried to quit but couldn't manage.

SECOND INTERVIEWER I'm a three-pack-a-day man, I guess.

THIRD INTERVIEWER If I'm gonna go I'd rather go smoking.

FOURTH INTERVIEWER I'm down to five a day.

(*Applicants all start to sneeze.*)

FIRST APPLICANT Excuse me, I'm gonna sneeze.

SECOND APPLICANT Have you got a hanky?

THIRD APPLICANT I have a cold coming on.

FOURTH APPLICANT I thought I had some tissues in my bag.

(*Applicants all sneeze.*)

FIRST INTERVIEWER Gezundheit.

SECOND INTERVIEWER God bless you.

THIRD INTERVIEWER Gezundheit.

FOURTH INTERVIEWER God bless you.

(*Applicants all sneeze simultaneously.*)

FIRST INTERVIEWER God bless you.

SECOND INTERVIEWER Gezundheit.

THIRD INTERVIEWER God bless you.

FOURTH INTERVIEWER Gezundheit.

(*Applicants return to their seats.*)

FIRST APPLICANT Thanks, I said.

SECOND APPLICANT I said thanks.

THIRD APPLICANT Thank you, I said.

FOURTH APPLICANT I said thank you.

(*Interviewers stand on their seats and say the following as if one person were speaking.*)

FIRST INTERVIEWER Do you

SECOND INTERVIEWER speak any

THIRD INTERVIEWER foreign

FOURTH INTERVIEWER languages?

FIRST INTERVIEWER Have you

SECOND INTERVIEWER got a

THIRD INTERVIEWER college

FOURTH INTERVIEWER education?

FIRST INTERVIEWER Do you

SECOND INTERVIEWER take

THIRD INTERVIEWER shorthand?

FOURTH INTERVIEWER Have you

FIRST INTERVIEWER any

SECOND INTERVIEWER special

THIRD INTERVIEWER qualifications?

FIRST INTERVIEWER Yes?

FIRST APPLICANT (*stepping up to Interviewers*) Sure, I can speak Italian, I said. My whole family is Italian so I oughta be able to, and I can match colors, like green to green, so that even your own mother couldn't tell the difference, begging your pardon, I said, I went through the eighth grade.
(*steps back*)

SECOND INTERVIEWER Next.

SECOND APPLICANT (*stepping up to Interviewers*) My grandmother taught me some Gaelic, I told the guy. And my old man could rattle off in Yiddish when he had a load on. I never went to school at all excepting church school, but I can write my name good and clear. Also, I said, I can smell an Irishman or a Yid a hundred miles off.
(*steps back*)

THIRD INTERVIEWER Next.

THIRD APPLICANT (*stepping up to Interviewers*) I've never had any need to take shorthand in my position, I said to him. I've a Z.A. in business administration from Philadelphia, and a Z.Z.A. from M.Y.U. night school. I mentioned that I speak a little Spanish, of course, and that I'm a whiz at model frigates and warships.
(*steps back*)

FOURTH INTERVIEWER Next.

FOURTH APPLICANT (*stepping up to Interviewers*) I can sew a straight seam, I said, hand or machine, and I have been exclusively a lady's maid although I CAN cook and will too if I have someone to assist me, I said. Unfortunately, aside from self-education, grammar school is as far as I have progressed. (*steps back*)

(*Each Interviewer, during his next speech, bows or curtsies to the Applicant nearest him.*)

FIRST INTERVIEWER Good.

SECOND INTERVIEWER Fine.

THIRD INTERVIEWER Very helpful.

FOURTH INTERVIEWER Thank you.

(*Each Applicant, during his next speech, jumps on the back of the Interviewer nearest him.*)

FOURTH APPLICANT You're welcome, I'm sure.

THIRD APPLICANT Anything you want to know.

SECOND APPLICANT Just ask me.

FIRST APPLICANT Fire away, fire away.

(*The next eight speeches are spoken simultaneously, with Applicants on Interviewers' backs.*)

FIRST INTERVIEWER Well unless there's anything special you want to tell me, I think—

SECOND INTERVIEWER Is there anything more you think I should know about before you—

THIRD INTERVIEWER I wonder if we've left anything out of this questionnaire or if you—

FOURTH INTERVIEWER I suppose I've got all the information down here unless you can—

FIRST APPLICANT I've got kids to support, you know, and I need a job real quick—

SECOND APPLICANT Do you think you could try and get me something today because I—

THIRD APPLICANT How soon do you suppose I can expect to hear from your agency? Do you—

FOURTH APPLICANT I don't like to sound pressureful, but you know I'm currently on unemploy—

(*Each Applicant, during his next speech, jumps off Interviewer's back.*)

FIRST APPLICANT Beggin' your pardon.

SECOND APPLICANT So sorry.

THIRD APPLICANT Excuse me.

FOURTH APPLICANT Go ahead.

(*Each Interviewer, during his next speech, bows or curtsies and remains in that position.*)

FIRST INTERVIEWER That's quite all right.

SECOND INTERVIEWER I'm sorry.

THIRD INTERVIEWER I'm sorry.

FOURTH INTERVIEWER My fault.

(*Each Applicant, during his next speech, begins leapfrogging over Interviewers' backs.*)

FIRST APPLICANT My fault.

SECOND APPLICANT My fault.

THIRD APPLICANT I'm sorry.

FOURTH APPLICANT My fault.

(*Each Interviewer, during his next speech, begins leapfrogging too.*)

FIRST INTERVIEWER That's all right.

SECOND INTERVIEWER My fault.

THIRD INTERVIEWER I'm sorry.

FOURTH INTERVIEWER Excuse me.

*(The leap-frogging continues as the preceding eight lines are repeated simultaneously. Then the Interviewers confer in a huddle and come out of it.)*

FIRST INTERVIEWER Do you enjoy your work?

FIRST APPLICANT Sure, I said, I'm proud. Why not? Sure I know I'm no Rembrandt, I said, but I'm proud of my work, I said to him.

SECOND APPLICANT I told him it stinks. But what am I supposed to do, sit home and rot?

THIRD APPLICANT Do I like my work, he asked me. Well, I said, to gain time, do I like my work? Well, I said, I don't know.

FOURTH APPLICANT I told him right straight out: for a sensible person, a lady's maid is the ONLY POSSIBLE way of life.

SECOND INTERVIEWER Do you think you're irreplaceable?

ALL APPLICANTS Oh, yes indeed.

ALL INTERVIEWERS Irreplaceable?

ALL APPLICANTS Yes, yes indeed.

THIRD INTERVIEWER Do you like me?

FIRST APPLICANT You're a nice man.

SECOND APPLICANT Huh?

THIRD APPLICANT Why do you ask?

FOURTH APPLICANT It's not a question of LIKE.

FIRST INTERVIEWER Well, we'll be in touch with you.

*(This is the beginning of leaving the agency. Soft music under. Applicants and Interviewers push their seats into two masses of four boxes, one on each side of the stage. Applicants leave first, joining hands to form a revolving door.*

*All are now leaving the agency, not in any orderly fashion. Interviewers start down one of the subway stairs at the back of the stage and Applicants start down the other. The following speeches overlap and are heard indistinctly as crowd noise.*)

FOURTH INTERVIEWER What sort of day will it be?

FIRST APPLICANT I bet we'll have rain.

SECOND APPLICANT Cloudy, clearing in the afternoon.

THIRD APPLICANT Mild, I think, with some snow.

FOURTH APPLICANT Precisely the same as yesterday.

SECOND APPLICANT Can you get me one?

FIRST INTERVIEWER See you tomorrow.

THIRD APPLICANT When will I hear from you?

SECOND INTERVIEWER We'll let you know.

FOURTH APPLICANT Where's my umbrella?

THIRD INTERVIEWER I'm going to a movie.

FIRST APPLICANT So how about it?

FOURTH INTERVIEWER Good night.

THIRD APPLICANT Can you help me, Doctor, I asked.

(*When all of the actors are offstage, the Fourth Interviewer makes a siren sound and the following speeches continue from downstairs as a loud crowd noise for a few moments; they overlap so that the stage is empty only briefly.*)

FIRST INTERVIEWER It'll take a lot of work on your part.

SECOND INTERVIEWER I'll do what I can for you.

THIRD INTERVIEWER Of course I'll do my best.

FIRST INTERVIEWER God helps those who help themselves.

FIRST APPLICANT I have sinned deeply, Father, I said.

FIRST INTERVIEWER You certainly have. I hope you truly repent.

SECOND INTERVIEWER In the name of the Father, etcetera, and the Holy Ghost.

THIRD INTERVIEWER Jesus saves.

FOURTH APPLICANT I said can you direct me to Fourteenth Street, please?

FIRST INTERVIEWER Just walk down that way a bit and then turn left.

SECOND INTERVIEWER Just walk down that way a bit and then turn right.

THIRD INTERVIEWER Take a cab!

FOURTH APPLICANT Do you hear a siren?

ALL INTERVIEWERS What time is it?

FIRST APPLICANT Half-past three.

SECOND APPLICANT It must be about four.

THIRD APPLICANT Half-past five.

FOURTH APPLICANT My watch has stopped.

FIRST INTERVIEWER Do you enjoy your work?

SECOND INTERVIEWER Do you think you're irreplaceable?

THIRD INTERVIEWER Do you like me?

(*The actor who played the Fourth Interviewer comes on stage while continuing to make the loud siren noise. The actress who played the Fourth Applicant comes on stage and speaks directly to the audience.*)

FOURTH APPLICANT Can you direct me to Fourteenth Street, please, I said. I seem to have lost my—I started to say, and then I was nearly run down.

(*The remaining actors return to the stage to play various people on Fourteenth Street: ladies shopping, a panhandler, a man in a sandwich board, a peddler of "franks and orange," a snooty German couple, a lecher, a pair of sighing lovers, and so on. The actors walk straight forward toward the audience and then walk backwards to the rear of the stage. Each time they approach the audience, they do so as a different character. The actor will need to find the essential vocal and physical mannerisms of each character, play them, and drop them immediately to assume another character. The Fourth Applicant continues to address the audience directly, to involve them in her hysteria, going up the aisle and back.*)

FOURTH APPLICANT I haven't got my Social Security—I started to say, I saw someone right in front of me and I said, could you direct me please to Fourteenth Street, I have to get to Fourteenth Street, please, to get a bargain, I explained, although I could hardly remember what it was I wanted to buy. I read about it in the paper today, I said, only they weren't listening and I said to myself, my purpose for today is to get to—and I couldn't remember, I've set myself the task of—I've got to have—it's that I can save, I remembered, I can save if I can get that bargain at—and I couldn't remember where it was so I started to look for my wallet which I seem to have mislaid in my purse, and a man—please watch where you're going, I shouted with my purse half-open, and I seemed to forget—Fourteenth Street, I remembered, and you'd think with all these numbered streets and avenues a person wouldn't get lost—you'd think a person would HELP a person, you'd think so. So I asked the most respectable looking man I could find, I asked him, please can you direct me to Fourteenth Street. He wouldn't answer. Just wouldn't. I'm lost, I said to myself. The paper said—the television said —they said, I couldn't remember what they said. I turned for help: "Jesus Saves" the sign said, and a man was carrying it, both sides of his body, staring straight ahead. "Jesus Saves" the sign said.

(*The passers-by jostle her more and more.*)

FOURTH APPLICANT I couldn't remember where I was going. "Come and be saved" it said, so I asked the man with the sign, please, sir, won't you tell me how to, dear Lord, I thought, anywhere, please, sir, won't you tell me how to—can you direct me to Fourteenth Street, PLEASE!

*(The passers-by have covered the Fourth Applicant. All actors mill about until they reach designated positions on the stage where they face the audience, a line of women and a line of men, students in a gym class. The Second Interviewer has stayed coolly out of the crowd during this last; now he is the Gym Instructor.)*

GYM INSTRUCTOR I took my last puff and strode resolutely into the room. Ready men, I asked brightly. And one and two and three and four and one and two and keep it up.

*(The Gym Instructor is trying to help his students mold themselves into the kind of people seen in advertisements and the movies. As he counts to four the students puff out their chests, smile, and look perfectly charming. As he counts to four again, the students relax and look ordinary.)*

GYM INSTRUCTOR You wanna look like the guys in the movies, don't you, I said to the fellahs. Keep it up then. You wanna radiate that kinda charm and confidence they have in the movies, don't you, I said to the girls. Keep it up then, stick 'em out, that's what you got 'em for. Don't be ashamed. All of you, tuck in your butts, I said loudly. That's the ticket, I said, wishing to hell I had a cigarette. You're selling, selling all the time, that right, miss? Keep on selling, I said. And one and two and three and four and ever see that guy on TV, I said. What's his name, I asked them. What's his name? Aw, you know his name, I said, forgetting his name. Never mind, it'll come to you, I said. He comes in here too. See that, I said, grabbing a guy out of line and showing 'em his muscle. See that line, I said, making the guy feel good, know what that is? It's boyishness, I said. You come here, I said, throwing him back into the line, and it'll renew your youthfulness, I said, taking a deep breath. And one and two and three and four and smile, I said, smiling. Not so big, I said, smiling less. You look like creeps, I said, when you smile that big. When you smile, hold something back. Make like you're holding back something big, I said, a secret, I said. That's the ticket. And one and two and three and four and . . .

(*accelerating the rhythm to a double count*)
Anybody got a cigarette, I said suddenly, without thinking. I was just kidding, I said then, sheepishly. One and two and three and four, I said, wishing I had a cigarette. And one and two and three and four . . .

(*The rapid movements of the gym class become the vibrations of passengers on a moving subway train. The actors rush to the boxes stage left, continuing to vibrate. Two of the actors stand on the boxes and smile like subway advertisements while the others, directly in front of them, are pushed against each other on the crowded train. They make an appropriate soft subway noise, a kind of rhythmic hiss and, as the subway passengers, form their faces into frozen masks of indifference.*)

SECOND APPLICANT (*squeezing her way to an uncomfortable front seat and speaking half to herself*) God forgive me . . . you no-good chump, I said to him, I used to love you . . . not now. Not now . . . God forgive me . . . God forgive me for being old. Not now, I said. I wouldn't wipe the smell off your uncle's bottom now, not for turnips, no. God forgive me . . . Remember how we used to ride the roller coaster out at Coney Island, you and me? Remember? Holding hands in the cold and I'd get so scared and you'd get so scared and we'd hug each other and buy another ticket . . . Remember? . . . Look now, I said. Look at me now! God forgive you for leaving me with nothing . . . God forgive you for being dead . . . God forgive me for being alive . . .

(*The actress who played the Third Interviewer slips out of the subway as though it were her stop and sits on a box, stage right, as a Telephone Operator. The other actors form a telephone circuit by holding hands in two concentric circles around the boxes, stage left; they change the hissing sound of the subway into the whistling of telephone circuits.*)

TELEPHONE OPERATOR Just one moment and I will connect you with Information.

(*The Telephone Operator alternates her official voice

*with her ordinary voice; she uses the latter when she talks to her friend Roberta, another operator whom she reaches by flipping a switch. When she is talking to Roberta, the whistling of the telephone circuit changes into a different rhythm and the arms of the actors, which are forming the circuit, move into a different position.*)

TELEPHONE OPERATOR Just one moment and I will connect you with Information. Ow! Listen, Roberta, I said, I've got this terrible cramp. Hang up and dial again, please; we find nothing wrong with that number at all. You know what I ate, I said to her, you were there. Baked macaroni, Wednesday special, maple-nut fudge, I said. I'm sorry but the number you have reached is not—I can feel it gnawing at me at the bottom of my belly, I told her. Do you think it's serious, Roberta? Appendicitis? I asked. Thank you for giving us the area code but the number you have reached is not in this area. Roberta, I asked her, do you think I have cancer? One moment, please, I'm sorry the number you have reached—ow! Well, if it's lunch, Roberta, I said to her, you know what they can do with it tomorrow. Ow! One moment, please, I said. Ow, I said, Roberta, I said, it really hurts.

(*The Telephone Operator falls off her seat in pain. The whistling of the telephone circuit becomes a siren. Three actors carry the Telephone Operator over to the boxes, stage left, which now serve as an operating table. Three actors imitate the Telephone Operator's breathing pattern while four actors behind her make stylized sounds and movements as surgeons and nurses in the midst of an operation. The Telephone Operator's breathing accelerates, then stops. After a moment the actors begin spreading over the stage and making the muted sounds of a cocktail party: music, laughter, talk. The actors find a position and remain there, playing various aspects of a party in slow motion and muted tones. They completely ignore the First Interviewer who, as a Girl At The Party, goes from person to person as if she were in a garden of living statues.*)

GIRL AT THE PARTY (*rapidly and excitedly*) And then after the ambulance took off I went up in the elevator and into the party. Did you see the accident, I asked, and they said they did, and what did he look like, and I said he wore a brown coat and had straight brown hair. He stepped off the curb right in front of me. We had been walking up the same block, he a few feet ahead of me, this block right here, I said, but she wasn't listening. Hi, my name is Jill, I said to somebody sitting down and they looked at me and smiled so I said his arm was torn out of its socket and his face was on the pavement gasping but I didn't touch him and she smiled and walked away and I said after her, you aren't supposed to touch someone before—I WANTED to help, I said, but she wasn't listening. When a man came up and said was it someone you knew and I said yes, it was someone I knew slightly, someone I knew, yes, and he offered me a drink and I said no thanks, I didn't want one, and he said well how well did I know him, and I said I knew him well, yes, I knew him very well. You were coming together to the party, he said. Yes, I said, excuse me. Hi, my name is Jill, did you hear a siren, and they said oh you're the one who saw it, was he killed?

(*becoming resigned to the fact that no one is listening*) And I said yes I was, excuse me, and went back across the room but couldn't find another face to talk to until I deliberately bumped into somebody because I had to tell them one of us couldn't come because of the accident. It was Jill. Jill couldn't come. I'm awfully sorry, I said, because of the accident. She had straight brown hair, I said, and was wearing a brown coat, and two or three people looked at me strangely and moved off. I'm sorry, I said to a man, and I laughed, and moved off. I'm dead, I said to several people and started to push them over, I'm dead, thank you, I said, thank you, please, I said, I'm dead, until two or three of them got hold of my arms and hustled me out. I'm sorry, I said, I couldn't come because of the accident. I'm sorry. Excuse me.

(*The Girl At The Party is lowered to the floor by two of the men and then all fall down except the actor who played the Fourth Interviewer. He remains seated as a Psychiatrist. The Third Applicant, on the floor, props his head up on his elbow and speaks to the audience.*)

THIRD APPLICANT Can you help me, Doctor, I asked him.

*(The Psychiatrist crosses his legs and assumes a professional expression.)*

THIRD APPLICANT Well, it started, well it started, I said, when I was sitting in front of the television set with my feet on the coffee table. Now I've sat there hundreds of times, thousands maybe, with a can of beer in my hand. I like to have a can of beer in my hand when I watch the beer ads. But now for no reason I can think of, the ad was making me sick. So I used the remote control to get to another channel, but each channel made me just as sick. The television was one thing and I was a person, and I was going to be sick. So I turned it off and had a panicky moment. I smelled the beer in my hand and as I vomited I looked around the living room for something to grab on to, something to look at, but there was just our new furniture. I tried to get a hold of myself. I tried to stare straight ahead above the television set, at a little spot on the wall I know. I've had little moments like that before, Doctor, I said, panicky little moments like that when the earth seems to slip out from under, and everything whirls around and you try to hold onto something, some object, some thought, but I couldn't think of anything. Later the panic went away, I told him, it went away, and I'm much better now. But I don't feel like doing anything anymore, except sit and stare at the wall. I've lost my job. Katherine thought I should come and see you. Can you help me, Doctor, I asked him.

PSYCHIATRIST Blah, blah, blah, blah, blah, blah, HOSTILE.
Blah, blah, blah, blah, blah, blah, PENIS.
Blah, blah, blah, blah, blah, blah, MOTHER.
*(holding out his hand)*
Blah, blah, blah, blah, blah, blah, MONEY.

*(The Third Applicant takes the Psychiatrist's hand and gets up, extending his left hand to the next actor. This begins a grand right and left with all the actors all over the stage.)*

ALL *(chanting as they do the grand right and left)*
Blah, blah, blah, blah, blah, blah, HOSTILE.

Blah, blah, blah, blah, blah, blah, PENIS.
Blah, blah, blah, blah, blah, blah, MOTHER.
Blah, blah, blah, blah, blah, blah, MONEY.
Blah, blah, blah, blah, blah, blah, HOSTILE.
Blah, blah, blah, blah, blah, blah, PENIS.
Blah, blah, blah, blah, blah, blah, MOTHER.
Blah, blah, blah, blah, blah, blah, MONEY.
(*forming couples and locking hands with arms crossed, continuing to move, but in a smaller circle*)
Blah, blah, blah, blah, blah, blah, blah.
Blah, blah, blah, blah, blah, blah, blah.

(*Now they slow down to the speed of a church procession. The women bow their heads, letting their hair fall forward over their faces. The "blah, blah, blah" continues, but much more slowly while some of the women accompany it with a descant of "Kyrie Eleison." After they have gone around in a circle once this way, the actor who played the Fourth Interviewer sits with his back to the audience as a Priest. The First Applicant kneels next to him, facing the audience as if in a confessional booth. The other six actors are at the back of the stage in two lines, swaying slightly, heads down. The women are in front with their hair still down over their faces.*)

FIRST APPLICANT (*crossing himself perfunctorily and starting to speak; his manner is not impassioned; it is clear that he comes regularly to repeat this always fruitless ritual*) Can you help me, Father, I said, as I usually do, and he said, as usual, nothing. I'm your friend, the housepainter, I said, the good housepainter. Remember me, Father? He continued, as usual, to say nothing. Almost the only color you get to paint these days, Father, I said, is white. Only white, Father, I said, not expecting any more from him than usual, but going on anyway. The color I really like to paint, Father, is red, I said. Pure brick red. Now there's a confession, Father. He said nothing. I'd like to take a trip to the country, Father, I said, and paint a barn door red, thinking that would get a rise out of him, but it didn't. God, I said then, deliberately taking the Lord's name in vain, the result of taking a three-inch brush and lightly kissing a coat of red paint on a barn door is something stunning and beautiful to behold. He still said nothing. Father, I said, springing it on him, Father, I'd like to join a monastery. My wife's sister, she could take care of the kids. Still nothing. Father, I said again, I'd like to join a monastery. Can you help me, Father? Nothing. Father, I said, I've tried lots of things in my life, I've gone in a lot of different directions, Father, and none of them seems any better than any other, Father, I said. Can you help me, Father, I said. But he said nothing as usual, and then, as usual, I went away.

(*The First Applicant and the Fourth Interviewer, who haven't moved at all during the confession, move upstage to join the others as the music starts up violently in a rock beat. The actors do a rock version of the Virginia reel.*)

SECOND INTERVIEWER (*loudly*) My

(*All bow to partners.*)

FOURTH APPLICANT (*loudly*) fault.

(*All dos-à-dos.*)

SECOND APPLICANT (*loudly*) Excuse

(*All circle around.*)

FOURTH INTERVIEWER (*loudly*) me.

(*All peel off.*)

FIRST INTERVIEWER (*loudly*) Can you

SECOND APPLICANT (*loudly*) help

FIRST APPLICANT (*loudly*) me?

FOURTH INTERVIEWER (*loudly*) Next.

(*All continue dancing, joining hands at the center to form a revolving door again. They repeat the preceding eight speeches. Then the Second Interviewer speaks rapidly, as a Square Dance Caller.*)

SQUARE DANCE CALLER Step right up, ladies and gents, and shake the hand of the next governor of this state. Shake his hand and say hello. Tell your friends you shook the hand of the next governor of the state. Step right up and shake his hand. Ask him questions. Tell him problems. Say hello. Step right up, shake his hand, shake the hand, ladies and gents, of the next governor of the state. Tell your folks: I shook his hand. When he's famous you'll be proud. Step right up, ladies and gents, and shake his hand. Ask him questions. Tell him problems. Say hello. Step right up, ladies and gents. Don't be shy. Shake the hand of the next governor of this state.

*(The actors have formed a crowd, downstage right, facing the audience. They give the impression of being but a few of a great number of people, all trying to squeeze to the front to see and speak to the political candidate. The Fourth Interviewer, now playing a Politician, stands on a box, stage left, facing the audience. The Second Interviewer stands by the crowd and keeps it in order.)*

POLITICIAN Thank you very much, I said cheerfully, and good luck to you, I said, turning my smile to the next one.

*(The First Interviewer, panting as the Girl At The Party, squeezes out of the crowd and rushes up to the Politician, who smiles at her benignly.)*

POLITICIAN Our children ARE our most important asset, I agreed earnestly. Yes they are, I said solemnly. Children, I said, with a long pause, are our most important asset. I only wish I could, madame, I said earnestly, standing tall, but rats, I said regretfully, are a city matter.

*(The First Interviewer returns to the crowd while the Third Interviewer, as the Telephone Operator, rushes up to the Politician. She appeals to him, making the same noise she made when her stomach hurt her.)*

POLITICIAN Nobody knows more about red tape than I do, I said knowingly, and I wish you luck, I said, turning my smile to the next one.

*(The Third Interviewer returns to the crowd and the Fourth Applicant goes up to the Politician.)*

POLITICIAN I certainly will, I said, with my eyes sparkling, taking a pencil out of my pocket. And what's your name, I said, looking at her sweetly and signing my name at the same time. That's a lovely name, I said.

*(The Fourth Applicant returns to the crowd while the Third Applicant, as an Older Man, shakes the Politician's hand.)*

POLITICIAN Yes sir, I said, those were the days. And good luck to you, sir, I said respectfully but heartily, and look out for the curb, I said, turning my smile to the next one.

*(The Third Applicant returns to the crowd and the Second Applicant approaches the Politician.)*

POLITICIAN Indeed yes, the air we breathe IS foul, I said indignantly. I agree with you entirely, I said wholeheartedly. And if my opponent wins it's going to get worse, I said with conviction. We'd all die within ten years, I said. And good luck to you, madame, I said politely, and turned my smile to the next one.

*(The First Applicant approaches him, his cap in his hand.)*

POLITICIAN Well, I said confidingly, getting a bill through the legislature is easier said than done, and answering violence, I said warningly, with violence, I said earnestly, is not the answer, and how do you do, I said, turning my smile to the next one.

*(Next, two Sighing Lovers—we saw them on Fourteenth Street—played by the First and Second Interviewers, approach the Politician.)*

POLITICIAN No, I said, I never said my opponent would kill us all. No, I said, I never said that. May the best man win, I said manfully.

*(Half-hearted cheers. The First and Second Interviewers return to the crowd.)*

POLITICIAN I do feel, I said without false modesty, that I'm better qualified in the field of foreign affairs than my opponents are, yes, I said, BUT, I said, with a pause for emphasis, foreign policy is the business of the President, not the Governor, therefore I will say nothing about the war, I said with finality.

(*The crowd makes a restive sound, then freezes.*)

POLITICIAN Do you want us shaking hands, I asked the photographer, turning my profile to the left. Goodbye, I said cheerfully, and good luck to you too.

(*The crowd makes a louder protest, then freezes.*)

POLITICIAN I'm sorry, I said seriously, but I'll have to study that question a good deal more before I can answer it.

(*The crowd makes an angry noise, then freezes.*)

POLITICIAN Of course, I said frowning, we must all support the President, I said as I turned concernedly to the next one.

(*The crowd makes a very angry sound, then freezes.*)

POLITICIAN I'm sorry about the war, I said. Nobody could be sorrier than I am, I said sorrowfully. But I'm afraid, I said gravely, that there are no easy answers.
(*smiles, pleased with himself*)
Good luck to you too, I said cheerfully, and turned my smile to the next one.

(*The Politician topples from his box, beginning his speech all over again. Simultaneously, all the other actors lurch about the stage, speaking again in character: the Shopper On Fourteenth Street, the Gym Instructor, the Subway Rider, the Telephone Operator, the Girl At The Party, the Analysand, and the Housepainter. Simultaneously, they all stop and freeze, continue again, freeze again, then continue with music under. The Second Interviewer, acting as policeman, begins to line them up in a diagonal line, like marching dolls, one behind the other. As they are put into line they begin to move their mouths without sound, like fish in a tank. The music stops. When all are in line the Second Interviewer joins them.*)

SECOND INTERVIEWER My

FOURTH APPLICANT fault.

SECOND APPLICANT Excuse

FOURTH INTERVIEWER me.

FIRST INTERVIEWER Can you

SECOND APPLICANT help

FIRST APPLICANT me?

FOURTH INTERVIEWER Next.

(*All continue marching in place, moving their mouths, and shouting their lines as the lights come slowly down.*)

SECOND INTERVIEWER My

FOURTH APPLICANT fault.

SECOND APPLICANT Excuse

FOURTH INTERVIEWER me.

FIRST INTERVIEWER Can you

SECOND APPLICANT help

FIRST APPLICANT me?

FOURTH INTERVIEWER Next.

# Strawberry Fields: Reality Busting

One thing the Beatles are good for is to get you outside the processes of your own head to show you that there are other ways of organizing reality than the ones you have learned. All good art can have this effect—to make you question values that you've taken for granted. But the works in this section do more than question social and political "realities." They can make you aware of your psychic environment, the constructs you have been socialized into using to cope with what is "out there"—constructs of time, space, perception, logic. For these constructs are relative rather than absolute. How can a fish become aware that he lives in water? How can a human become aware that his mind lives in a similarly pervasive and invisible milieu? They often have to get outside of their respective environments—and run the risk of dying or of developing into a new species.

Americans have made a very specialized and exclusive standard of "objectivity" and "rationality" into the sole test for the validity of our experiences—we often think there is only one "right" way of perceiving things. The works below show some alternatives. Some of them could be described as "surrealist"—works by artists who live within the Western reality framework and who alter or negate it through their writing. Others are by writers outside of our cultural frame of reference, from societies that Western observers for many years labeled as "primitive." Now it has become clear that we have much to learn from so-called "inferior" peoples—that the American Indian's attitude toward the earth, for example, may be more humane *and pragmatic* than the European method of aggressive exploitation of natural resources.

The selections which follow can show you that there is more than one way of perceiving reality, and they can also demonstrate different ways of conceptualizing alternative solutions to some of the issues American society now faces and will confront in the future. These works should thus be viewed as a means of posing alternatives and opening you up to the myriad of possibilities which relationships in American society hold. Social change comes from exploration—open your mind, "let the sun shine in." American society will be much different in the future—largely as a result of your efforts and the options you and others pose.

These selections for the most part are much more "difficult" than the others; the methods of literary analysis you have learned may not open them up easily to you. Also, their applicability to American society in the concrete is not obvious. We have provided minimal introductory comments to each selection suggesting ways into them and ways to apply them; but we do not imply that there is only one way to interpret any of these works. Moreover, we have arranged them in an increasing order of "difficulty."

**BUD FOOTE** (*better known as* Og, *is King of Bashan*).

*In this selection, reprinted from one of the leading underground newspapers, Atlanta's* Great Speckled Bird, Og *transposes values applicable to law and order in one area of* American *society, and applies them to more controversial aspects of this same society. As such, he "busts reality," and many familiar social problems suddenly arise viewed in a new light.*

# THE FOIBLE OF THE SENATOR AND THE SPEEDER

Well, the week Wore On and eventually it Got To Be the weekend: and late Sunday Morning while his wife had gone off to Church, why Officer Johnson, who was known Far and Wide throughout the Length and Breadth of the county as one of the Metropolice's Finest, switched on the Tube and Settled Back with a Tin of Suds poking out of his Ample Paw.

Well, it happened to be that Hiatus in Sunday TV-watching between the Popeye Cartoons on the one hand and the Pro Ballgames on the other, and thus it was that Officer Johnson found himself eyeball to eyeball with a U and S Senator who was Meeting the Press.

Senator, said a Reporter from *The New York Times,* just how do you Account for the Situation the U S and A finds Itself in *vis-a-vis* the VietNamese?

Well Sir, said the Respected Solon, I don't see that you can Blame it on Anybody in Particular: I mean, after all, it was good old Dwight D. of Honored Memory who began sending Aid and Comfort to Saigon; and it was the Martyred JFK who began Sending Military Advisors, and it was his Successor who Officially promoted the Advisors to Combat troops; and so I don't see that you can Blame it on Anybody in Particular: it just Sort Of Crept Up on Us.

Senator, asked a representative of the St. Louis *Post-Dispatch,* what is your reaction to the Problem of Pollution of our Air and Water?

I am Glad you Asked that question, replied the Senator. The way I see it, it all Began with the Indian Campfires and with

Riverside Latrines, and the First thing you Know why here we are with Smog a Hundred miles Square and a Hundred miles deep over Los Angeles and the Rivers so crusted over with Kahkah that you don't have to be J.C. to Walk on the Water no more: you might say Sir that it Just sort of Crept up on Us.

Senator, asked a Third Reporter, would you Care to Comment on the question of Urban Poverty?

Certainly I would, said the Lawmaker as he shook his Hoary Locks. It seems to me that Poor People have been Slipping into the Cities Unbeknownst to the Government for Lo, these Many Years, until all of a Sudden we are up to our Nostrils in Urban Poor. It just sort of You Might Say crept Up on Us.

Well all this Seemed most Reasonable to Officer Johnson of the Metropolice's finest, and as he finished off his Falstaff and dressed himself for Work it was Quite a Comfort to him to Reflect that the Affairs of the Republic were in such Competent Hands.

As Officer Johnson was overseeing the Safety of the City on his motorcycle, all of a sudden he Espied a two-year-old Pontiac rolling merrily down the Expressway doing seven and a half miles an hour over the Speed Limit, and he Quite Naturally gave Chase and pulled the Offender over to the Curb.

Lissen he said What do you Mean doing 7½ miles an hour over the Limit?

Officer, I am real Sorry, responded the Culprit. I was just rolling Innocently along and the Speed just Crept Up on Me.

And as Johnson grimly wrote out the Ticket he said, Goddamn, anybody who Don't know how Fast he's goin ain't got No Business drivin a Automobile.

*Moral: All deliberate Speed Kills.*

## DONALD BARTHELME

*was born in Texas and currently lives in New York. Since the publication of his first collection of stories,* Come Back, Dr. Caligari, *he has been recognized as a leading writer of experimental, "reality busting" fiction. His other books are a novel,* Snow White, *and two collections of short works,* Unspeakable Practices, Unnatural Acts *and* City Life. *In the following short story, Barthelme introduces a balloon into a relatively structured environment—American society—and records various possible reactions to it. Everyday reality is expanded and the balloon becomes a part of societal existence. It is an amorphous possibility to be made into whatever one wants for such an opportunity does not exist in "normal" society. The balloon is thus* what could be.

# THE BALLOON

The balloon, beginning at a point on Fourteenth Street, the exact location of which I cannot reveal, expanded northward all one night, while people were sleeping, until it reached the Park. There, I stopped it; at dawn the northernmost edges lay over the Plaza; the free-hanging motion was frivolous and gentle. But experiencing a faint irritation at stopping, even to protect the trees, and seeing no reason the balloon should not be allowed to expand upward, over the parts of the city it was already covering, into the "air space" to be found there, I asked the engineers to see to it. This expansion took place throughout the morning, soft imperceptible sighing of gas through the valves. The balloon then covered forty-five blocks north-south and an irregular area east-west, as many as six crosstown blocks on either side of the Avenue in some places. That was the situation, then.

But it is wrong to speak of "situations," implying sets of circumstances leading to some resolution, some escape of tension; there were no situations, simply the balloon hanging there—muted heavy grays and browns for the most part, contrasting with walnut and soft yellows. A deliberate lack of finish, enhanced by skillful installation, gave the surface a rough, forgotten quality; sliding weights on the inside, carefully adjusted, anchored the great, vari-shaped mass at a number of points. Now, we have had a flood of original ideas in all media, works of singular beauty as well as significant milestones in the history of inflation, but at that moment there was only *this balloon,* concrete particular, hanging there.

There were reactions. Some people found the balloon "interesting." As a response this seemed inadequate to the immensity of the balloon, the suddenness of its appearance over the city; on the other hand, in the absence of hysteria or other societally-induced anxiety, it must be judged a calm, "mature" one. There was a certain amount of initial argumentation about the "meaning" of the balloon; this subsided, because we have learned not to insist on meanings, and they are rarely even looked for now, except in cases involving the simplest, safest phenomena. It was agreed that since the meaning of the balloon could never be known absolutely, extended discussion was pointless, or at least less purposeful than the activities of those who, for example, hung green and blue paper lanterns from the warm gray underside, in certain streets, or seized the occasion to write messages on the surface, anouncing their availability for the performance of unnatural acts, or the availability of acquaintances.

Daring children jumped, especially at those points where the balloon hovered close to a building, so that the gap between balloon and building was a matter of a few inches, or points where the balloon actually made contact, exerting an ever-so-slight pressure against the side of a building, so that balloon and building seemed a unity. The upper surface was so structured that a "landscape" was presented, small valleys as well as slight knolls, or mounds; once atop the balloon, a stroll was possible, or even a trip, from one place to another. There was pleasure in being able to run down an incline, then up the opposing slope, both gently graded, or in making a leap from one side to the other. Bouncing was possible, because of the pneumaticity of the surface, and even falling, if that was your wish. That all these varied motions, as well as others, were within one's possibilities, in experiencing the "up" side of the balloon, was extremely exciting for children, accustomed to the city's flat, hard skin. But the purpose of the balloon was not to amuse children.

Too, the number of people, children and adults, who took advantage of the opportunities described was not so large as it might have been: a certain timidity, lack of trust in the balloon, was seen. There was, furthermore, some hostility. Because we had hidden the pumps, which fed helium to the interior, and because the surface was so vast that the authorities could not determine the point of entry—that is, the point at which the gas was injected—a degree of frustration was evidenced by those city officers into whose province such manifestations normally fell. The apparent purposelessness of the balloon was vexing (as was the fact that it was "there" at all). Had we painted, in great letters,

"LABORATORY TESTS PROVE" or "18% MORE EFFECTIVE" on the sides of the balloon, this difficulty would have been circumvented, but I could not bear to do so. On the whole, these officers were remarkably tolerant, considering the dimensions of the anomaly, this tolerance being the result of, first, secret tests conducted by night that convinced them that little or nothing could be done in the way of removing or destroying the balloon, and, secondly, a public warmth that arose (not uncolored by touches of the aforementioned hostility) toward the balloon, from ordinary citizens.

As a single balloon must stand for a lifetime of thinking about balloons, so each citizen expressed, in the attitude he chose, a complex of attitudes. One man might consider that the balloon had to do with the notion *sullied*, as in the sentence *The big balloon sullied the otherwise clear and radiant Manhattan sky.* That is, the balloon was, in this man's view, an imposture, something inferior to the sky that had formerly been there, something interposed between the people and their "sky." But in fact it was January, the sky was dark and ugly; it was not a sky you could look up into, lying on your back in the street, with pleasure, unless pleasure, for you, proceeded from having been threatened, from having been misused. And the underside of the balloon, was a pleasure to look up into—we had seen to that. Muted grays and browns for the most part, contrasted with walnut and soft, forgotten yellows. And so, while this man was thinking *sullied*, still there was an admixture of pleasurable cognition in his thinking, struggling with the original perception.

Another man, on the other hand, might view the balloon as if it were part of a system of unanticipated rewards, as when one's employer walks in and says, "Here, Henry, take this package of money I have wrapped for you, because we have been doing so well in the business here, and I admire the way you bruise the tulips, without which bruising your department would not be a success, or at least not the success that it is." For this man the balloon might be a brilliantly heroic "muscle and pluck" experience, even if an experience poorly understood.

Another man might say, "Without the example of —— it is doubtful that —— would exist today in its present form," and find many to agree with him, or to argue with him. Ideas of "bloat" and "float" were introduced, as well as concepts of dream and responsibility. Others engaged in remarkably detailed fantasies having to do with a wish either to lose themselves in the balloon, or to engorge it. The private character of these wishes, of their origins, deeply buried and unknown, was such that they were not much spoken of; yet there is evidence that they were widespread. It was also argued that what was important was what you felt when you stood under the balloon; some people claimed that they felt sheltered, warmed, as never before, while enemies of the balloon felt, or reported feeling, constrained, a "heavy" feeling.

Critical opinion was divided:

"monstrous pourings"

"harp"

XXXXXXX "certain contrasts with darker portions"

"inner joy"

"large, square corners"

"conservative eclecticism that has so far governed modern balloon design"

: : : : : : : "abnormal vigor"

"warm, soft, lazy passages"

"Has unity been sacrificed for a sprawling quality?"

"*Quelle catastrophe!*"

"munching"

People began, in a curious way, to locate themselves in relation to aspects of the balloon: "I'll be at that place where it dips down into Forty-seventh Street almost to the sidewalk, near the Alamo Chile House," or "Why don't we go stand on top, and take the air, and maybe walk about a bit, where it forms a tight, curving line with the façade of the Gallery of Modern Art—" Marginal intersections offered entrances within a given time duration, as well as "warm, soft, lazy passages" in which . . . But it is wrong to speak of "marginal intersections." Each intersection was crucial, none could be ignored (as if, walking there, you might not find someone capable of turning your attention, in a flash, from old exercises to new exercises, risks and escalations). Each intersection was crucial, meeting of balloon and building, meeting of balloon and man, meeting of balloon and balloon.

It was suggested that what was admired about the balloon was finally this: that it was not limited, or defined. Sometimes a bulge, blister, or sub-section would carry all the way east to the river on its own initiative, in the manner of an army's movements on a map, as seen in a headquarters remote from the fighting. Then that part would be, as it were, thrown back again, or would withdraw into new dispositions; the next morning, that part would have made another sortie, or disappeared altogether. This ability on the part of the balloon to shift its shape, to change, was very pleasing, especially to people whose lives were rather rigidly patterned, persons to whom change, although desired, was not available. The balloon, for the twenty-two days of its existence, offered the possibility, in its randomness, mislocation of the self, in contradistinction to the grid of precise, rectangular pathways under our feet. The amount of specialized training currently needed, and the consequent desirability of long-term commitments, has been occasioned by the steadily growing importance of complex machinery, in virtually all kinds of operations; as this tendency increases, more and more people will turn, in bewildered inadequacy, to solutions for which the balloon may stand as a prototype, or "rough draft."

I met you under the balloon, on the occasion of your return from Norway; you asked if it was mine; I said it was. The balloon, I said, is a spontaneous autobiographical disclosure, having to do with the unease I felt at your absence, and with sexual deprivation, but now that your visit to Bergen has been terminated, it is no longer necessary or appropriate. Removal of the balloon was easy; trailer trucks carried away the depleted fabric, which is now stored in West Virginia, awaiting some other time of unhappiness, sometime, perhaps, when we are angry with one another.

## WILLIAM BURROUGHS

*is the author of several novels revolving primarily around his experience with drugs and addiction. Among his works are* The Soft Machine, Nova Express *and* Naked Lunch. *The following selection was taken from the latter novel which represents an attack on the sterility of the suburban America out of which Burroughs grew. He rejects the suburban America and substitutes his own, one in which time and space are manipulated, where the flesh itself becomes a "naked lunch" to be consumed by each and every one, for there is nothing else left. Moreover, there are other forms of addiction: addiction to power, addiction to love, addiction to other people. You are the* Naked Lunch. *In being able to recognize such "addiction" within yourself, and the causes of it, you can come to see yourself as perhaps the locus of many social problems in American society, rather than attributing this malaise to others. In this sense, it is your reality which is being busted, for as time and space come to be manipulated, one can no longer depend on existing forms. Form, in the end, disappears or changes so rapidly that such change becomes a form of its own. American society again becomes a creative possibility when one can see that there are many ways of interpreting this society.*

*From*

# NAKED LUNCH

## MEETING OF INTERNATIONAL CONFERENCE OF TECHNOLOGICAL PSYCHIATRY

Doctor "Fingers" Schafer, the Lobotomy Kid, rises and turns on the Conferents the cold blue blast of his gaze:

"Gentlemen, the human nervous system can be reduced to a compact and abbreviated spinal column. The brain, front, middle and rear must follow the adenoid, the wisdom tooth, the appendix. . . . I give you my Master Work: *The Complete All American Deanxietized Man. . . .*"

Blast of trumpets: The Man is carried in naked by two Negro Bearers who drop him on the platform with bestial, sneering brutality. . . . The Man wriggles. . . . His flesh turns to viscid, transparent jelly that drifts away in green mist, unveiling a monster black centipede. Waves of unknown stench fill the room, searing the lungs, grabbing the stomach. . . .

Schafer wrings his hands sobbing: "Clarence!! How can you do this to me?? Ingrates!! Every one of them ingrates!!"

The Conferents start back muttering in dismay:

"I'm afraid Schafer has gone a bit too far. . . ."

"I sounded a word of warning. . . ."

"Brilliant chap Schafer . . . but . . ."

"Man will do anything for publicity. . . ."

Gentlemen, this unspeakable and in every sense illegitimate child of Doctor Schafer's perverted brain must not see the light. . . . Our duty to the human race is clear. . . ."

"Man he done seen the light," said one of the Negro Bearers.

"We must stomp out the Un-American crittah," says a fat, frog-faced Southern doctor who has been drinking corn out of a mason jar. He advances drunkenly, then halts, appalled by the formidable size and menacing aspect of the centipede. . . .

"Fetch gasoline!" he bellows. "We gotta burn the son of a bitch like an uppity Nigra!"

"I'm not sticking my neck out, me," says a cool hip young doctor high on LSD25. . . . "Why a smart D.A. could . . ."

Fadeout. "Order in The Court!"

D.A.:"Gentlemen of the jury, these 'learned gentlemen' claim that the innocent human creature they have so wantonly slain suddenly turned himself into a huge black centipede and it was 'their duty to the human race' to destroy this monster before it could, by any means at its disposal, perpetrate its kind. . . .

"Are we to gulp down this tissue of horse shit? Are we to take these glib lies like a greased and nameless asshole? Where *is* this wondrous centipede?

" 'We have destroyed it,' they say smugly. . . . And I would like to remind you, Gentlemen and Hermaphrodites of the Jury, that this Great Beast"—he points to Doctor Schafer—"has, on several previous occasions, appeared in this court charged with the unspeakable crime of brain rape. . . . In plain English"—he pounds the rail of the jury box, his voice rises to a scream—"in plain English, Gentlemen, *forcible lobotomy*. . . ."

The Jury gasps. . . . One dies of a heart attack. . . . Three fall to the floor writhing in orgasms of prurience. . . .

The D.A. points dramatically: "He it is. . . . He and no other who has reduced whole provinces of our fair land to a state bordering on the far side of idiocy. . . . He it is who has filled great warehouses with row on row, tier on tier of helpless creatures who must have their every want attended. . . . 'The Drones' he calls them with a cynical leer of pure educated evil. . . . Gentlemen, I say to you that the wanton murder of Clarence Cowie must not go unavenged: This foul crime shrieks like a wounded faggot for justice at least!"

The centipede is rushing about in agitation.

"Man, that mother fucker's hungry," screams one of the Bearers.

"I'm getting out of here, me."

A wave of electric horror sweeps through the Conferents. . . . They storm the exits screaming and clawing. [ . . . ]

## ORDINARY MEN AND WOMEN

Luncheon of Nationalist Party on balcony overlooking the Market. Cigars, scotch, polite belches. . . . The Party Leader strides about in a jellaba smoking a cigar and drinking scotch. He wears expensive English shoes, loud socks, garters, muscular, hairy legs—overall effect of successful gangster in drag.

P.L. (pointing dramatically): "Look out there. What do you see?"

LIEUTENANT: "Huh? Why, I see the Market."

P.L. "No you don't. You see men and women. *Ordinary* men and women going about their ordinary everyday tasks. Leading their ordinary lives. That's what we need. . . ."

A street boy climbs over the balcony rail.

LIEUTENANT: "No, we do not want to buy any used condoms! Cut!"

P.L.: "Wait! . . . Come in, my boy. Sit down. . . . Have a cigar. . . . Have a drink."

He paces around the boy like an aroused tom cat.

"What do you think about the French?"

"Huh?"

"The French. The Colonial bastards who is sucking your live corpuscles."

"Look mister. It cost two hundred francs to suck my corpuscle. Haven't lowered my rates since the year of the rindpest when all the tourists died, even the Scandinavians."

P.L.: "You see? This is pure uncut boy in the street."

"You sure can pick 'em, boss."

"M.I. never misses."

P.L.: "Now look, kid, let's put it this way. The French have dispossessed you of your birthright."

"You mean like Friendly Finance? . . . They got this toothless Egyptian eunuch does the job. They figure he arouse less antagonism, you dig, he always take down his pants to show you his condition. 'Now I'm just a poor old eunuch trying to keep up my habit. Lady, I'd like to give you an extension on that artificial kidney, I got a job to do is all. . . . Disconnect her, boys.' He shows his gums in a feeble snarl. . . . 'Not for nothing am I known as Nellie the Repossessor.'

"So they disconnect my own mother, the sainted old gash, and she swell up and turn black and the whole souk stink of piss and the neighbors beef to the Board of Health and my father say: 'It's the will of Allah. She won't piss any more of my loot down the drain.'

"Sick people disgust me already. When some citizen start telling me about his cancer of the prostate or his rotting septum make with that purulent discharge I tell him: 'You think I am innarested to hear about your horrible old condition? I am not innarested at all.' "

P.L.: "All *right*. Cut . . . You hate the French, don't you?"

"Mister, I hate everybody. Doctor Benway says it's metabolic, I got this condition of the blood. . . . Arabs and Americans got it special. . . . Doctor Benway is concocting this serum."

P.L.: "Benway is an infiltrating Western Agent."

L.1: "A rampant French Jew . . ."

L.2: "A hog-balled, black-assed Communist Jew Nigger."

P.L.: "Shut up, you fool!"

L.2: "Sorry, chief. I am after being stationed in Pigeonhole."

P.L.: "Don't go near Benway." (Aside: "I wonder if this will go down. You never know how primitive they are. . . .") "Confidentially he's a black magician."

L.1: "He's got this resident djinn."

"Uhuh . . . Well I got a date with a high-type American client. A real classy fellah."

P.L.: "Don't you know it's shameful to peddle your ass to the alien unbelieving pricks?"

"Well that's a point of view. Have fun."

P.L.: "Likewise." Exit boy. "They're hopeless I tell you. Hopeless."

L.1: "What's with this serum?"

P.L.: "I don't know, but it sounds ominous. We better put a telepathic direction finder on Benway. The man's not to be trusted. Might do almost anything. . . . Turn a massacre into a sex orgy. . . ."

"Or a joke."

"Precisely. Arty type . . . No principles . . ."

AMERICAN HOUSEWIFE (opening a box of Lux): "Why don't it have an electric eye the box flip open when it see me and hand itself to the Automat Handy Man he should put it inna water already. . . . The Handy Man is outa control since Thursday, he been getting physical with me and I didn't put it in his combination at all. . . . And the Garbage Disposal Unit snapping at me, and the nasty old Mixmaster keep trying to get up under my dress. . . . I got the most awful cold, and my intestines is all constipated. . . . I'm gonna put it in the Handy Man's combination he should administer me a high colonic awready."

SALESMAN (he is something between an aggressive Latah and a timid Sender): "Recollect when I am travelling with K. E., hottest idea man in the gadget industry.

" 'Think of it!' he snaps. 'A cream separator in your own kitchen!'

" 'K. E., my brain reels at the thought.'

" 'It's five, maybe ten, yes, maybe twenty years away. . . . But it's coming.'

" 'I'll wait, K. E. No matter how long it is I'll wait. When the priority numbers are called up yonder I'll be there.'

"It was K. E. put out the Octopus Kit for Massage Parlors, Barber Shops and Turkish Baths, with which you can administer a high colonic, an unethical massage, a shampoo, whilst cutting the client's toenails and removing his blackheads. And the M.D.'s Can Do Kit for busy practitioners will take out your appendix, tuck in a hernia, pull a wisdom tooth, ectomize your piles and circumcise you. Well, K. E. is such an atomic salesman if he runs out of Octopus Kits he is subject, by sheer charge, to sell an M.D. Can Do to a barber shop and some citizen wakes up with his piles cut out. . . .

" 'Jesus, Homer, what kinda creep joint you running here? I been gang fucked.'

" 'Well, landsake, Si, I was just aiming to administer our complimentary high colonic free and gratis on Thanksgiving Day. K. E. musta sold me the wrong kit again. . . .' "

MALE HUSTLER: "What a boy hasta put up with in this business.

> Gawd! The propositions I get you wouldn't believe it. . . . They wanta play Latah, they wanta merge with my protoplasm, they want a replica cutting, they wanta suck my orgones, they wanta take over my past experience and leave old memories that disgust me. . . .
>
> "I am fucking this citizen so I think, 'A straight John at last'; but he comes to a climax and turns himself into some kinda awful crab. . . . I told him, 'Jack, I don't hafta stand still for such a routine like this. . . . You can take that business to Walgreen's.' Some people got no class to them. Another horrible old character just sits there and telepathizes and creams in his dry goods. So nasty."

The bum boys fall back in utter confusion to the brink of the Soviet network where Cossacks hang partisans to the wild wail of bagpipes and the boys march up Fifth Avenue to be met by Jimmy Walkover with the keys to The Kingdom and no strings attached carry them loose in your pocket. . . .

Why so pale and wan, fair bugger? Smell of dead leeches in a rusty tin can latch onto that live wound, suck out the body and blood and bones of Jeeeeesus, leave him paralyzed from the waist down.

Yield up thy forms, boy, to thy sugar daddy got the exam three years early and know all the answer books fix the World Series. [ . . . ]

Now a word about the parties of Interzone. . . .

It will be immediately clear that the Liquefaction Party is, except for one man, entirely composed of dupes, it not being clear until the final absorption who is whose dupe. . . . The Liquefactionists are much given to every form of perversion, especially sado-masochistic practices. . . .

Liquefactionists in general know what the score is. The Senders, on the other hand, are notorious for their ignorance of the nature and terminal state of sending, for barbarous and self-righteous manners, and for rabid fear of any *fact*—. It was only the intervention of the Factualists that prevented the Senders from putting Einstein in an institution and destroying his theory. It may be said that only a very few Senders know what they are doing and these top Senders are the most dangerous and evil men in the world. . . . Techniques of Sending were crude at first. Fadeout to the National Electronic Conference in Chicago.

The Conferents are putting on their overcoats. . . . The speaker talks in a flat shopgirl voice:

"In closing I want to sound a word of warning. . . . The logical extension of encephalographic research is biocontrol; that is control of physical movement, mental processes, emotional reactions and *apparent* sensory impressions by means of bioelectric signals injected into the nervous system of the subject."

"Louder and funnier!" The Conferents are trouping out in clouds of dust.

"Shortly after birth a surgeon could install connections in the brain. A miniature radio receiver could be plugged in and the subject controlled from State-controlled transmitters."

Dust settles through the windless air of a vast empty hall—smell of hot iron and steam; a radiator sings in the distance. . . . The Speaker shuffles his notes and blows dust off them. . . .

"The biocontrol apparatus is prototype of one-way telepathic control. The subject could be rendered susceptible to the transmitter by drugs or other processing without installing any apparatus. Ultimately the Senders will use telepathic transmitting exclusively. . . . Ever dig the Mayan codices? I figure it like this: the priests—about one per cent of population—made with one-way telepathic broadcasts instructing the workers what to feel and when. . . . A telepathic sender has to send all the time. He can never receive, because if he receives that means someone else has feelings of his own could louse up his continuity. The sender has to send all the time, but he can't ever recharge himself by contact. Sooner or later he's got no feelings to send. You can't have feelings alone. Not alone like the Sender is alone—and you dig there can only be one Sender at one place-time. . . . Finally the screen goes dead. . . . The Sender has turned into a huge centipede. . . . So the workers come in on the beam and burn the centipede and elect a new Sender by consensus of the general will. . . . The Mayans were limited by isolation. . . . Now one Sender could control the planet. . . . *You see control can never be a means to any practical end. . . . It can never be a means to anything but more control. . . . Like junk . . .*"

The Divisionists occupy a mid-way position, could in fact be termed moderates. . . . They are called Divisionists because they literally divide. They cut off tiny bits of their flesh and grow exact replicas of themselves in embryo jelly. It seems probable, unless the process of division is halted, that eventually there will be only one replica of one sex on the planet: that is one person in the world with millions of separate bodies. . . . Are these bodies actually independent, and could they in time develop varied characteristics? I doubt it. Replicas must periodically recharge with the Mother Cell. This is an article of faith with the Divisionists, who live in fear of a replica revolution. . . . Some Divisionists think that the process can be halted short of the eventual monopoly of one replica. They say: "Just let me plant a few more replicas all over so I won't be lonely when I travel. . . . And we must strictly control the division of Undesirables. . . ." Every replica but your own is eventually an "Undesirable." Of course if someone starts inundating an area with Identical Replicas, everyone knows what is going on. The other citizens are subject to declare a "Schluppit" (wholesale massacre of all identifiable replicas). To avoid extermination of their replicas, citizens dye, distort, and alter them with face and body molds. Only the most abandoned and shameless characters venture to manufacture I.R.s—Identical Replicas.

A cretinous albino Caid, product of a long line of recessive genes (tiny toothless mouth lined with black hairs, body of a huge crab, claws instead of arms, eyes projected on stalks) accumulated 20,000 I.R.s.

"As far as the eye can see, nothing but replicas," he says, crawling around on his terrace and speaking in strange insect chirps. "I don't have to skulk around like a nameless asshole growing replicas in my cesspool and sneaking them out disguised as plumbers and delivery men. . . . My replicas don't have their dazzling beauty marred by plastic surgery and barbarous dye and bleach processes. They stand forth naked in the sun for all to see, in their incandescent loveliness of body, face and soul. I have made them in my image and enjoined them to increase and multiply geometric for they shall inherit the earth."

A professional witch was called in to make Sheik Aracknid's replica cultures forever sterile. . . . As the witch was preparing to loose a blast of anti-orgones, Benway told him: "Don't knock yourself out. Frederick's ataxia will clean out that replica nest. I studied neurology under Professor Fingerbottom in Vienna . . . and he knew every nerve in your body. Magnificent old thing . . . Came to a sticky end. . . . His falling piles blew out the Duc de

Ventre's Hispano Suiza and wrapped around the rear wheel. He was completely gutted, leaving an empty shell sitting there on the giraffe skin upholstery. . . . Even the eyes and brain went with a horrible schlupping sound. The Duc de Ventre says he will carry that ghastly schlup to his mausoleum."

Since there is no sure way to detect a disguised replica (though every Divisionist has some method he considers infallible) the Divisionists are hysterically paranoid. If some citizen ventures to express a liberal opinion, another citizen invariably snarls: "What are you? Some stinking Nigger's bleached-out replica?"

The casualties in barroom fights are staggering. In fact the fear of Negro replicas—which may be blond and blue-eyed—has depopulated whole regions. The Divisionists are all latent or overt homosexuals. Evil old queens tell the young boys: "If you go with a woman your replicas won't grow." And citizens are forever putting the hex on someone else's replica cultures. Cries of "Hex my culture will you, Biddy Blair!" followed by sound effects of mayhem, continually ring through the quarter. . . . The Divisionists are much given to the practice of black magic in general, and they have innumerable formulas of varying efficacy for destroying the Mother Cell, also known as the Protoplasm Daddy, by torturing or killing a captured replica. . . . The authorities have finally given up the attempt to control, among the Divisionists, the crimes of murder and unlicensed production of replicas. But they do stage pre-election raids and destroy vast replica cultures in the mountainous regions of the Zone where replica moonshiners hole up.

Sex with a replica is strictly forbidden and almost universally practised. There are queer bars where shameless citizens openly consort with their replicas. House detectives stick their heads into hotel rooms saying: "Have you got a replica in here?"

Bars subject to be inundated by low class replica lovers put up signs in ditto marks: *" " " "*s Will Not Be Served Here. . . . It may be said that the average Divisionist lives in a continual crisis of fear and rage, unable to achieve either the self-righteous complacency of the Senders or the relaxed depravity of the Liquefactionists. . . . However the parties are not in practice separate but blend in all combinations.

The Factualists are Anti-Liquefactionist, Anti-Divisionist, and above all Anti-Sender.

Bulletin of the Coordinate Factualist on the subject of replicas: "We must reject the facile solution of flooding the planet with 'desirable replicas.' It is highly doubtful if there are any desirable replicas, such creatures constituting an attempt to circumvent process and change. Even the most intelligent and genetically perfect replicas would in all probability constitute an unspeakable menace to life on this planet. . . ."

T.B.—Tentative Bulletin-Liquefaction: "We must not reject or deny our protoplasmic core, striving at all time to maintain a maximum of flexibility without falling into the morass of liquefaction. . . ." Tentative and Incomplete Bulletin: "Emphatically we do not oppose telepathic research. In fact, telepathy properly used and understood could be the ultimate defense against any form of organized coercion or tyranny on the part of pressure groups or individual control addicts. We oppose, as we oppose atomic war, the use of such knowledge to control, coerce, debase, exploit or annihilate the individuality of another living creature. Telepathy is not, by its nature, a one-way process. To attempt to set up a one-way telepathic broadcast must be regarded as an unqualified evil. . . ."

D.B.—Definitive Bulletin: "The Sender will be defined by negatives. A low pressure area, a sucking emptiness. He will be portentously anonymous, faceless, colorless. He will—probably—be born with smooth disks of skin instead of eyes. He always knows where he is going like a virus knows. He doesn't need eyes."

"Couldn't there be more than one Sender?"

"Oh yes, many of them at first. But not for long. Some maudlin citizens will think they can send something edifying, not realizing that sending *is* evil. Scientists will say: 'Sending is like atomic power. . . . If properly harnessed.' At this point an anal technician mixes a bicarbonate of soda and pulls the switch that reduces the earth to cosmic dust. ('Belch . . . They'll hear this fart on Jupiter.') . . . Artists will confuse sending with creation. They will camp around screeching 'A new medium' until their rating drops off. . . . Philosophers will bat around the ends and means hassle not knowing that *sending can never be a means to anything but more sending, Like Junk.* Try using junk as a means to something else. . . . Some citizens with 'Coca Cola and aspirin' control habits will be talking about the evil glamor of sending. But no one will talk about anything very long. *The Sender,* he don't like talking."

The Sender is not a human individual. . . . It is The Human Virus. (All virus are deteriorated cells leading a parasitic existence. . . . They have specific affinity for the Mother Cell; thus deteriorated liver cells seek the home place of hepatitis, etc. So every species has a Master Virus: Deteriorated Image of that species.)

The broken image of Man moves in minute by minute and cell by cell. . . . Poverty, hatred, war, police-criminals, bureaucracy, insanity, all symptoms of The Human Virus.

*The Human Virus can now be isolated and treated.*

## THE COUNTY CLERK

The County Clerk has his office in a huge red brick building known as the Old Court House. Civil cases are, in fact, tried there, the proceeding inexorably dragging out until the contestants die or abandon litigation. This is due to the vast number of records pertaining to absolutely everything, all filed in the wrong place so that no one but the County Clerk and his staff of assistants can find them, and he often spends years in the search. In fact, he is still looking for material relative to a damage suit that was settled out of court in 1910. Large sections of the Old Court House have fallen in ruins, and others are highly dangerous owing to frequent cave-ins. The County Clerk assigns the more dangerous missions to his assistants, many of whom have lost their lives in the service. In 1912 two hundred and seven assistants were trapped in a collapse of the North-by-North-East wing.

When suit is brought against anyone in the Zone, his lawyers connive to have the case transferred to the Old Court House. Once this is done, the plaintiff has lost the case, so the only cases that actually go to trial in the Old Court House are those instigated by eccentrics and paranoids who want "a public hearing," which they rarely get since only the most desperate famine of news will bring a reporter to the Old Court House.

The Old Court House is located in the town of Pigeon Hole outside the urban zone. The inhabitants of this town and the surrounding area of swamps and heavy timber are people of such great stupidity and such barbarous practices that the Administration has seen fit to quarantine them in a reservation surrounded by a radioactive wall of iron bricks. In retaliation the citizens of Pigeon Hole plaster their town with signs: "*Urbanite Don't Let The Sun Set On You Here,*" an unnecessary injunction, since nothing but urgent business would take any urbanite to Pigeon Hole.

Lee's case is urgent. He has to file an immediate affidavit that he is suffering from bubonic plague to avoid eviction from the house he has occupied ten years without paying the rent. He exists in perpetual quarantine. So he packs his suitcase of affidavits and petitions and injunctions and certificates and takes a bus to the Frontier. The Urbanite customs inspector waves him through: "I hope you've got an atom bomb in that suitcase."

Lee swallows a handful of tranquilizing pills and steps into the Pigeon Hole customs shed. The inspectors spend three hours pawing through his papers, consulting dusty books of regulations and duties from which they read incomprehensible and ominous excerpts ending with: "And as such is subject to fine and penalty under act 666." They look at him significantly.

They go through his papers with a magnifying glass.

"Sometimes they slip dirty limericks between the lines."

"Maybe he figures to sell them for toilet paper. Is this crap for your own personal use?"

"Yes."

"He says yes."

"And how do we know that?"

"I gotta affidavit."

"Wise guy. Take off your clothes."

"Yeah. Maybe he got dirty tattoos."

They paw over his body probing his ass for contraband and examine it for evidence of sodomy. They dunk his hair and send the water out to be analyzed. "Maybe he's got dope in his hair."

Finally, they impound his suitcase; and he staggers out of the shed with a fifty pound bale of documents.

A dozen or so Recordites sit on the Old Court House steps of rotten wood. They watch his approach with pale blue eyes, turning their heads slow on wrinkled necks (the wrinkles full of dust) to follow his body up the steps and through the door. Inside, dust hangs in the air like fog, sifting down from the ceiling, rising in clouds from the floor as he walks. He mounts a perilous staircase—condemned in 1929. Once his foot goes through, and the dry splinters tear into the flesh of his leg. The staircase ends in a painter's scaffold, attached with frayed rope and pullies to a beam almost invisible in dusty distance. He pulls himself up cautiously to a ferris wheel cabin. His weight sets in motion hydraulic machinery (sound of running water). The wheel moves smooth and silent to stop by a rusty iron balcony, worn through here and there like an old shoe sole. He walks down a long corridor lined with doors, most of them nailed or boarded shut. In one office, *Near East Exquisitries* on a green brass plaque, the Mugwump is catching termites with his long black tongue. The door of the County Clerk's office is open. The County Clerk sits inside gumming snuff, surrounded by six assistants. Lee stands in the doorway. The County Clerk goes on talking without looking up.

"I run into Ted Spigot the other day . . . a good old boy, too. Not a finer man in the Zone than Ted Spigot. . . . Now it was a Friday I happen to remember because the Old Lady was down with the menstral cramps and I went to Doc Parker's drugstore on Dalton Street, just opposite Ma Green's Ethical Massage Parlor, where Jed's old livery stable used to be. . . . Now, Jed, I'll remember his second name directly, had a cast in the left eye and his wife came from some place out East, Algiers I believe it was, and after Jed died she married up again, and she married one of the Hoot boys, Clem Hoot if my memory serves, a good old boy too, now Hoot was around fifty-four fifty-five year old at the time. . . . So I says to Doc Parker: 'My old lady is down bad with the menstral cramps. Sell me two ounces of paregoric.'

"So Doc says, 'Well, Arch, you gotta sign the book. Name, address and date of purchase. It's the law.'

"So I asked Doc what the day was, and he said, 'Friday the 13th.'

"So I said, 'I guess I already had mine.'

" 'Well,' Doc says, 'there was a feller in here this morning. City feller. Dressed kinda flashy. So he's got him a RX for a mason jar of morphine. . . . Kinda funny looking prescription writ out on toilet paper. . . . And I told him straight out: "Mister, I suspect you to be a dope fiend.' "

" ' "I got the ingrowing toe nails, Pop. I'm in agony." ' he says.

" ' "Well," I says, "I gotta be careful. But so long as you got a legitimate condition and an RX from a certified bona feedy M.D., I'm honored to serve you.' "

" ' "That croaker's really certified," he say. . . . Well, I guess one hand didn't know what the other was doing when I give him a jar of Saniflush by error. . . . So I reckon he's had his too.'

" 'Just the thing to clean a man's blood.'

" 'You know, that very thing occurred to me. Should be a sight better than sulphur and molasses. . . . Now, Arch, don't think I'm nosey; but a man don't have no secrets from God and his druggist I always say. . . . Is you still humping the Old Gray Mare?'

" 'Why, Doc Parker . . . I'll have you know I'm a family man and an Elder in the First Denominational Non-sextarian Church and I ain't had a pieca hoss ass since we was kids together.'

" 'Them was the days, Arch. Remember the time I got the goose grease mixed up with the mustard? Always was a one to grab the wrong jar, feller say. They could have heard you squealing over in Cunt Like County, just a squealing like a stoat with his stones cut off.'

" 'You're in the wrong hole, Doc. It was you took the mustard and me as had to wait till you cooled off.'

" 'Wistful thinking, Arch. I read about it one time inna magazine settin' in that green outhouse behind the station. . . . Now what I meant awhile back, Arch, you didn't rightly understand me. . . . I was referring to your wife as the Old Gray Mare. . . . I mean she ain't what she used to be what with all them carbuncles and cataracts and chilblains and haemorrhoids and aftosa.'

" 'Yas, Doc, Liz is right sickly. Never was the same after her eleventh miscarriaging. . . . There was something right strange about that. Doc Ferris he told me straight, he said: "Arch, 'tain't fitting you should see that critter." And he gives me a long look made my flesh crawl. . . . Well, you sure said it right, Doc. She ain't what she used to be. And your medicines don't seem to ease her none. In fact, she ain't been able to tell night from day since using them eye drops you sold her last month. . . . But, Doc, you oughtta know I wouldn't be humping Liz, the old cow, meaning no disrespect to the mother of my dead monsters. Not when I got that sweet little ol' fifteen year old thing. . . . You know that yaller girl used to work in Marylou's Hair Straightening and Skin Bleach Parlor over in Nigga town.'

" 'Getting that dark chicken meat, Arch? Gettin' that coon pone?'

" 'Gettin' it steady, Doc. Gettin' it steady. Well, feller say duty is goosing me. Gotta get back to the old crank case.'

" 'I'll bet she needs a grease job worst way.'

" 'Doc, she sure is a dry hole. . . . Well, thanks for the paregoric.'

" 'And thanks for the trade, Arch. . . . He he he . . . Say, Archy boy, some night when you get caught short with a rusty load drop around and have a drink of Yohimbiny with me.'

" 'I'll do that, Doc, I sure will. It'll be just like old times.'

"So I went on back to my place and heated up some water and mixed up some paregoric and cloves and cinnamon and sassyfrass and give it to Liz, and it eased her some I reckon. Leastwise she let up aggravatin' me. . . . Well, later on I went down to Doc Parker's again to get me a rubber . . . and just as I was leaving I run into Roy Bane, a good ol' boy too. There's not a finer man in this Zone than Roy Bane. . . . So he said to me he says, 'Arch, you see that ol' nigger over there in that vacant lot? Well, sure as shit and taxes, he comes there every night just as regular you can set your watch by him. See him behind them nettles? Every night round about eight thirty he goes over into that lot yonder and pulls himself off with steel wool. . . . Preachin' Nigger, they tell me.'

"So that's how I come to know the hour more or less on Friday the 13th and it couldn't have been more than twenty minutes half an hour after that, I'd took some Spanish Fly in Doc's store and it was jest beginning to work on me down by Grennel Bog on my way to Nigger town. . . . Well the bog makes a bend, used to be nigger shack there. . . . They burned that ol' nigger over in Cunt Lick. Nigger had the aftosa and it left him stone blind. . . . So this white girl down from Texarkana screeches out:

" 'Roy, that ol' nigger is looking at me so nasty. Land's sake I feel just dirty all over.'

" 'Now, Sweet Thing, don't you fret yourself. Me an' the boys will burn him.'

" 'Do it slow, Honey Face. Do it slow. He's give me a sick headache.'

'So they burned the nigger and that ol' boy took his wife and went back up to Texarkana without paying for the gasoline and old Whispering Lou runs the service station couldn't talk about nothing else all Fall: 'These city fellers come down here and burn a nigger and don't even settle up for the gasoline.'

"Well, Chester Hoot tore that nigger shack down and rebuilt it just back of his house up in Bled Valley. Covered up all the windows with black cloth, and what goes on in there ain't fittin' to speak of. . . . Now Chester he's got some right strange ways. . . . Well it was just where the nigger shack used to be, right across from the Old Brooks place floods out every Spring, only it wasn't the Brooks place then . . . belonged to a feller name of Scranton. Now that piece of land was surveyed back in 1919. . . . I reckon you know the man did the job too. . . . Feller name of Hump Clarence used to witch out wells on the side. . . . Good ol' boy too, not a finer man in this Zone than Hump Clarence. . . . Well it was just around about in there I come on Ted Spigot ascrewin a mud puppy."

Lee cleared his throat. The Clerk looked up over his glasses. "Now if you'll take care, young feller, till I finish what I'm asaying, I'll tend to your business."

And he plunged into an anecdote about a nigra got the hydrophobia from a cow.

"So my pappy says to me: 'Finish up your chores, son, and let's go see the mad nigger. . . .' They had that nigger chained to the bed, and he was bawling like a cow. . . . I soon got enough of that ol' nigger. Well, if you all will excuse me I got business in the Privy Council. He he he!"

Lee listened in horror. The County Clerk often spent weeks in the privy living on scorpions and Montgomery Ward catalogues. On several occasions his assistants had forced the door and carried him out in an advanced state of malnutrition. Lee decided to play his last card.

"Mr. Anker," he said, "I'm appealing to you as one Razor Back to another," and he pulled out his Razor Back card, a memo of his lush-rolling youth.

The Clerk looked at the card suspiciously: "You don't look like a bone feed mast-fed Razor Back to me. . . . What you think about the Jeeeeews. . . ?"

"Well, Mr. Anker, you know yourself all a Jew wants to do is doodle a Christian girl. . . . One of these days we'll cut the rest of it off."

"Well, you talk right sensible for a city feller. . . . Find out what he wants and take care of him. . . . He's a good ol' boy."

## SMOKEY THE BEAR SUTRA

*is an anonymous work by a well-known American poet who circulated the poem as a broadside with the stipulation: "may be reproduced free forever." In this sutra (technically, one of the sermons of Buddha), one of America's most beloved folk heroes, Smokey the Bear, is used as a vehicle for discussing man's relationship to the land in an age of technology. As the myth comes to be altered, so too does our conception of what is real—in this case, the view of our environment which has had catastrophic ecological results.*

Once in the Jurassic, about 150 million years ago,
the Great Sun Buddha in this corner of the Infinite
Void gave a great Discourse to all the assembled elements
and energies: to the standing beings, the walking beings,
the flying beings, and the sitting beings—even grasses,
to the number of thirteen billion, each one born from a
seed, were assembled there: a Discourse concerning
Enlightenment on the planet Earth.

"In some future time, there will be a continent called
America. It will have great centers of power called
such as Pyramid Lake, Walden Pond, Mt. Rainier, Big Sur,
Everglades, and so forth; and powerful nerves and channels
such as Columbia River, Mississippi River, and Grand Canyon.
The human race in that era will get into troubles all over
its head, and practically wreck everything in spite of
its own strong intelligent Buddha-nature."

"The twisting strata of the great mountains and the pulsings
of great volcanoes are my love burning deep in the earth.
My obstinate compassion is schist and basalt and
granite, to be mountains, to bring down the rain. In that

future American Era I shall enter a new form: to cure
the world of loveless knowledge that seeks with blind hunger;
and mindless rage eating food that will not fill it."

And he showed himself in his true form of

SMOKEY THE BEAR.

A handsome smokey-colored brown bear standing on his
hind legs, showing that he is aroused and watchful.

Bearing in his right paw the Shovel that digs to the
truth beneath appearances; cuts the roots of useless attachments, and flings damp sand on the fires of greed and war;

His left paw in the Mudra of Comradely Display—indicating
that all creatures have the full right to live to their limits
and that deer, rabbits, chipmunks, snakes, dandelions,
and lizards all grow in the realm of the Dharma;

Wearing the blue work overalls symbolic of slaves and
laborers, the countless men oppressed by a civilization
that claims to save but only destroys;

Wearing the broad-brimmed hat of the West, symbolic of
the forces that guard the Wilderness, which is the Natural
State of the Dharma and the True Path of man on earth;
all true paths lead through mountains—

With a halo of smoke and flame behind, the forest fires
of the kali-yuga, fires caused by the stupidity of those
who think things can be gained and lost whereas in truth all
is contained vast and free in the Blue Sky and Green Earth
of One Mind;

Round-bellied to show his kind nature and that the great
earth has food enough for everyone who loves her and trusts
her;

Trampling underfoot wasteful freeways and needless
suburbs; smashing the worms of capitalism and totalitarianism;

Indicating the Task: his followers, becoming free of cars, houses, canned food, universities, and shoes, master the Three Mysteries of their own Body, Speech, and Mind; and fearlessly chop down the rotten trees and prune out the sick limbs of this country America and then burn the leftover trash.

Wrathful but Calm, Austere but Comic, Smokey the Bear will Illuminate those who would help him; but for those who would hinder or slander him,

HE WILL PUT THEM OUT.

Thus his great Mantra:

Namah samanta vajranam chanda maharoshana
Sphataya hum traka ham mam

"I DEDICATE MYSELF TO THE UNIVERSAL DIAMOND
BE THIS RAGING FURY DESTROYED"

And he will protect those who love woods and rivers, Gods and animals, hobos and madmen, prisoners and sick people, musicians, playful women, and hopeful children;

And if anyone is threatened by advertising, air pollution, or the police, they should chant SMOKEY THE BEAR'S WAR SPELL:

DROWN THEIR BUTTS
CRUSH THEIR BUTTS
DROWN THEIR BUTTS
CRUSH THEIR BUTTS

And SMOKEY THE BEAR will surely appear to put the enemy out with his vajra-shovel.

Now those who recite this Sutra and then try to put it in practice will accumulate merit as countless as the sands of Arizona and Nevada,
Will help save the planet Earth from total oil slick,

Will enter the age of harmony of man and nature,
Will win the tender love and caresses of men, women, and
beasts
Will always have ripe blackberries to eat and a sunny spot
under a pine tree to sit at,

AND IN THE END WILL WIN HIGHEST PERFECT ENLIGHTENMENT.

thus have we heard.

*(may be reproduced free forever)*

# Two American Indian Works

The literature of the American Indian is particularly pertinent to any attempt to break out of the reality patterns of our society because his case is so lucidly symbolic of the crisis in white American civilization. The Indian's mystical relation to his land made him easy prey for the European method of technological economic exploitation. But now that it is clear that our technological-economic system is quite capable of destroying itself and the rest of the planet, American Indian culture is being closely studied for the insights it may reveal for reorganizing our lives on a more humane basis. The two myths below—the first from the Wintu, the second from the Pawnee—go beyond environmental matters to the metaphysical realm of man's relation to his fellows and to his inner spirit. These are myths relating to the Christian conception of original sin: they attempt to explain the origin of the separation of the living and the dead. It would be useful to compare the attitudes toward death in these fables to traditional Western ideas about the afterlife, and to the ideas implicit in the American funeral parlor industry. To change your preconceptions about death is to alter your attitude to life.

# COYOTE AND DEATH

A long time ago, when the first people lived, all of them came together and decided to build a staircase to heaven. They set to work. Buzzard was their leader. He said, "When people are old and blind they will go to heaven and become young and healthy again. There will be a camping place there with plenty of wood and a spring."

Coyote came along. They were working. Coyote said, "Nephews, what are you doing?" They paid no attention to him. Then he said, "Get in the shade and rest. It is too hot to work." So finally they did. They told Coyote what they were doing. Coyote said, "It would be a good idea to have people die. People can go to burials and cry. It would be nice."

"Your idea is not good," they said.

Coyote argued in favor of death. Then Buzzard and the others said, "When acorns ripen they will have no shells. Snow will be salmon flour."

Coyote was against this too. He said, "Acorns should have shells so that the boys and girls can shell them and throw them at each other in the evening and have a good time. Snow should be cold, and when people go out to hunt in it they will die. That is the way it will be good."

Finally all the people became very angry and destroyed their work.

From *Wintu Myths,* by Cora Dubois and D. Demetracopoulou. *University of California Publications in American Archaeology and Ethnology,* Vol. 28, No. 5 (Berkeley, 1931). Reprinted by permission of the Regents of the University of California.

# SPIRIT LAND

There was a village, and among the people was a man who had a beautiful wife. He thought much of her and spent his time in hunting game, so that they might have plenty to eat.

After a time they had a son, who grew up. When he was about twelve years old his mother died. Then the man took good care of the boy, for he was his only son. The boy became sick and died.

The man did not know what to do, whether to kill himself or to wander over the country. He decided to wander over the country. He mourned four days at the grave of his son; now he was to roam over the country. He went many days, and after a while he came to some timbered country. He went through it. He had his quiver filled with arrows and a bow. While in this timber he heard people talk in his language, and he stopped. . . . One came to him and said: "What a wonderful tree! All of you come! I have found a wonderful tree. It looks like a man." The man stood still, and the others came and said: "Truly this is a wonderful tree. Look, it has eyes, nose, and hair! Look, here is a quiver and bow." At this saying the man shrieked, and said: "I thought you were all dead! Here you are wandering over the country." As soon as he spoke they ran away. He could hear some of them say, "He has caught me!" Another would say, "He has caught my foot," when the creature was caught by briers and grapevines. They ran a long way, then they stopped; and they began to tell how narrowly they had escaped from the man.

While they were talking, the man came upon them again, and away they went. The man followed them up. This time they disappeared on the side of a hill, and, as it was now late in the day, the man made up his mind to follow and to try to stand with them. He thought, as he was wandering, "Why not remain with these people?" He got to the place where they had disappeared,

From *Traditions of the Skidi Pawnee* by George A. Dorsey. American Folklore Society. Boston and New York: Houghton Mifflin, 1904.

and under a thick grapevine found an entrance large enough for a man to crawl in; there, far within, was a cave. He knew the leader. He had carried the sacred bundle and had led the war party; but he now saw them and knew they were lost; that they had been attacked by the enemy, and that they had been scalped. He sat there looking at them. They were talking about him. The man did not go entirely inside, for he himself was afraid. While they were talking, someone shrieked, "There he is!" and they would pile themselves one on top of another. . . .

The leader, who was sitting under the bundle, said: "Boys, keep quiet! This man is of our people. Get up and make a fire, and we will hear what he has to say." Fire was made, and each took his place where he belonged in the circle. And then the leader asked him what brought him there.

"Nava," said the man, "I lost my wife. We had a son and he died, too. I was left all alone. I have mourned for him a long time, longing for death, so that I might join my wife and son. I wandered from home until I came here. I am here, and I am glad I can now make my home with you, my brothers: for I do not care to be with my people any more."

The leader spoke and said: "It is good, but we cannot let you live with us. We are dead. What you see are spirits. We should have gone to the Spirit Land but for this bundle which you see. It belongs to our people, and Tirawa released our spirits, so that we could wander back and return the bundle. Brother, I am glad you came to us. We will teach you the ceremony of this bundle; then take it home, and let our people know that the bundle is again found."

The man sat a long time, for he knew that to accept what this man said was to become a power among his people and be a leader. But at last he spoke and said: "My people, I am poor in heart. I cannot accept what my brother has offered, for I am never to return to my people. If I cannot see my son I am ready to die." Here he stood up and continued: "My brothers, take pity on me; take me with you to Spirit Land that I can see my boy. I cannot take the bundle to my people, for I am not happy." He passed his hands over the leader's head and on down the arms. "Take pity on me," he said once more.

The leader sat with downcast head. Then he stood up, took down the bundle, took out sweet grass and put it in the fire, then opened the bundle. He looked at all the things in the bundle; he took them outside, so that the gods who gave them might look at them. Then he said: "My brothers, I must help this man to remain here. I will go to the gods in the west, who will receive this man's words. I pity him. I think the gods will pity him. I go."

He disappeared. The others watched and watched. At last they heard the wind descend. The leader had come back. He went to the bundle, took out native tobacco and burnt it, offering it to the gods. Then he spoke: "My son, the gods in the west have received your words. All the gods sent their words to Tirawa, and Tirawa has given his consent for the people in Spirit Land to come and see the living. They are to camp with them four days and four nights, without speaking one to another. You are to be allowed to be near your son and to speak with him, but not to touch him. . . . Those who wish to remain with their relatives as well as those who wish to go to Spirit Land will be permitted to do so. Now, my son, go. Get your people. Let them come and make their camp in the neighborhood."

So the man left that same night. He noticed that he was very swift. Why, he could not understand. Finally he reached the village. A crier was called and told to go through the camp and let the people know that they were wanted at a certain place; that they were to meet their dead friends.

The next day they broke camp and went south. For a long time they traveled, until finally they came to a timbered country. Here they pitched their camp. The man went to the camp of the spirits. He was told that the dead people were also on the way, and that the next morning they would arrive. The man went to the camp, and notified the crier to go quietly and tell the people to be ready to see their friends. Some mocked and others believed. . . .

The next day people began to make preparations to meet their dead friends. Medicine ointment was put upon their heads, faces, and hands. Some time in the afternoon they saw a great dust which reached the heavens. People began to get frightened: others rejoiced, for they were again to see their dead friends. People rejoiced with song. Then the spirits began to pass through. As they passed, the people saw their dead friends, but they did not dare to touch or speak to them. As they kept up the marching, the man's son came. He caught his son. Now he was told . . . not to speak [touch?] to him. . . . He did not do this, for as soon as he caught his son he spoke to him and hugged him, and in his heart he said: "I will not let you go!"

As soon as this was done the spirits went off. The other spirits also disappeared. The man went away broken-hearted. The people returned home, and the man never came back. The people said: "He is with the scalped men." But afterwards he was seen, and had over him a horse robe. He was wild, did not seem to care to be with his people. So he was forgotten; for had he not caught his son, then the spirits and the people were to have lived once more together, and death was to have been unknown.

## HERMANN HESSE

*is the author of some of the most celebrated works of fiction of the twentieth century, including* The Glass Bead Game, *from which the following selection is taken. Among the Nobel Prize winner's other works are* Journey to the East, Narcissus and Goldmund, Steppenwolf, Demian, *and* Siddartha. *In all these novels the conflict between passion and reason is exemplified, as is the contrast between East and West. "The Indian Life" is one of the three "incarnations" written by Joseph Knecht, the chief character in* The Glass Bead Game, *as an exercise in projecting himself imaginatively into an alien temporal and cultural situation. In this selection, spatial, temporal, and cultural realities are shifted in a way that could demonstrate possibilities for altering your attitudes toward American society, which in turn could enable you to change undesirable aspects of that society. By immersing yourself in a different reality, you can see the one you live in with greater clarity.*

# THE INDIAN LIFE

When Vishnu, or rather Vishnu in his avatar as Rama, fought his savage battles with the prince of demons, one of his parts took on human shape and thus entered the cycle of forms once more. His name was Ravana and he lived as a warlike prince by the Great Ganges. Ravana had a son named Dasa. But the mother of Dasa died young, and the prince took another wife. Soon this beauteous and ambitious lady had a son of her own, and she resented the young Dasa. Although he was the firstborn, she determined to see her own son Nala inherit the rulership when the time came. And so she contrived to estrange Dasa's father from him, and meant to dispose of the boy at the first opportunity. But one of Ravana's court Brahmans, Vasudeva the Sacrificer, became privy to her plan. He was sorry for the boy who, moreover, seemed to him to possess his mother's bent for piety and feeling for justice. So the Brahman kept an eye on Dasa, to see that the boy came to no harm until he could put him out of reach of his stepmother.

Now Rajah Ravana owned a herd of cows dedicated to Brahma. These were regarded as sacred, and frequent offerings of their milk and butter were made to the god. The best pastures in the country were reserved for these cows.

One day a herdsman of these sacred cows came to the palace to deliver a batch of butter and report that there were signs of drought in the region where the herd had been grazing. Hence the band of herdsmen were going to lead the cows up into the mountains, where water and grass were available even in the driest of times.

The Brahman had known the herdsman for many years as a friendly and reliable man. He took him into his confidence. Next

From *The Glass Bead Game* (*Magister Ludi*) by Hermann Hesse. Translated by Richard and Clara Winston. 

day, when little Prince Dasa could not be found, only Vasudeva and the herdsman knew the secret of his disappearance. The herdsman took the boy Dasa into the hills with him. They caught up with the slowly moving herd, and Dasa gladly joined the band of herdsmen. He helped to guard and drive the cows, learned to milk, played with the calves, and idled about in the mountain meadows, drinking sweet milk, his bare feet smeared with cow-dung. He liked the life of the herdsmen, learned to know the forest and its trees and fruits, loved the mango, the wild fig, and the varinga tree, plucked the sweet lotus root out of green forest pools, on feast days wore a wreath of the red blossoms of the flame-of-the-woods. He became acquainted with the ways of all the animals of the wilderness, learned how to shun the tiger, to make friends with the clever mongoose and the placid hedgehog, and to while away the rainy seasons in the dusky shelter of a makeshift hut where the boys played games, recited verse, or wove baskets and reed mats. Dasa did not completely forget his former home and his former life, but soon these seemed to him like a dream.

One day, when the herd had moved on to another region, Dasa went into the forest to look for honey. Ever since he had come to know the woods he had loved them, and this particular forest seemed to him uncommonly beautiful. The rays of sunlight wound through leaves and branches like golden serpents; the noises of the forest, bird calls, rustle of treetops, jabber of monkeys, twined into a lovely, mildly luminescent network resembling the light amid the branches. Smells, too, similarly joined and parted again, the perfumes of flowers, varieties of wood, leaves, waters, mosses, animals, fruits, earth and mold, pungent and sweet, wild and intimate, stimulating and soothing, gay and sad. In some unseen gorge a stream gurgled; a velvety green butterfly with black and yellow markings danced over white flowers; deep among the blue shadows of the trees a branch broke and leaves dropped heavily into leaves, or a stag bellowed in the darkness, or an irritable she-ape scolded her family.

Dasa forgot about looking for honey. While listening to the singing of several jewel-bright small birds, he noticed a trail running between tall ferns that stood like a dense miniature forest within the great forest. It was the narrowest of footpaths, and he silently and cautiously pressed between the ferns and followed where it led. After a while he came upon a great banyan tree with many trunks. Beneath it stood a small hut, a kind of tent woven of fern leaves. Beside the hut a man sat motionless. His back was straight as a rod and his hands lay between his crossed feet. Under the white hair and broad forehead his eyes, still and sightless, were focused on the ground. They were open, but looking inward. Dasa realized that this was a holy man, a yogi. He had seen others before; they were men favored by the gods. It was good to bring them gifts and pay them respect. But this man here, sitting before his beautifully made and well-concealed fern hut, so perfectly motionless, so lost in meditation, more strongly attracted the boy and seemed to him rarer and more venerable than any of the others he had seen. He seemed to be floating above the ground as he sat there, and it was as if his abstracted gaze saw and knew everything. An aura of holiness surrounded him, a magic circle of dignity, a flame of concentrated intensity and a wave of radiant yoga energies, which the boy could not pass through, which he would not have dared to breach by a word of greeting or a cry. The majesty of his form, the light from within which radiated from his face, the composure and bronze unassailability of his features, emanated waves and rays in the midst of which he sat enthroned like a moon; and the accumulated spiritual force, the calmly concentrated will, wove such a spell around him that Dasa sensed that here was someone who, by a mere wish or thought, without even raising his eyes, could kill and restore to life.

More motionless than a tree, whose leaves and twigs stir in respiration, motionless as the stone image of a god, the yogi sat before his hut; and from the moment he had seen him the boy too remained motionless, fascinated, fettered, magically attracted by the sight. He stood staring at the Master. He saw a spot of sunlight on his shoulder, a spot of sunlight on one of his relaxed hands; he saw the flecks of light move slowly away and new ones come into being, and he began to understand that the streaks of light had nothing to do with this man, nor the songs of birds and the chatter of monkeys from the woods all around, nor the brown wild bee that settled on the sage's face, sniffed at his skin, crawled a short distance along his cheek, and then flew off again, nor all the multifarious life of the forest. All this, Dasa sensed, everything the eyes could see, the ears could hear, everything beautiful or ugly, engaging or frightening—all of it had no connection at all to this holy man. Rain would not chill or incommode him; fire could not burn him. The whole world around him had become meaningless superficiality. There came to the princely cow-herd an inkling that the whole world might be no more than a breath of wind playing over the surface, a ripple of waves over unknown depths. He was not conscious of this as a thought, but as a physical quiver and slight giddiness, a feeling of horror and danger, and at the same time of intense yearning. For this yogi, he felt, had plunged through the surface of the world, through the superficial world, into the ground of being, into the secret of all things. He had broken through and thrown off the magical net of the senses, the play of light, sound, color, and sensation, and lived secure in the essential and unchanging. The boy, although once tutored by Brahmans who had cast many a ray of spiritual light upon him, did not understand this with his intellect and would have been unable to say anything about it in words, but he sensed it as in blessed moments one senses the presence of divinity; he sensed it as a shudder of awe and admiration for this man, sensed it as love for him and longing for a life such as this man sitting in meditation seemed to be living. Strangely, the old man had reminded him of his origins, of his royalty. Touched to the quick, he stood there on the edge of the fern thicket, ignoring the flying birds and the whispered conversations of the trees, forgetting the forest and the distant herd, yielding to the spell while he stared at the sage, captivated by the incomprehensible stillness and impassivity of the man, by the bright serenity of his face, by the power and composure of his posture, by the complete dedication of his service.

Afterward he could not have said whether he had spent two or three hours, or days, at the hut. When the spell released him, when he noiselessly crept back between the ferns, found the path out of the woods, and finally reached the open meadows and the herd, he did so without being aware of what he was doing. His soul was still entranced, and he did not really come to until one of the herdsmen called him. The man was angry with him for having been away so long, but when Dasa only stared at him in wide-eyed astonishment, as if he did not understand what was being said to him, the herdsman broke off, disconcerted by the boy's strange look and solemn bearing. "Where have you been, my boy?"

he asked. "Have you seen a god by any chance, or run into a demon?"

"I was in the woods," Dasa said. "Something drew me there; I wanted to look for honey. But then I forgot about it because I saw a man there, a hermit, who sat lost in meditation or prayer, and when I saw the way his face glowed I could not help standing still and watching him for a long time. I would like to go again this evening and bring him gifts. He is a holy man."

"Do so," the herdsman said. "Bring him milk and sweet butter. We should honor the holy men and give them what we can."

"But how am I to address him?"

"There is no need to address him, Dasa. Only bow and place the gifts before him. No more is needed."

Dasa did so. It took him a while to find the place again. The clearing in front of the hut was deserted, and he did not dare go into the hut itself. He therefore laid his gifts on the ground at the entrance and left.

As long as the herdsmen remained with the cows in this vicinity, Dasa brought gifts every evening, and once he went there by day again. He found the holy man deep in meditation, and this time too felt impelled to stand there in a state of bliss, receiving those rays of strength and felicity that emanated from the yogi.

Long after they had left the neighborhood and were driving the herd to new pastures, Dasa remembered his experience in the forest. And as is the way of boys, when he was alone he sometimes daydreamed of himself as a hermit and practitioner of yoga. But with time the memory and the dream faded, all the more so since Dasa was now rapidly growing into a strong young man who threw himself with zest into the sports and brawls of his fellows. But a gleam, a faint inkling remained in his soul, a suggestion that the princely life and the sovereignty he had lost might some day be replaced by the dignity and power of yoga.

One day, when they had come to the vicinity of the capital, they heard that a great festival was in preparation. Old Prince Ravana, bereft of his former strength and grown quite frail, had appointed the day for his son Nala to succeed him.

Dasa wanted to go to the festival. He wished to see the city once more, for he had only the faintest memories of it from his childhood. He wanted to hear the music, to watch the parade and the tournament among the nobles; and he also wanted to have a look at that unknown world of townsfolk and magnates who figured so largely in tales and legends, for he knew, although this was only a tale or legend or something even more insubstantial, that once upon a time, ages ago, their world had been his own.

The herdsmen were supposed to deliver a load of butter to the court for the festival sacrifices, and to his joy Dasa was one of the three young men chosen by the chief herdsman for this task.

They brought their butter to the palace on the eve of the festival. The Brahman Vasudeva received it from them, for it was he who had charge of the sacrifices, but he did not recognize the youth. Then the three herdsmen joined the throngs attending the celebrations. Early in the morning they watched the beginning of the sacrifices under the Brahman's direction. They saw the masses of shining golden butter given to the flames, watched as it was transformed into leaping fire; flickering, its light and fatty smoke soared toward the Infinite, a delight to the thrice-ten gods. They watched the elephants leading the parade, their riders in howdahs with gilded roofs. They beheld the flower-decked royal carriage containing the young Rajah Nala, and heard the mighty reverberations of the drums. It was all very magnificent and glittering and also a little ridiculous, or at least that is how it seemed to young Dasa. He was stunned and enraptured, intoxicated by the noise, by the carriages and caparisoned horses, by all the pomp and extravagance; he was also delighted by the dancing girls who cavorted in front of the royal carriage, their limbs slender and tough as lotus stems. He was astonished at the size and beauty of the city, but still and all he regarded everything, in the midst of his excitement and pleasure, with the sober good sense of the herdsman who basically despises the townsman.

That he himself was really the firstborn, that his stepbrother Nala, whom he had forgotten completely, was being anointed, consecrated, and hailed in his stead, that he himself, Dasa, ought by rights to be riding in the flower-decked carriage—such thoughts did not even occur to him. On the other hand, he took a strong dislike to this Nala; the young man seemed to him stupid and mean in his self-indulgence, unbearably vain and swollen with self-importance. He would rather have liked to play a trick on this youth acting the part of rajah, to teach him a lesson; but there was surely no opportunity for anything of the sort, and in any case he quickly forgot all about it, for there was so much to see, to hear, to laugh at, to enjoy. The townswomen were pretty and had pert, alluring looks, movements, and turns of speech. A good many phrases were flung at the three herdsmen which rang in their ears for a long while afterward. These phrases were called out with overtones of mockery, for townsfolk feel about herdsmen just the way herdsmen do about townsfolk: each despises the other. But still and all those handsome, stalwart young men, nourished on milk and cheese and living under the open sky almost all the year, were much to the liking of the townswomen.

By the time Dasa returned from this festival, he had become a man. He chased girls and had to hold his own in a good many hard boxing and wrestling matches with other young fellows. They were now making their way into a different region, a region of flat meadows and wetlands planted to rushes and bamboo trees. Here he saw a girl by the name of Pravati, and was seized by a mad love for this beautiful young woman. She was a tenant farmer's daughter, and Dasa was so infatuated that he forgot everything else and threw away his freedom in order to win her. When the time came for the herdsmen to move along to fresh pastures, he brushed aside advice and warnings, bade farewell to them and the herdsman's life he had dearly loved, and settled down. He succeeded in winning Pravati as his wife. In return he tilled his father-in-law's millet fields and rice paddies, and helped with the work in mill and woodlot. He built a bamboo and mud hut for his wife, and kept her shut up within it.

It must be a tremendous power that can move a young man to give up his previous joys and friends and habits, to change his existence entirely, and to live among strangers in the unenviable role of son-in-law. But so great was Pravati's beauty, so great and alluring the promise of amorous delights that radiated from her face and figure, that Dasa became blind to everything else and surrendered utterly to this woman. And in fact he found great happiness in her arms. Many stories are told of gods and holy men so enraptured by an enchanting woman that they remain locked in intimate embrace with her for days, moons, and years, wholly absorbed by voluptuousness and forgetting all other matters. Dasa, too, would have wished his lot and his love to be like that. But he was destined for other things, and his happiness did not last long. It lasted about a year, and this period, too, was not filled with pure felicity. There was ample room for much else, for vexatious demands on the part of his father-in-law, for the taunts of his brothers-in-law, and for the whims of his young wife. But whenever he went to lie with her on their pallet, all this was forgotten, vanished into thin air, such was the magic of her smile, so sweet was it to caress her slender limbs, so wonderfully did the garden of delight in her young body bloom with a thousand flowers, fragrances, and lovely shadows.

His happiness was not a whole year old when, one day, noise and unrest stirred the neighborhood. Mounted messengers appeared announcing the coming of the young Rajah. Then came troops, horses, the supply train, and finally Rajah Nala himself, to hunt in the countryside. Tents were pitched here and there; horses could be heard neighing and horns blowing.

Dasa paid no attention to all this. He worked in the fields, tended the mill, and kept out of the way of hunters and courtiers. But one day when he returned to his hut he found his wife missing. He had strictly forbidden her to set foot outside during this period, while the court was in the neighborhood, and now he felt at once a stabbing pain in his heart and a premonition of disaster. He hurried to his father-in-law's house. Pravati was not there either, and no one would admit to having seen her. The pang in his heart intensified. He searched the cabbage patch and the fields; he spent a whole day and then another going back and forth between his hut and his father-in-law's; he lurked in the field, climbed down into the well, called her name, coaxed, cursed, hunted for footprints.

At last the youngest of his brothers-in-law, who was still a boy, told him the truth. Pravati was with the Rajah; she was living in his tent and had been seen riding on his horse.

Dasa lurked invisibly about Nala's encampment, carrying the sling he had used during his days as a herdsman. Day or night, whenever the prince's tent seemed to be unguarded for a moment, he would steal closer; but each time guards soon appeared and he had to flee. Hiding in the branches of a tree, he looked down on the camp and saw the Rajah, whose repellent face he remembered from the time of the festival. Dasa watched him mount his horse and ride off. When he returned hours later, dismounted, and threw back the tent flap, Dasa could see into the shadowy interior where a young woman came forward to welcome the prince. He nearly fell from the tree as he recognized his wife Pravati. Now he was certain, and the pressure upon his heart grew unbearable. Great as the happiness of his love for Pravati had been, the anguish, the rage, the sense of loss and insult were greater now. That is how it is when a man fastens all his capacity for love upon a single object. With its loss everything collapses for him, and he stands impoverished amid ruins.

For a day and a night Dasa drifted about the woods in the neighborhood. He was utterly exhausted, but after every brief rest the misery in his heart lashed him on. He had to stir and keep moving; he felt as if he would have to tramp on to the end of the world and to the end of his life, which had lost all its meaning and all its glory. Nevertheless, he did not wander off to distant, unknown regions. He remained in the vicinity of his misfortunes. He circled about his hut, the mill, the fields, the Rajah's hunting tent. Finally he concealed himself again in the trees overlooking the tent. He crouched in his leafy hiding place, bitter and burning as a hungry beast of prey, until the moment came for which he had been saving his last energies—until the Rajah stepped outside the tent. Then he slipped silently down from the branch, raised the sling, and struck his enemy squarely in the forehead with the stone. Nala fell and lay motionless on his back. There seemed to be no one about. For a moment the storm of voluptuous, vengeful delight that roared through Dasa's senses was checked, fearfully and strangely, by a profound silence. Then, before a clamor broke out around the slain man and the space in front of the tent began to swarm with servants, Dasa was in the woods, lost in the bamboo thickets that sloped down toward the valley.

In the delirium of action, as he leaped from the tree and aimed the sling, letting it hurl forth its death, he had felt as if he were extinguishing his own life also, as if he were discharging his last spark of vitality and flinging himself, along with the deadly stone, into the abyss of annihilation, content to die if only his hated foe fell a moment before him. But now that the deed had been followed by that unexpected moment of silence, a craving for life which he had not realized was in him drew him back from the abyss. A primitive instinct took possession of his senses and his limbs, drove him into the depths of the woods and the bamboo thickets, commanded him to flee and hide.

Awareness of what was happening came to him only after he had reached a refuge and was safe from immediate danger. As he collapsed exhausted, struggling for breath, his frenzy giving way to weakness and sobriety, he felt disappointment and revulsion at having escaped. But when his breathing slowed and his dizziness passed, this repugnance yielded to a defiant determination to live, and once more his heart gloried savagely in the deed.

The hunt for the killer began. Soon searchers were swarming through the woods. They beat the thickets throughout the day, and he evaded them only because he kept utterly still in his hiding place in the marsh, which no one dared penetrate too deeply for fear of tigers. He slept a little, lay on the alert for a while, crawled on a bit, rested again, and by the third day had made his way beyond the hills, whence he pushed on toward the higher mountains.

The homeless life he led thereafter took him here and there. It made him harder and more callous, but also wiser and more resigned. Nevertheless, during the nights he repeatedly dreamed of Pravati and his former happiness, or what he had in the past called his happiness. He also dreamed many times of the pursuit and his flight—frightful, heart-stopping dreams such as this: He would be fleeing through woods, the pursuers close behind him with drums and hunting horns. Through forest and swamp and briers, over rotting, collapsing bridges, he would be carrying something, a burden, a bale, something wrapped up, concealed, unknown. All he knew about it was that it was precious and that under no circumstances must he let it out of his hands; it was something valuable and imperiled, a treasure, perhaps something stolen, wrapped in a bright cloth with a russet and blue pattern, such as Pravati's holiday dress had been. Laden with this pack, this treasure, or these stolen goods, he would be fleeing and skulking, amid toil and danger, creeping under low-hanging branches or overhanging rocks, stealing past snakes and crossing rivers full of crocodiles on vertiginous narrow planks, until at last he stopped in exhaustion, fumbled with the knot of the string that tied his pack, slowly unwrapped the cloth and spread it out, and the treasure he took out at last and held in shuddering hands was his own head.

He led the stealthy life of a vagabond, no longer actually fleeing from people, but rather avoiding them. And one day his roaming led him through a hilly region of lush grass which looked lovely and serene and seemed to welcome him, as though he ought to know it. In one place he recognized a meadow with softly swaying grasses in flower, in another a willow grove which reminded him of the serene and innocent days when he had not yet known love and jealousy, hatred and revenge. It was the pastureland where he had once tended the herd with his companions; that had been the most untroubled period of his youth. Now he looked back upon it across vast chasms of irrevocability. A sweet melancholy in his heart answered the voices that welcomed him here, the wind fluttering the silvery willows, the jolly song of the little brooks, the trilling of the birds, and the deep golden buzz of bumblebees. It all sounded and smelled of refuge, home; never before, used as he was to the roaming herdsman's life, had he ever felt that a countryside was so homelike, so much part of him.

Accompanied and guided by these voices in his soul, with feelings like those of a soldier home from the wars, he wandered about this pleasant landscape, for the first time in many terrible months not a stranger, a fugitive, a candidate for death, but with an open heart, thinking of nothing, desiring nothing, surrendering utterly to the tranquil present, grateful and somewhat astonished at himself and at this new, unwonted, rapturous state of mind, this undemanding receptivity, this serenity without tensions, this new mode of taking delight in close observation. He felt drawn to the forest which lay beyond the green meadows. In among the trees, amid the dusk speckled by sunlight, the feeling of returning home intensified, and led him along paths which his feet seemed to find by themselves, until he passed through a fern thicket, a dense little forest of ferns in the midst of the greater woods, and reached a tiny hut. On the ground in front of the hut sat the motionless yogi whom he had once watched, and to whom he had brought milk and butter.

Dasa stopped, as if he had just awakened. Everything here was the same as it had been; here no time had passed, there had been no killing and suffering. Here, it seemed, time and life were hard as crystal, frozen in eternity. He stood looking at the old man, and there returned to his heart that admiration, love, and longing which he had felt upon his first sight of the yogi. He looked at the hut and thought that it probably needed some repairs before the onset of the next rainy season. Then he ventured a few cautious steps forward. He entered the hut and peered around. There was little there, almost nothing: a pallet of leaves, a gourd containing some water, and an empty pouch made of bast. He took the pouch and went into the woods searching for food. He returned with fruit and the sweet pith of certain trees. Then he went off with the gourd and filled it with fresh water.

Now he had done all that could be done here. There was so little a man needed to live. Dasa kneeled on the ground and sank into reveries. He was content with this silent repose and dreaming in the woods, content with himself, with the voice within him that had led him here where as a boy he had once sensed something like peace, happiness, and home.

And so he remained with the silent yogi. He renewed the pallet of leaves, found food for the two of them, repaired the old hut, and began building a second for himself a short distance away. The old man appeared to tolerate him, but Dasa could not quite make out whether he had actually taken notice of him. When he rose from his meditation, it was only in order to go to sleep in the hut, to eat a bite, or to walk a bit in the woods. Dasa lived with him like a servant in the presence of a nobleman, or rather the way a small pet, a tame bird or a mongoose, say, lives along with human beings, useful and scarcely noticed. Since he had been a fugitive for so long, unsure of himself, suffering pangs of conscience, seeking concealment and perpetually fearing pursuit, this life of repose, the effortless small labors and the presence of a man who did not seem to notice him, did him a great deal of good for a while. His sleep was not troubled by frightful dreams; for half and then whole days at a time he forgot what had happened. The future did not enter his mind, and if ever a longing or desire came to him, it was to remain where he was, to be accepted by the yogi and initiated into the secret of a hermit's life, to become a yogi himself and partake of the proud indifference of yoga. He had begun to imitate the venerable ascetic's posture, to sit motionless like him with crossed legs, like him to gaze into an unknown and superreal world, and to cultivate apathy to everything around him. Whenever he made such attempts, he tired quickly; he found his limbs stiff and his back aching, was plagued by mosquitoes or bothered by all sorts of itches and twitches which compelled him to move, to scratch himself, and finally to stand up again. But several times he had felt something different, a sense of emptiness, lightness, and floating in air, such as sometimes comes in dreams in which we touch the ground only lightly now and then, gently pushing off from it to drift like a wisp of fluff. At such moments he had an inkling of what it must be like to float about that way all the time, body and soul divesting themselves of all weight and sharing the movements of a greater, purer, sunnier life, exalted and absorbed by a beyond, by timelessness and immutability. But these intimations had lasted only a moment. And every time he plummeted back into his ordinary self, disappointed, he thought that he must persuade the master to become his teacher, to initiate him into his exercises and secret arts and make a yogi of him also. But how was he to do that? It did not seem as if the old man would ever notice him, that there would ever be an exchange of words between them. Just as the yogi seemed beyond the day and hour, beyond the forest and hut, he also seemed beyond all words.

Nevertheless, one day he spoke a word. There came a time during which Dasa again dreamt night after night, often bewilderingly sweet and often bewilderingly dreadful dreams, either of his wife Pravati or the horrors of life as a fugitive. And by day he made no progress, could not long endure sitting and practicing, could not help thinking about women and love. He tramped about the forest a great deal. He blamed the weather for his condition; these were sultry days with sudden gusts of hot wind.

One more such bad day came. The mosquitoes hummed. Dasa had had another of his anguished dreams that left him with a sense of fear and oppression. He no longer remembered it, but upon waking it seemed to him that it had been a wretched, outrageous, and shameful relapse into earlier states and stages of his life. All day long he moved restively about the hut, or squatted gloomily. He dabbed at odd tasks, several times sat down for meditation exercises, but would each time be seized by a feverish unrest. His limbs twitched, he felt as if ants were crawling over his feet, had a burning sensation in the nape of his neck, and was unable to endure stillness for more than a few moments. Now and then he cast shy and ashamed glances at the old man, who sat in the perfect posture, eyes turned inward, face floating above his body in inviolable serenity like the head of a flower.

On this day, when the yogi rose and turned toward the hut, Dasa went up to him. He had waited long for this moment, and now blocked his way and with the courage of fear addressed him.

"Forgive me for disturbing your peace, reverend father," he said. "I am seeking peace, tranquility; I would like to live as you do and become like you. As you see, I am still young, but I have already tasted much suffering. Destiny has played cruelly with me. I was born to be a prince and cast out to become a herdsman. I became a herdsman, grew up, strong and happy as a young bull, innocent in my heart. Then my eyes were opened to women, and when I beheld the most beautiful of them, I put my life at her service. Not to possess her would have killed me. I left my companions, the herdsmen. I sued for Pravati's hand, was granted it, became a son-in-law, and labored hard for her. But Pravati was mine and loved me, or so I thought. Every evening I returned to her arms, lay upon her heart. Then, behold, the Rajah came to the neighborhood, the same on whose account I had been cast out as a child. He came and took Pravati from me; I was condemned to see her in his arms. That was the greatest agony I have ever experienced; it changed me and my whole life. I slew the Rajah. I killed and led the life of a criminal and fugitive. Every man's hand was against me; my life was not safe for an hour until I stumbled upon this place. I am a foolish man, reverend father; I am a killer and perhaps may still be caught and drawn and quartered. I can no longer endure this terrible life; I want to be done with it."

The yogi had listened quietly to this outburst, with downcast eyes. Now he opened them and fixed his gaze upon Dasa's face, a bright, piercing, almost unbearably firm, composed, and lucid gaze. And while he studied Dasa's face, seemingly pondering his tale, his mouth slowly twisted into a smile, then a laugh. Soundlessly laughing, he shook his head, and said: "Maya! Maya!"

Utterly bewildered and shamed, Dasa stood stock still. The yogi, before his evening meal, took a short walk on the narrow path that led into the ferns. With quiet, rhythmic step he paced back and forth. After several hundred paces, he returned and entered his hut. His face was once more as it had always been, turned toward something other than the world of appearances. What had been the meaning of the laugh breaking through that impassive countenance? Had that terrible laughter at Dasa's anguished confession and plea been benevolent or mocking, comforting or condemning, divine or demonic? Had it been merely the cynical bleat of an old man no longer able to take things seriously, or the amusement of a sage at another's folly? Had it been rejection, farewell, dismissal? Or was it meant as advice, an invitation to Dasa to follow his example and join in his laughter? Dasa could not solve the riddle. Late into the night he continued to ponder the meaning of this laughter with which the old man seemed to have summed up his life, his happiness, and his misery. His thoughts chewed on it as if it were a tough root that somehow had a hidden savor. And likewise he chewed upon and pondered and mulled over the word that the old man had called out so loudly, so laughingly and gaily and with such incomprehensible amusement: "Maya! Maya!" He half knew, half guessed the general meaning of the word, and the intonation the laughing old man had given it seemed also to suggest a meaning. Maya—that was Dasa's life, Dasa's youth, Dasa's sweet felicity and bitter misery. Beautiful Pravati was Maya; love and its delights were Maya; all life was Maya. To the eyes of this yogi Dasa's life, all men's lives, everything was Maya, was a kind of childishness, a spectacle, theater, an illusion, emptiness in bright wrappings, a soap bubble—something one could laugh at and at the same time despise, but by no means take seriously.

But although the yogi might be able to dismiss Dasa's life with laughter and the word Maya, Dasa himself could not. Much as he might wish to become a laughing yogi himself, and to see his own life as nothing but Maya, the whole of that life had been roused in him once more during these restive days and nights. He remembered now all the things he had nearly forgotten when he found refuge here after the stresses of his life as a fugitive. There seemed to him only the slightest hope that he would ever be able to learn the art of yoga, let alone to become as adept at it as the old man himself. But then—what was the sense of his lingering in this forest? It had been an asylum; he had recuperated a bit and gathered strength, had come to his senses somewhat. That was something, was in fact a great deal. And perhaps out in the country the hunt for the Rajah's murderer had ended and he could continue his wanderings without any great danger.

He decided to do so. He would depart next day. The world was vast; he could not remain in this hiding place forever.

This decision gave him a measure of peace.

He had intended to leave at dawn. But when he awoke after a long sleep the sun was already high in the sky. The yogi had begun his meditation, and Dasa did not want to leave without bidding good-by. Moreover, he still had a request to make. And so he waited, hour after hour, until the man rose, stretched his limbs, and began his pacing. Then Dasa once more blocked his way, bowed repeatedly, and obstinately remained until the master directed an inquiring look at him.

"Master," he said humbly, "I am going my way. I shall no longer disturb your tranquility. But permit me a request this one last time, venerable father. When I told you about my life, you laughed and exclaimed, 'Maya!' I implore you, teach me more about Maya."

The yogi turned toward the hut, his eyes commanding Dasa to follow. Picking up the water gourd, the old man held it out to Dasa, signing to him to wash his hands. Obediently, Dasa did so. Then the master poured the remainder of the water into the ferns, held the gourd out to Dasa once again, and asked him to fetch fresh water. Dasa obeyed. He ran, emotions of parting tugging at his heart, for the last time down the little footpath to the spring. For the last time he carried the light husk with its smooth, worn rim to the little pool which so often reflected in scattered flecks of light the muzzles of deer, the arching of treetops, and the sweet blue of the sky. Now, as he stooped over it, it reflected for the last time his own face in the russet dusk. He dipped the gourd slowly and thoughtfully into the water, feeling a weird sense of uncertainty. He could not understand why, or why it had hurt him, since he meant to leave anyhow, that the old man had not asked him to stay a while longer, or perhaps stay forever.

Crouching by the brink of the spring, he took a drink. Then he rose, holding the gourd carefully so as not to spill any of the water. He was about to return along the path when his ear caught a tone that both delighted and horrified him. This was the voice he had heard in so many of his dreams, that he had remembered with such bitter longing in many a waking hour. It coaxed so sweetly, sounded so charming, so childlike and loving in the dusk of the forest, that his heart shivered with fright and pleasure. It was his wife Pravati's voice. "Dasa," she called coaxingly.

Incredulously, he looked around, still holding the gourd; and suddenly she appeared among the tree trunks, slender as a reed on her long legs—Pravati, his unforgettable, faithless beloved. He dropped the gourd and ran toward her. Smiling, somewhat abashed, she stood before him, looking up at him with her big doe's eyes. As he approached he saw that she wore red leather sandals and a beautiful, costly dress. There was a gold bracelet on her arm, and precious stones flashed in her black hair. He checked his stride. Was she still a rajah's concubine? Had he not killed Nala? Was she still going about with his gifts? How could she come before him adorned with these clasps and gems and dare to call his name?

But she was lovelier than ever, and before he had time to demand an explanation he could not resist taking her into his arms, pressing his forehead against her hair, raising her face and kissing her mouth; and as he did so he felt that everything had returned to him, that everything was his once more, all that he had ever possessed, his happiness, love, lust, joy in life, passion. All his thoughts had already moved far from the forest and the old hermit; the woods, the hermitage, meditation, and yoga had vanished, were forgotten. He gave not another thought to the old man's gourd, which he was to bring back filled with water. It remained where he had dropped it by the spring as he rushed toward Pravati. And she, for her part, began hastily to tell him how it was she had come here, and all that had happened in the interval.

Her story was astonishing, astonishing and delightful, like a fairy tale, and Dasa plunged into his new life as if it were a fairy tale. Pravati was his again; the odious Rajah Nala dead. The pursuit of the murderer had long since ceased. But more than all that, Dasa, the prince who had become a herdsman, had been proclaimed the rightful heir and ruler. In the city an old herdsman and an old Brahman had revived the almost forgotten story of his expulsion and made it the talk of the country. He who had been hunted high and low to be tortured and executed as Nala's murderer was now being sought much more ardently throughout the land, so that he could be brought solemnly to his father's palace and installed as Rajah.

It was like a dream, and what pleased and amazed Dasa most was the pretty chance that of all the seekers sent about the country, it had been Pravati who had found him and been the first to salute him. On the edge of the forest he found tents erected. The smell of smoke and roasting game filled the air. Pravati was joyously hailed by her retinue, and a great feast began at once when she presented Dasa, her husband. Among the throng was a man who had been Dasa's companion in his days as a herdsman. It was he who had led Pravati and the retinue here, with the thought that Dasa might be found at one of the places dear to him from earlier days. The man laughed with pleasure when he recognized Dasa. He ran up to him, ready to embrace him or give him a friendly pat on the back. But his fellow herdsman had become a rajah, and he stopped as if suddenly numbed, then moved slowly and respectfully forward and bowed low. Dasa raised him, clasped him to his breast, affectionately called him by name, and asked how he could reward him. The herdsman wanted a heifer calf, and three were promptly assigned to him from the Rajah's best stock.

More and more people were introduced to the new prince: officials, huntsmen, court Brahmans. He received their salutations. A meal was served; music of drums, sitars, and nose-flutes sounded; and all the festivity and pomp seemed to Dasa like a dream. He could not fully believe in it. For the present the only reality seemed to him Pravati, his young wife, whom he again held in his arms.

Moving by small daily stages, the procession approached the capital city. Runners had been sent ahead to announce that the young Rajah had been found and was on his way. The city resounded with the boom of gongs and drums as Dasa and his retinue approached. A white-clad parade of Brahmans came forward to meet him, headed by the successor of that Vasudeva who some twenty years before had sent Dasa to the herdsmen. The old man had died only recently. The Brahmans hailed the new Rajah, sang hymns, and led him to the palace, where several great sacrificial fires had been lit. Dasa was shown into his new home. There were more welcomings, homages, benedictions, and speeches. Outside the palace, the city celebrated joyfully until late into the night.

Instructed daily by two Brahmans, Dasa quickly acquired the knowledge necessary to a ruler. He attended sacrifices, pronounced judgments, and practiced the arts of chivalry and war. A Brahman named Gopala taught him politics. He explained the position of his house and its regal privileges, what claims his future sons would have, and who were his enemies. The principal one was Nala's mother who in the past had robbed Prince Dasa of his rights and had sought to take his life, and who now must certainly hate her son's murderer. She had fled to the protection of their neighbor, Prince Govinda, and was living in his palace. This Govinda and his house had been dangerous foes from time immemorial. They had made war upon Dasa's forefathers and claimed certain parts of his territory. On the other hand the Prince of Gaipali, Dasa's neighbor to the south, had been friendly with his father and had always disliked Rajah Nala. Visiting him, lavishing gifts upon him, and inviting him to the next great hunt belonged among Dasa's important duties.

The lady Pravati had rapidly adapted to the ways of the nobility. She had the bearing of a princess, and in her beautiful dresses and jewelry she looked splendid, as if she sprang from as fine a lineage as her husband. Year after year they lived together in harmonious love, and their happiness gave them a certain glow, like those whom the gods favor, so that the people adored them. And when, after long waiting, Pravati at last bore him a beautiful boy to whom he gave his father's name, Ravana, his happiness was complete. All that he possessed, all the land and power, the estates and barns, dairies, cattle, and horses, acquired a fresh importance in his eyes, an added glory and value. His wealth had pleased him because it could be lavished on Pravati, whose loveliness could be enhanced with apparel and jewelry. Now his rich possessions delighted him all the more, and seemed far more important, because he saw in them his son Ravana's inheritance and future happiness.

Pravati's chief pleasures lay in festivals, parades, and pomp, luxury in dress and finery, and a large corps of servants. Dasa preferred the joys of his garden. He had ordered rare and precious trees and flowers planted there, and stocked the grounds with parrots and other brilliantly plumaged birds. Feeding and talking with these pets became one of his daily pleasures. In addition, learning attracted him. He proved a grateful pupil of the Brahmans, learned to read and write, memorized many poems and proverbs, and kept a personal scribe who understood the art of making scrolls out of palm leaves. Under the scribe's skillful hands a modest library grew. The books were kept in a small opulent room with gilded paneling of precious woods, carved with reliefs representing incidents in the lives of the gods. Here he sometimes invited his Brahmans, the foremost scholars and thinkers among the priests, to conduct disputations on sacred subjects: on the creation of the world and on great Vishnu's Maya, on the holy Vedas, the power of sacrifice, and the still greater power of penance, by virtue of which a mortal man can make the very gods tremble with fear of him. Those Brahmans who had spoken best and advanced the most elegant arguments received fine gifts. As the prize for a successful disputation, some departed leading away a fine cow. On occasion there was something both ridiculous and touching when great scholars, who a few moments before had been reciting maxims from the Vedas along with brilliant exegeses of the same, or who had just proved the depth of their knowledge of all the heavens and seas, stalked off swollen with pride in their awards, or fell to bickering with one another over their prizes.

In general, for all his happiness, his wealth, his garden, and his books, Prince Dasa at times could not help regarding everything that pertained to human life and human nature as both strange and dubious, at once touching and ridiculous, like those same sagacious and vain Brahmans, at once bright and dark, desirable and contemptible. When his gaze dwelt on the lotus flowers in the ponds of his garden, on the lovely iridescent plumage of his peacocks, pheasants, and rhinoceros birds, on the gilded carvings of his palace, these things sometimes seemed to him virtually divine, aglow with the fires of eternal life. But other times, and even at the same times, he sensed in them something unreal, unreliable, questionable, a tendency toward perishability and dissolution, a readiness to relapse into formlessness, into chaos. Just as he himself had been a prince, became a herdsman, descended to the nadir of a murderer and outlaw, and ultimately became a prince once more, moved and guided by unknown powers, with all his tomorrows forever uncertain, so life's wayward Maya everywhere contained simultaneously nobility and baseness, eternity and death, grandeur and absurdity. Even his beautiful, beloved Pravati had sometimes, for brief moments, appeared to him in a ludicrous light, stripped of her charm; she wore too many bracelets, had too much of pride and triumph in her eyes, and tried too hard to move majestically.

Even dearer to him than his garden and his books was his son Ravana, the fulfillment of his love and his life, the object of his tenderness and solicitude. He was a true prince, a lovely, delicate child, doe-eyed like his mother and inclined to pensiveness and reverie like his father. Often, when Dasa saw the boy standing for a long time in front of one of the ornamental trees in the garden, or sitting on a rug, absorbed in contemplation of a stone, a carved toy, or a feather, eyebrows slightly raised and eyes staring quietly, somewhat absently, it seemed to him that this son was very like himself. Dasa realized fully how intensely he loved him the first time that he had to leave the boy for an indefinite period.

One day a messenger arrived from the frontier region where his land bordered on that of his neighbor Govinda and reported that Govinda's men had launched a raid, stolen cattle, and even kidnapped a number of Dasa's subjects. Dasa immediately made his preparations. He took with him the colonel of his bodyguard and a few dozen horses and men, and set off in pursuit of the raiders. The moment before he rode off, he took his small son into his arms and kissed him; and love flared in his heart like a fiery pang. The force of that pang surprised him; it affected him like some bidding from the unknown; and during the long ride his reflections on it ripened into understanding. For as he rode he pondered the reason he was sitting in the saddle and galloping so sternly and swiftly over the countryside. What power, he wondered, was causing him to undertake such efforts? Pondering, he realized that at the bottom of his heart it was of small concern to him that cattle and men should have been snatched from him somewhere on his borders. Thievery and the flouting of his authority could not suffice to kindle his rage and spur him to action. It would have been more natural to him to have dismissed the news of the raid with a compassionate smile. But to have done so, he knew, would have been to commit a bitter injustice to the messenger. The poor fellow had run all the way with his news until he was ready to drop with exhaustion. No less would he have wronged the people who had been captured and who were now prisoners, carried away from their homes and their peaceful life into foreign slavery. Moreover, all his other subjects, though they had not been harmed in the least, would also have felt wronged. They would have resented his passivity, not understanding why the prince could not protect his country better. They took it for granted that if violence were done to any of them they could count upon their ruler for aid and vengeance.

He realized that it was his duty to undertake this expedition of reprisal. But what is duty? How many duties there are that we so often neglect without the slightest compunction? What was the reason that this duty of vengeance was no trivial one, that he could not neglect it, and that in fact he was not performing it perfunctorily and halfheartedly but with zest and passion? As soon as the question arose in his mind, his heart answered it, for once again it quivered with the pang he had felt on parting from little Prince Ravana. If the Rajah, he realized, made no resistance when cattle and people were taken from him, robbery and violence would spread from the borders of his country closer and closer to the center, and ultimately the enemy would stand directly before him and would strike him where he was prone to the bitterest pain: in the person of his son. They would take his son, his successor, from him; they would carry the boy off and kill him, perhaps under torture; and that would be the most extreme suffering he could ever experience, even worse, far worse, than the death of Pravati herself. So that was the reason he was riding off so zealously and was so dutiful a sovereign. Not from concern for the loss of cattle and land, not from kindness for his subjects, not from ambition to match his father's noble name, but out of intense, painful, irrational love for this child, and out of intense, irrational fear of the pain he would feel at the loss of this child.

Thus far he had come in understanding during that ride. He had not, however, managed to apprehend and punish Govinda's men. They escaped with their booty, and in order to show his determination and prove his courage he himself now had to raid across the border, damage one of his neighbor's villages, and carry off some cattle and a few slaves.

He had been away many days. On the homeward ride, a victor, he had again sunk into meditation, and returned home very quietly and rather sorrowful. For in the course of his meditations he had realized how entirely ensnared he was, without any hope of escaping; his whole nature and all his actions were caught and being strangled in a diabolic net. While his leaning toward philosophy, his love for quiet contemplation and a life of innocence and inaction, were constantly growing, there was likewise growing from another source his love for Ravana, his anxiety about his son's life and future, an equally forceful compulsion to action and entanglement. Out of affection grew conflict, out of love war. Already, in the effort to mete out justice, he had seized a herd, terrified a village, and forcibly carried off poor innocent people. Out of that, of course, would grow a new act of vengeance, new violence, and so on and on until his whole life and his whole country were plunged in warfare and violence and the clash of arms. It was this insight, or vision, which made him so silent and sorrowful upon his homecoming.

He had been right, for the hostile neighbor gave him no peace. The incursions and raids were repeated. Dasa had to march out again for reprisals and defense, and when the enemy withdrew, his own soldiers and chasseurs had to be turned upon the neighboring people. Mounted and armed men were more and more a familiar sight in the capital. In a good many frontier villages there were now permanent garrisons of soldiers on guard. Military conferences and preparations troubled Dasa's days. He could not see what purpose this endless guerrilla warfare served; he grieved for the plight of his victims, for the lives of the dead. He grieved because more and more he had to neglect his garden and his books. He grieved for the lost peace of his days and his heart. Often he spoke with Gopala, the Brahman, about these matters, and sometimes with his wife Pravati.

Should they not ask one of the respected neighboring princes to act as mediator? For his part he would gladly help to bring about peace by conciliation and surrendering a few pastures and villages. He was disappointed and somewhat angered when neither the Brahman nor Pravati would hear of anything of the kind.

His difference of opinion with Pravati on this question led to an extremely violent quarrel, and ended with a serious estrangement. Insistently, he pleaded his points with her. But she behaved as if every word were directed not against the war and the useless killing, but solely against herself. In a verbose, furious retort she declared that it was precisely the enemy's aim to take advantage of Dasa's good nature and love of peace (not to say his fear of war); the enemy would persuade him to conclude one peace treaty after another, each paid for in small concessions of territory and population. And in the end he would still not be satisfied, but as soon as Dasa was sufficiently weakened, would return to open war and seize everything that was left to him. She was not concerned about herds and villages, merits and demerits, but with the fate of the whole, their survival or annihilation. And if Dasa did not know what he owed to his dignity, his son, and his wife, she would have to be the one to teach him. Her eyes blazed; her voice shook; it was long since he had seen her so beautiful and so passionate, but he felt only sorrow.

Meanwhile the border raids and breaches of peace continued; they came to a temporary end only with the beginning of the rainy season. By now there were two factions at Dasa's court. One side, the peace party, was very small; aside from Dasa it numbered only a few of the older Brahmans. These were all learned men absorbed in their meditations. But the war party, the party of Pravati and Gopala, had the majority of priests and all the army officers on its side. The country armed feverishly, and it was known that the hostile neighbor was doing the same. The chief huntsman instructed Prince Ravana in the art of the bow, and his mother took him along to every inspection of troops.

During this period Dasa sometimes thought of the forest where he had lived for a while as a poor fugitive, and of the white-haired old hermit who lived there absorbed in contemplation. Sometimes he felt a desire to call upon the yogi, to see him again and ask his advice. But he did not know whether the old man was still living, nor whether he would listen and give counsel. And even if he were alive and would advise, everything would nevertheless take its course. Nothing could be changed. Meditation and wisdom were good, were noble things, but apparently they throve only on the margin of life. If you swam in the stream of life and struggled with its waves, your acts and suffering had nothing to do with wisdom. They came about of their own accord, were fated, and had to be done and suffered. Even the gods did not live in eternal peace and eternal wisdom. They too experienced danger and fear, struggle and battle; that he knew from the many tales of the gods.

And so Dasa yielded. He no longer contended with Pravati. He reviewed the troops, saw the war coming, anticipated it in debilitating dreams, and as his body grew leaner, and his face darker, he saw his happiness fading, his gaiety shriveling. There remained only his love for his son. That increased along with his anxiety, increased along with the arming and the drilling of soldiers. It was the flaming red flower in his parching garden. He wondered at how much emptiness and joylessness a man could endure, at how easy it was to grow accustomed to care and gloom, and he also wondered that so anxious and solicitous a love could so painfully dominate a life that had seemingly lost the capacity for passion. Although his life might be meaningless, it was certainly not without a center; it revolved around his love for his son. It was on Ravana's account that he rose from his bed in the morning and spent his days in occupations and exertions directed solely toward war, and therefore repugnant to him. On Ravana's account he patiently conferred with his generals, and withstood majority opinion only to the extent that he prevailed on them to wait and see, not plunge recklessly into adventures.

Just as his joys, his garden, and his books had gradually deserted him, so he was also deserted by those who for so many years had shaped his happiness and represented his pleasures. It had begun with politics, with Pravati's passionate speech excoriating his fear of sinning and love of peace, almost openly calling all that cowardice. She had spoken with flushed cheeks and in fiery phrases of heroism, a prince's honor, and the prospect of disgrace. At that time, stunned and with a sense of giddiness, he had suddenly realized how far his wife had become estranged from him, or he from her. Ever since, the gulf between them had widened. It was still growing, and neither of them did anything to check its growth. Or rather, it should have fallen to Dasa to do something about it. For only he saw the gulf for what it was. In his imagination it more and more grew into the gulf of gulfs, became a cosmic abyss between man and woman, between yes and no, between soul and body. In retrospect he thought he saw the whole thing with complete clarity. He remembered how Pravati, magically beautiful, had captivated him until he parted with his friends, gave up his carefree life as a herdsman, and for her sake lived as a servant in an alien world, the son-in-law in the house of unkind people who exploited his infatuation to extract labor from him. Then Nala had come along, and his misfortunes had begun. The wealthy, handsome Rajah with his fine clothes and tents, his horses and servants, had seduced his wife. That might have cost him little effort, for poor Pravati had not been accustomed to regal splendor. But would she really have been led astray so easily and quickly if she had been faithful and virtuous at heart? Very well, the Rajah had seduced her, or simply taken her, and thus inflicted upon him the most horrible grief he had ever experienced. But he, Dasa, had taken revenge. He had killed the thief of his happiness, and had felt the killing as a moment of high triumph. But scarcely was the deed done than he had had to flee. For days, weeks, and months he had lived in swamp and forest, an outlaw, trusting no man.

And what had Pravati being doing all that time? The two of them had never spoken much about that. In any case, she had not fled also. She had sought and found him only after he had been proclaimed Nala's successor, because of his birth, and she needed him in order to enter the palace and ascend the throne. Then she had appeared, had fetched him from the forest and the venerable hermit's purlieus. He had been dressed in fine garments, made Rajah, and since then he had had nothing but glory and felicity—but in reality: what had he abandoned at that time, and what had he gained in exchange? He had gained the splendor and the duties of a sovereign, duties that had been initially easy and had ever since grown harder and harder. He had regained his beautiful wife, the sweet hours of lovemaking with her, and then his son, who had taught his heart a new kind of love and increasing concern for his imperiled life and happiness, so that now the whole country was on the brink of war. This was what Pravati had conferred upon him when she discovered him by the spring in the woods. But what had he left behind, what had he sacrificed? He had left behind the peace of the forest, pious solitude, and the presence and the example of a holy yogi. In addition he had sacrificed the hope of becoming a disciple and successor, of sharing the sage's profound, radiant, unshakable peace of soul, of being liberated from the struggles and passions of life. Seduced by Pravati's beauty, entangled by the woman, and infected by her ambition, he had abandoned the only way that led to liberation and peace.

That was how the story of his life appeared to him now. And in fact it could easily be interpreted thus. Only a few blurrings and omissions were needed to see it that way. He had omitted, among other things, the fact that he had not been the hermit's disciple at all. On the contrary, he had been on the point of leaving him voluntarily. But perspectives often shift in hindsight.

Pravati regarded these matters quite differently, although she was far less inclined to reflection than her husband. She did not think about Nala at all. On the other hand, if she remembered rightly it had been she alone who had founded Dasa's good fortune. She was responsible for his becoming the Rajah. She had given him a son, had lavished love and happiness upon him. But in the end she had found him unable to match her greatness, unworthy of her soaring projects. For it was clear to her that the coming war could have no outcome other than the destruction of the enemy and the doubling of her own power and possessions. But instead of exulting in this prospect and collaborating enthusiastically, Dasa, most unlike a prince, hung back from war and conquest and would have preferred to grow old idling away his time with his flowers, trees, parrots, and books. On the other hand there was Vishwamitra, the commander of the cavalry forces. He was a different sort of man, next to herself the most ardent partisan of the war, repeatedly urging that they strike for victory as soon as possible. In any comparison between the two, Vishwamitra could not help showing to advantage.

Dasa had not failed to notice his wife's growing friendship with Vishwamitra. He saw how much she admired him and let herself be admired by this brave and cheerful but possibly rather shallow, perhaps somewhat unintelligent army officer with his manly smile, his fine strong teeth and well-tended beard. Dasa observed it all with bitterness and at the same time with contempt. He deceived himself into thinking he felt only scornful indifference. He did not spy on them or try to discover whether their friendship had overstepped the limits of decency. He regarded Pravati's infatuation with the handsome cavalryman, and the looks which showed how she preferred him to her unheroic husband, with the same outwardly indifferent, inwardly embittered calm with which he was wont to view everything that happened. Whether his wife was determined upon infidelity and betrayal, or whether she was merely expressing her contempt for Dasa's principles, it did not matter. The thing had come and was developing, was beginning to confront him like the war and the disaster whose imminence he sensed. There was nothing to be done about it. The only possible attitude toward it was one of acceptance, of stoic endurance. For that, instead of attack and conquest, was Dasa's kind of manliness and heroism.

Whether or not Pravati's admiration for the cavalry captain, and his for her, remained within the bounds of morality, in any case Pravati was less guilty than he, Dasa, himself. That much he understood. To be sure, thinker and doubter that he was, he tended to blame her for the evaporation of his happiness. Or any any rate he considered that she was partly responsible for his having stumbled into the complexities of life, into love, into ambition, into acts of revenge and raids. In his thoughts he even blamed woman, love, and lust for everything on earth, for the whole crazy dance, the whole wild chase of passions and desires, of adultery, of death, of killing, of war. But at the same time he knew quite well that Pravati was not to blame. She was not a cause, but herself a victim. She had not made, and could not be held accountable for, either her beauty or his love for her. She was only a grain of dust in the rays of the sun, a ripple in the stream. It should have been his task, and his alone, to withdraw from woman and love, from ambition and the hunger for happiness. He should have remained either a contented cowherd among herdsmen, or else he should have tried to overcome his own inadequacy by the mysterious path of yoga. He had neglected to do so, had failed; he had no vocation for greatness, or else he had not kept faith with his vocation, so that after all his wife was right to regard him as a coward. On the other hand, she had given him this son, this frail, handsome boy for whom he felt so fearful but whose existence filled his own life with meaning, who was in fact a great joy—a painful and fearful joy, certainly, but still a joy, his true happiness. Now he was paying for this happiness with the sorrow and bitterness in his heart, with his readiness for war and death, with his consciousness of moving toward a dire fate.

Meanwhile Rajah Govinda sat in his own capital, listening to the bidding of the mother of Nala, the slain seducer of evil memory. Govinda's incursions and challenges were growing ever more frequent and brazen. Only an alliance with the powerful Rajah of Gaipali could have made Dasa strong enough to enforce peace and neighborly relations. But this Rajah, although he was well disposed toward Dasa, was Govinda's kinsman and had politely repulsed all efforts to win him over to such an alliance. There was no escape, no hope of sanity or humanity. The fated outcome was drawing nearer and would have to be undergone. Dasa himself almost longed for the war now. If only the accumulated lightnings would strike; if only the calamity would come speedily, since it could no longer be averted.

Once more he paid a visit to the Rajah of Gaipali and exchanged fruitless courtesies with him. In his council he urged moderation and patience, but by now he was doing so without hope. For the rest, he improved his armaments. The council was divided only on the question of whether to respond to the enemy's next raid with invasion of his territory and outright war, or whether to await his major offensive, so that the people and all neutrals would see who was truly guilty of violating the peace.

The enemy, unconcerned with such questions, put an end to reflection, discussion, and hesitation. One day he struck. He staged a major raid which inveigled Dasa, along with the cavalry captain and his best troops, into rushing to the frontier. While they were on the way, Govinda's main force invaded the country, stormed the gates of Dasa's capital, and besieged the palace. As soon as Dasa heard the news he turned back. He knew that his wife and his son were encircled in the palace, and that bloody battles were raging in the streets of the city. His heart pounded with fury and sorrow when he thought of his loved ones and the dangers that faced them. Now he was no longer a reluctant and cautious commander. He burned with anguish and rage, urged his men homeward in wild haste, found the battle surging through the streets, cut his way through to the palace, confronted the enemy and fought like a madman until, at twilight on that bloody day, he collapsed exhausted, bleeding from several wounds.

When he recovered consciousness, he found himself a prisoner. The battle was lost. City and palace were in the hands of his enemies. Bound, he was taken before Govinda, who greeted him disdainfully and led him into one of the other rooms of the palace. It was the room with the carved and gilded walls where Dasa kept his scrolls. Here, sitting bolt upright on one of the rugs, stony-faced, was his wife, Pravati. Armed guards stood behind her. Across her knees lay their son. Like a broken flower that frail body lay dead, face gray, his garments soaked with blood. The woman did not turn when her husband was led in. She did not see him;

she sat staring expressionlessly at the small corpse. But she seemed to Dasa strangely transformed. It took a while before he realized that her hair, which only a few days before he had seen raven black, was now everywhere shot through with gray. She seemed to have been sitting that way for a long time, the boy on her lap, numbed, her face a mask.

"Ravana!" Dasa exclaimed. "Ravana, my child, my flower!" He knelt. His face fell forward upon the dead boy's head. As if in prayer he knelt before the mute woman and the child, mourning both, paying homage to both. He smelled the odor of blood and death, mingled with the fragrance of the aromatic pomade on the child's hair.

With numbed gaze Pravati stared blankly down at the two of them.

Someone touched his shoulder. It was one of Govinda's captains, who ordered him to stand up. The soldiers led him out. He had not addressed a word to Pravati, or she to him.

Bound, he was placed on a wagon and taken to a dungeon in Govinda's capital. There his fetters were partly loosened. A soldier brought a jug of water and put it on the stone floor. The door was closed and barred, and he was left alone. A wound on his shoulder burned like fire. He groped for the water jug and moistened his hands and face. He wanted to drink, but forbore; this way he would die faster, he thought. How much longer would it take, how much longer! He longed for death as his parched throat longed for water. Only death would still the torture in his heart. Only then would the picture of the mother with their dead son be erased. But in the midst of his agony, merciful weariness and weakness overcame him. He sank down and fell asleep.

When he returned hazily to consciousness after this brief slumber, he tried to rub his eyes, but could not. Both hands were occupied, were holding something tightly. When he took heart and forced his eyes open, he saw that he was no longer surrounded by dungeon walls. Greenish light flowed bright and strong over leaves and moss. He blinked several times. The light struck him like a fierce though noiseless blow. A twitch of horror, a shudder of fear, passed through the nape of his neck and down his spine. Once more he blinked, screwed up his face as if he were weeping, and opened his eyes wide.

He was standing in a forest, holding in both hands a gourd

full of water. At his feet the basin of a spring reflected browns and greens. Beyond the fern thicket, he recalled, stood the hut and the waiting yogi who had sent him to fetch water, who had laughed so strangely and whom he had asked to teach him something about Maya.

He had lost neither a battle nor a son. He had been neither a rajah nor a father. Rather, the yogi had granted his wish and taught him about Maya. Palace and garden, library and aviary, the cares of sovereignty and paternal love, war and jealousy, his love for Pravati and his violent suspicion of her—all that had been nothing. No, not nothing. It had been Maya! Dasa stood there shattered. Tears ran down his cheeks. His hands trembled, shaking the gourd he had just filled for the hermit. Water spilled over the rim and onto his feet. He felt as if someone had just amputated one of his limbs, removed something from his head. Suddenly the long years he had lived, the treasures cherished, the delights enjoyed, the pangs suffered, the fears endured, the despair he had tasted to the brink of death—all this had been taken from him, extinguished, reduced to nothingness. And yet not to nothingness! For the memory was there. The images had remained with him. He still saw Pravati sitting, tall and rigid, with her hair so suddenly gray, her son in her lap, as though she herself had killed him. The child lay there like the prey of some beast, his legs dangling limply across her knees.

Oh how swiftly, how swiftly and horribly, how cruelly and thoroughly, had he been taught about Maya! Everything had been deranged; charged years had shrunk to moments. All that crowded reality had been a dream. Perhaps, too, he had dreamed all that had happened previously; the tales of Prince Dasa, of his life as a herdsman, his marriage, his vengeance upon Nala, his taking refuge with the hermit. All that had been pictures such as one might admire on a carved palace frieze where flowers, stars, birds, monkeys, and gods could be seen amid the foliage. And was what he was experiencing this moment, what he saw before his eyes, awakening from rulership and war and imprisonment, standing beside the spring, this gourd from which he had just spilled a little water, together with what he was now thinking about it all—was not all this made of the same stuff? Was it not dream, illusion, Maya? And everything he would still experience in the future, would see with his eyes and feel with his hands, up to the moment of his death—was it any different in substance, any different in kind? It was all a game and a sham, all foam and dream. It was Maya, the whole lovely and frightful, delicious and desperate kaleidoscope of life with its searing delights, its searing griefs.

Dasa still stood numbed. Again the gourd shook in his hands and its water spilled, wetting his toes and running into the ground. What ought he to do? Fill the bowl again, carry it back to the yogi, and be laughed at for all that he had suffered in his dream? That was not alluring. He let the gourd tilt, emptied it, and threw it into the moss. Then he sat down on the green bed and began to reflect seriously. He had had enough and more than enough of this dreaming, of this diabolic texture of experiences, joys, and sufferings that crushed your heart and made your blood stand still, only to be suddenly revealed as Maya, so that you were nothing but a fool. He had had enough of everything. He no longer craved either wife or child, either a throne or victory or revenge, either happiness or cleverness, either power or virtue. He desired nothing but peace, nothing but an end of turmoil. He no longer wanted anything but to check this endlessly turning wheel, to stop this endless spectacle, to extinguish it all. He wanted to find rest for himself and extinguish himself. That was what he had wanted when he hurled himself at the enemy in that last battle, slashing all about and being slashed at in return, giving wounds and receiving them, until he collapsed. But what then? Then there was a brief pause of unconsciousness, or slumber, or death, and immediately afterward you were awake again, had to admit the currents of life into your heart once more and once more let the dreadful, lovely, terrible flood of pictures pour into your eyes, endlessly, inescapably, until the next unconsciousness, until the next death. That was, perhaps, a pause, a moment of rest, a chance to catch your breath. But then it went on, and once again you were one of the thousand figures engaged in the wild, intoxicating, desperate dance of life. Ah, there was no extinction. It went on forever.

Unrest drove him to his feet once more. If there were no rest in this accursed round-dance, if his one most acute desire could not be fulfilled, then he might just as well fill his gourd again and bring it to this old man who had sent him on this errand, although he did not really have any right of command over him. It was a service that had been asked of him. It was an assignment. He might just as well obey and carry it out. That was better than sitting here and pondering methods of self-destruction. Altogether, obeying and serving were better and far easier, seemlier and far more harmless, than commanding and taking responsibility. That much he knew. Very well, Dasa, take the gourd, fill it carefully with water, and bring it to your master!

When he reached the hut, the master received him with a strange look, a slightly questioning, half-compassionate, half-amused look of complicity—such a look as an older boy might have for a younger one whom he sees returning from a strenuous and somewhat shameful adventure, a test of courage that has been assigned to him. This herdsman prince, this poor fellow who had stumbled in here, was only coming back from the spring, where he had been for water, and had been gone no more than fifteen minutes. But still he was also coming from a dungeon, had lost a wife, a son, and a principality, had completed a human life and had caught a glimpse of the revolving wheel. The chances were that this young man had already been wakened once or several times before, and had breathed a mouthful of reality, for otherwise he would not have come here and stayed so long. But now he seemed to have been properly awakened and become ripe for setting out on the long journey. It would take a good many years just to teach this young man the proper posture and breathing.

By this look alone, this look which contained a trace of benevolent sympathy and the hint of a relationship that had come into being between them, the relationship between master and disciple—by this look alone the yogi accepted the disciple. This one look banished the fruitless thoughts from the disciple's head. It bound him in discipline and service. There is no more to be told about Dasa's life, for all the rest took place in a realm beyond pictures and stories. He never again left the forest.

# A Selection of Works from *Technicians of the Sacred*

The poet Jerome Rothenberg has assembled an extraordinary collection of writings from "primitive" socicties entitled *Technicians of the Sacred.* In a lengthy and illuminating appendix he presents works by various contemporary writers within our cultural framework who are experimenting with ways of getting their minds outside of that environment—and these writings have remarkable affinities to the "uncivilized" works that make up the main body of Rothenberg's book. The Cherokee "Friendship Dance," and excerpts from the "Song of the Dead" from China and "The Legend of Saveasi'uleo" from Oceania (Samoa) are presented here.

Many poets are trying to regain the ancient, venerable role of *shaman* or prophet, and their works naturally begin to resemble forms from cultures that recognize poets as seers. In reading these works, see what associations your imagination can provide between them and your own culture's modes of thought and social organization. (For example, compare the "Friendship Dance" to such modes of social intercourse as the cocktail party and the sensitivity group.)

# FRIENDSHIP DANCE

## PREPARATION

Men participants form a single file and are joined by women who dance in front of them as partners. During the song they dance counterclockwise with a shuffling trot, and in the intervals walk in a circle. At the song, when the leader begins to insert words suggestive of intimacy (see translations below), the humorous gestures and acts of the pantomime begin.

## SONG & PANTOMIME

A free rendering of the song is as follows: "Ha!-Ha! I am called an old man [poor and ugly] but I am not this. I am going to take this woman home with me, as I did not know that there was such a good shell-shaker, none like her. I'll take her home to my town."

During the song the leader may raise his hands, palms in, to shoulder height, at times turning halfway to the left and moving sideways. Throughout he is imitated by the men. Toward the end, the leader reaches the climax of his humor in the following phrase, "Ha!-Ha! We are going to touch each other's privates"; the men, holding their partners' hands, suit actions to words.

## MOVEMENTS (SEQUENCE OF INTIMACY)

1. Greeting, holding hands facing.
2. Side by side, holding hands crossed.
3. Facing, putting palms upon partners' palms.
4. Placing hands on partners' shoulders while facing.
5. Placing arms over partners' shoulders while side by side.
6. Placing hats on women partners' heads while facing.

From *Cherokee Dance and Drama,* by Frank Speck and Leonard Bloom (University of California Press, 1931). Reprinted by permission of the Regents of the University of California. Adaptation by Jerome Rothenberg, from *Technicians of the Sacred* (Doubleday, 1968). 

7. Stroking partners under chin while facing.
8. Putting hands on female partners' breasts while side by side.
9. Touching the clothing over the partners' genitals while side by side.

# THE LEGEND OF SAVEASI'ULEO [1]

*Ulufanuasesee.* Why do you want to
eat me, brother?

*Saveasi'uleo.* Can't you see I'm
a sea-monster?

*U.* Slippery as you are, an
eel, I can slip through
your fingers.

*S.* You don't stand a chance
against me, I've already eaten
your four older brothers.

*U.* But, brother, why eat
your brothers? Aren't we
born of the same father?



[1] The following note is reprinted from *Technicians of the Sacred:*

*The Myth.* Saveasi'uleo, the first-born of Muli & Muli, a couple on the island of Savaii, devoured four of his younger brothers when they went swimming. His grieving parents moved inland to a hill named Alao. Their youngest son, Ulufanuasesee (lit. "moving panorama"), was undaunted. When he went swimming, he faced his brother Saveasi'uleo & challenged him.

Later, in Faletatai, Ulufanuasesee married a woman, who gave birth to Siamese twins, who separated when some men accidentally dropped heavy firewood on the ground & frightened them. One of the Siamese twins, Taema, swimming near the island of Annuu, met her uncle Saveasi'uleo & married him. This fulfilled Ulufanuasesee's prediction that the brothers would be united again through their descendants.

[The translator adds]: "Like most poems in the oral tradition (consider, e.g., the ballads in Scotland and America), the 'Legend' has various slightly different versions. But the freakish Saveasi'uleo has been as integral a part of the Samoan imagination as the Monkey among the Chinese."

*S.* I didn't choose to be
born a monster. It was
Father who screwed me up.

*U.* Here I stand on this flat
rock. See if you can
get closer.

*S.* It will be too late to
tell Muli, your father and
your mother, by the time you're
squirming in my stomach.

*U.* But I'm not weak like
my older brothers. I can
swim against the tides
in shark-filled waters.

*S.* I'm Saveasi'uleo, the sea
eel, who makes even
the sharks quiver.

*U.* I can catch you by your
tail and dash you
against the rocks.

*S.* How I would love to get
at you, brother! Your boast
whets my appetite for blood.

*U.* Come, if you like,
let's wrestle. I'll
give you such a hold
you'll be crushed.

*S.* Oh, you make my mouth
water. Your hairless legs
are fine to start with.

*U.* A kick in your middle
and you'll split.

*S.* Oh, let me slip up
your legs, wrap around
your thighs, and enter.

U. Ha, ha, keep your
itch to yourself. I don't
care for a slimey eel's touch.

S. Let my body move against
yours all over. Your body
is more muscular than your
brothers'.

U. That's why I can swim
faster and better. And I
conquer the waves
when I surf.

S. Your tempting body and words
are hard to resist. Let me
work on you this instance.

U. So you still want me,
water-monster. Then, come
up and eat your youngest
brother. Come on! Eat me!

(*Ulufanuasesee beats on his chest.*)

S. Your courage has moved me,
brother. Though I won't
eat you until later, the
taste of your words I shall
savor. Let us make
a pact: Our children shall
be united.

U. I shall swim to Faletatai
in Upolu. When I have
a daughter, she shall be
yours.

S. Brother, let us pledge our
kinship. On this rock
let us lean wet and naked
and press our bodies
against each other's.

# SONG OF THE DEAD, RELATING THE ORIGIN OF BITTERNESS [1]

The following note is reprinted from *Technicians of the Sacred:*

The Na-Khi tribe (a branch of the Ch'iang) settled in the Li-chiang district probably during the Han Dynasty. Their main funeral ceremony, the Zhi mä, involves the chanting of various "books" & songs, preserved until recently in mnemonic picture-writing. While much of this writing is based on the rebus principle (of the [eye pictograph] = I variety), there are places too where the pictograph seems to comment on matter in the spoken text; e.g., the first symbol in the song's title represents a large horsefly, such as occur on the high meadows in the summer, they emerge only when the sun shines & hide when overcast, they are blood suckers & a plague to both man & beast; the Na-Khi call them mun, here the symbol stands for mun = dead, it has also the meaning of old. . . .

But the picture itself (of a horsefly) is a presence also & adds to the meaning—whether by chance or intention is outside the present editor's concern. There are also purely literal pictographs of the [eye pictograph] = eye variety.

The song *per se* is "one of several types of funeral songs, sung at the death of an old man while the body is still in the house." The manuscript consists of eighteen pages from which the present editor has excerpted & slightly adapted pages 2, 3, 13, 14 15, juxtaposing pictures & words, etc. The song (to sum it up) proposes to relate "the origin of bitterness" & follows the dead man (possibly identified with the "first father") as he sees his image reflected, learns

[1] Joseph F. Rock, *The Zhi mä Funeral Ceremony of the Na-Khi of Southwest China* (Studie Instituti Anthropos, Posieux [Fribourg], Switzerland, 1955), Vol. 9, pp. 55, 58, 87, 90, 92. Adapted & arranged by Jerome Rothenberg, from *Technicians of the Sacred* (Doubleday, 1968). Copyright © 1968 by Jerome Rothenberg.

he's growing old, wanders to distant towns to buy long life, sees men selling silver & gold "but years he saw no one sell," then in an empty marketplace watches leaves of the bamboo turn yellow, thinks

> so trees must also die, it is the custom
> there is death after all

laughs & turns back.

The song now moves to a consideration of all who have died, including apparently "the father of heaven" & "the mother of the earth," so that "even in heaven there is bitterness." Then come the dance sections given here as sets 3, 4, & 5—*ritual description: "they form themselves into a circle, but not a closed one, & holding hands much like children do when at play, begin a dance"*—followed by further accounts of the dead man's ascent & the accomplishments & powers to be inherited by his son, his village, & his neighbors.

## SONG OF THE DEAD, RELATING THE ORIGIN OF BITTERNESS

(Set One)

| | | |
|---|---|---|
| | | |
|  To learn to do things here is bitterness |  Ssu-ssa-zo of Shu-lo |  when he was old but didn't know it |
|  |  |  |
| made a yellow wooden bowl | went to wash gold in it | Ssu-ssa-zo's shadow was projected on the water |
|  |  |  |
| he saw his shadow reflected on the water | his own shadow | that he saw reflected |

| | |
|---|---|
| | |
| he was old then & he knew it | on the horizon where the clouds touch heaven<br>the old crane still didn't know that he was old |

| (Set Two) | | |
|---|---|---|
| How he was shaking his own body | his own white feathers dropping down before him | now that he knew that he was old |
| old tiger of the place called Such-&-Such | still didn't know that he was old | his long white fangs were falling down before him |
| & now he knew that he was old | At Such-&-Such-Another-Place | the white stag didn't know that he was old |
| now he was shaking his own body | his white antlers were falling down before him | then he knew that he was old |

(Set Three)

| | | |
|---|---|---|
| Now we will go with the dead & will suffer the bitterness of the dead | we will dance again & vanquish demons again | but if no one had told us where the dance began |

| | | |
|---|---|---|
| we would never dare to speak about the dance | for unless one knows the origin of the dance | one cannot dance it |

| | | | |
|---|---|---|---|
| On top of Such-&-Such-a-Mountain | the yak said he would like to dance | but for the yak | there was no custom of the dance |

| | |
|---|---|
| no custom for the goat that followed | The sons of bitterness are here—they wear their hats |

| (Set Four) | | |
|---|---|---|
|  The yak will dance there, as the custom is |  on top of Such-&-Such-a-Mountain |  the stag said he would like to dance there |
|  but for the stag |  there was no custom of the dance |  Shoes of elfskin & white toes |
|  the sons of bitterness will wear them |  the stag will dance there, as the custom is |  & where the pinetrees grow the young deer try to dance |
|  they beat their cloven hoofs in rhythm |  swaying, dancing, as the custom is |  & all the people of the village |

| (Set Five) | |
|---|---|
| & all the sons of bitterness | who have slim hips & sway in rhythm |
| who sway & dance again, as is the custom | *we will follow the crane to his clouds* |
| *will go with the tiger to his high mountain* | *& with our ancestor into the sky* |
| the crane wants to fly to the shining white gate in the clouds | all those born with wings |
| have followed the crane to his clouds | *but his ability we do not allow to pass* |

(China: Na-Khi)

# Five Poems

These poems, all by Americans, take familiar words, images and ideas and refocus them through lenses of subjectivity, giving them new, often bizarre, contexts and associations. When you come across a commonplace object or concept in these poems—"the 6th avenue bus," "a wino on San Francisco's skidrow," "a hamburger stand," "Marxism," "a Campfire Girl," "sleep"—try to reconstruct the mind of the author and see how the object or concept behaves in the world the poet has set up around it. If you were to recondition your mind to become as a poet's, constantly seeing things in a strange and unfamiliar aspect, what consequences would your psychic reorganization have in your social life? Someone would doubtless accuse you of trying to "escape from reality." But what makes preestablished social conditions more "real" than the patterns of your mind? Simply the fact that most people conform to the preestablished. What would happen if large numbers of people restructured their minds in the manner of these poets? The possibilities you discover in your mind become the possibilities open to society at large, and thus reveal potential ways of dealing with seemingly insoluble societal issues.

## FRANK O'HARA

*died in an auto accident in 1966 after helping make a revolution in American poetry, developing a new ease of discourse and a sensibility which was deeply in touch with the mundane, concrete urban world while still reaching into the regions beyond. He worked for the Museum of Modern Art in New York and published art criticism as well as poetry.*

## ON THE WAY TO SAN REMO

The black ghinkos snarl their way up
the moon growls at each blinking window
the apartment houses climb deafeningly into the purple

A bat hisses northwards
the perilous steps lead to a grate
suddenly the heat is bearable

The cross-eyed dog scratches a worn patch of pavement
his right front leg is maimed in the shape of a V
there's no trace of his nails on the street a woman cajoles

She is very old and dirty
she whistles her filthy hope
that it will rain tonight

The 6th Avenue bus trunk-lumbers sideways
it is full of fat people who cough as at a movie
they eat each other's dandruff in the flickering glare

The moon passes into clouds
so hurt by the street lights
of your glance oh my heart

The act of love is also passing like a subway bison
through the paper-littered arches of the express tracks
the sailor sobers he feeds pennies to the peanut machines

Though others are in the night
far away lips upon a dusty armpit
the nostrils are full of tears

High fidelity reposed in a box a hand on the windowpane
the sweet calm the violin strings tie a young man's hair
the bright black eyes pin far away their smudged curiosity

Yes you are foolish smoking
the bars are for rabbits
who wish to outlive the men

1954

## TOM CLARK

*was born in Chicago in 1941 and attended the University of Michigan and Cambridge University. He is currently poetry editor of* The Paris Review. *Ted Berrigan* *(see p. 456)* *has written: "Tom Clark is the leader of us all." "Sunken Politics" is from his most recent book,* Stones.

# SUNKEN POLITICS

Inside my skull a secret
Female eats a cookie
Savages nine of them hug
The stomach of a penny
You know I tackled Marxism
O a baby has pride too mom
You who built me in an egg
Like a complicated ship
I threw you in the trash

Such thoughts are flak
Cast at the leaves
They break and the tree
Cusses mankind
Retire humble bean
For nothing is strange
And no one is ever
Hungry any more out there
So it doesn't matter about those
Men whose belts
Are made of all the food in the world

## TED BERRIGAN

*was born in 1934 in Providence, Rhode Island. He went to Catholic schools, and to Korea with the U.S. Army. His works have appeared in a great number of periodicals, and he has taught at the University of Iowa Writers' Workshop, the University of Michigan and Yale University. He is a visionary madman and a poet's poet with a tenacious sense of humor. He has a son and a daughter.*

# REAL LIFE

### *1. The Fool*

He eats of the fruits of the great Speckle
Bird, pissing in the grass! Is it possible
He is incomplete, bringing you Ginger Ale
Of the interminably frolicsome gushing summer showers?
You were a Campfire Girl,
Only a part-time mother and father; I
Was large, stern, acrid, and undissuadable!
Ah, Bernie, we wear complete
The indexed Webster Unabridged Dictionary.
And lunch is not lacking, ants and clover
On the grass. To think of you alone
Suffering the poem of these states!
Oh Lord, it is bosky, giggling happy here,
And you, and me, the juice, at last extinct!

### *2. The Fiend*

Red-faced and romping in the wind
I too am reading the technical journals, but
Keeping Christmas-safe each city block
With tail-pin. My angels are losing patience,
Never win. Except at night. Then
I would like a silken thread
Tied round the solid blooming winter.
Trees stand stark-naked guarding bridal paths;
The cooling wind keeps blowing, and
There is a faint chance in geometric boxes!
It doesn't matter, though, to show he is
Your champion. Days are nursed on science fiction
And you tremble at the books upon the earth
As my strength and I walk out and look for you.

## RICHARD BRAUTIGAN*

# THE GALILEE HITCH-HIKER

*The Galilee Hitch-hiker*

**Part 1**

Baudelaire was
driving a Model A
across Galilee.
He picked up a
hitch-hiker named
Jesus who had
been standing among
a school of fish,
feeding them
pieces of bread.
"Where are you
going?" asked
Jesus, getting
into the front
seat.
"Anywhere, anywhere
out of this world!"
shouted
Baudelaire.
"I'll go with you
as far as
Golgotha,"
said Jesus.
"I have a
concession

* See page 32.

Reprinted from *The Pill Versus the Springhill Mine Disaster* by Richard Brautigan.  A Seymour Lawrence Book/Delacorte Press. Used by permission. First published by Four Seasons Foundation in its Writing Series edited by Donald Allen.

at the carnival
there, and I
must not be
late."

*The American Hotel*

**Part 2**

Baudelaire was sitting
in a doorway with a wino
on San Francisco's skidrow.
The wino was a million
years old and could remember
   dinosaurs.
Baudelaire and the wino
were drinking Petri Muscatel.
"One must always be drunk,"
   said Baudelaire.
"I live in the American Hotel,"
said the wino.   "And I can
   remember dinosaurs."
"Be you drunken ceaselessly,"
   said Baudelaire.

1939

**Part 3**

Baudelaire used to come
to our house and watch
me grind coffee.
That was in 1939
and we lived in the slums
of Tacoma.
My mother would put
the coffee beans in the grinder.
I was a child
and would turn the handle,
pretending that it was
   a hurdy-gurdy,
and Baudelaire would pretend

that he was a monkey,
hopping up and down
and holding out
a tin cup.

*The Flowerburgers*

**Part 4**

Baudelaire opened
up a hamburger stand
in San Francisco,
but he put flowers
between the buns.
People would come in
and say, "Give me a
hamburger with plenty
of onions on it."
Baudelaire would give
them a flowerburger
instead and the people
would say, "What kind
of a hamburger stand
is this?"

*The Hour of Eternity*

**Part 5**

"The Chinese
read the time
in the eyes
of cats,"
said Baudelaire
and went into
a jewelry store
on Market Street.
He came out
a few moments
later carrying
a twenty-one
jewel Siamese

cat that he
wore on the
end of a
golden chain.

*Salvador Dali*

**Part 6**

"Are you
or aren't you
going to eat
your soup,
you bloody old
cloud merchant?"
Jeanne Duval
shouted,
hitting Baudelaire
on the back
as he sat
daydreaming
out the window.
Baudelaire was
startled.
Then he laughed
like hell,
waving his spoon
in the air
like a wand
changing the room
into a painting
by Salvador
Dali, changing
the room
into a painting
by Van Gogh.

A *Baseball Game*

**Part 7**

Baudelaire went
to a baseball game

and bought a hot dog
and lit up a pipe
of opium.
The New York Yankees
were playing
the Detroit Tigers.
In the fourth inning
an angel committed
suicide by jumping
off a low cloud.
The angel landed
on second base,
causing the
whole infield
to crack like
a huge mirror.
The game was
called on
account of
fear.

*Insane Asylum*

**Part 8**

Baudelaire went
to the insane asylum
disguised as a
psychiatrist.
He stayed there
for two months
and when he left,
the insane asylum
loved him so much
that it followed
him all over
California,
and Baudelaire
laughed when the
insane asylum
rubbed itself

up against his
leg like a
strange cat.

*My Insect Funeral*

**Part 9**

When I was a child
I had a graveyard
where I buried insects
and dead birds under
a rose tree.
I would bury the insects
in tin foil and match boxes.
I would bury the birds
in pieces of red cloth.
It was all very sad
and I would cry
as I scooped the dirt
into their small graves
with a spoon.
Baudelaire would come
and join in
my insect funerals,
saying little prayers
the size of
dead birds.

*San Francisco*
*February 1958*

## KENNETH PATCHEN

*since the 1930s, has been publishing poetry remarkable for its inventiveness, fantasy, and social commitment. He often works in the visionary picture-poem tradition of Blake; his picture-novel,* The Journal of Albion Moonlight, *has been much discussed on college campuses.*

## THE EDUCATION OF THE WATERS